DRUGS, PARASITES AND HOSTS

BIOLOGICAL COUNCIL

THE CO-ORDINATING COMMITTEE FOR SYMPOSIA ON
DRUG ACTION

DRUGS, PARASITES
AND HOSTS

A Symposium on
Relation Between Chemotherapeutic
Drugs, Infecting Organisms and Hosts

Editors

L. G. GOODWIN, M.B., B.S., B.PHARM., B.SC.
R. H. NIMMO-SMITH, M.A., D.PHIL., M.B., CH.B.
The Wellcome Laboratories of Tropical Medicine, London

With 56 Illustrations

LONDON

J. & A. CHURCHILL LTD.
104 GLOUCESTER PLACE, W.1

1962

PREFACE

BIOCHEMISTRY and immunology are advancing rapidly. The frontiers between these disciplines and chemotherapy, pharmacology, physiology, pathology, microbiology and physical and organic chemistry have become as meaningless as the political boundries in a 1913 atlas. The day of the "splitters" is over and an era of integration has begun. Of course, it began long ago in the laboratory of old Paul Ehrlich and it is astonishing how often we need to acknowledge our debts to him. When a basic concept or principle emerges from new knowledge or from the application of new techniques we often discover that Ehrlich thought of it first. There was no doubt in his mind of the need to consider all interactions between drugs, parasites and hosts in the problems raised by the science of chemotherapy, which he himself founded.

Chemotherapy bridges many of the artificial boundaries between the sciences. The main object of the Symposium was to bring together those who study the biochemical and immunological aspects of parasites, from helminths to viruses, and those who study the design and mode of action of the drugs that kill these parasites. The principles which underlie their work and the particular problems they have to face are variations on a common theme.

The Symposium was organized by the British Pharmacological Society, with the participation of The Biochemical Society, The Physiological Society, The Royal Society of Medicine and The Society for General Microbiology. The members of the Organizing Committee were: F. Bergel (Chairman), W. A. Bain, E. F. Gale, B. W. Lacey, H. McIlwain, H. O. Schild and L. G. Goodwin and R. H. Nimmo-Smith (Secretaries). The detailed secretarial work was organized and carried out by Miss P. E. Wright.

Grateful acknowledgment is made to the Wellcome Trust for a grant which enabled us to invite contributors from East Africa, Europe and the United States, and to the Ciba Foundation for hospitality afforded to overseas visitors.

The Symposium was held in the Edward Lewis Theatre of the Middlesex Hospital Medical School by permission of the Dean, Sir Brian Windeyer, and was attended by nearly 400 members of the participating Societies. We wish to thank the staff at the Middlesex Hospital Medical School for their help.

The formulae and many of the illustrations which appear in this volume were executed by Mr. W. H. G. Richards.

We are grateful to the publishers, J. & A. Churchill Ltd., for their help in a determined effort to publish this volume speedily.

L. G. GOODWIN
R. H. NIMMO-SMITH

CONTENTS

INTRODUCTION

F. Bergel

Chester Beatty Research Institute, London

THE subject of this year's meeting, the idea to discuss the relation between drugs, invaders and invaded, originated with Dr. Edith Bülbring of Oxford, and Dr. Len Goodwin; its transformation into a working proposition for a symposium was carried through under the guidance of Dr. Goodwin. It is hoped that by tomorrow night most of you will take home with you the impression that the main object of our symposia, namely not only to take stock, but more important to look forward, has been achieved. The processes of looking forward, of spontaneous honest speculation, of enumeration of unsolved problems, of tentative programming for the future, processes which on several occasions in the past have been actively helped along also by subsequent discussions at Ciba meetings (which unfortunately is not possible this year) are really essential. This is the more so if we do not wish to come into conflict with the ideas of Sir Lindor Brown, the Secretary of the Royal Society and Chairman of that Society's Committee on Scientific Information. In a recent issue of *Nature* (1962) he remarked that while a quick exchange of ideas and information between workers in different fields which border on each other is necessary, there are many instances of publication *in extenso* of papers delivered at symposia, such publication leading to repeated publication of the same material often one to two years after the event. He suggests that while encouragement should be given to an increased number of symposia there should be no obligation on participants to publish their observations in a special volume. Our reply, apart from the forward look of the matter presented, should be very early publication. If all, including the publishers, help the Committee in the right manner we should be able to do it, and spread our special gospel to a wider audience than this hall is capable of holding. I think that then even Sir Lindor Brown would not object, especially as there is a further reason for publication; the message of this symposium is *holism*, a word used by Field Marshal Smuts. In our case it stresses the importance of the eternal triangle in therapy of host, drug and invader. Many among us who deal experimentally or clinically with disease of multi-aetiological origin such as cancer, collagenous disorders and cardiovascular disease, are more and more inclined to tackle the problem at both ends with the lowest units of molecular nature and with the highest of the total organism, and all stages between. It is therefore gratifying that today and tomorrow we have not only the triangular idea to offer but also at the same time hope to demonstrate the soundness of the approach which combines all aspects of invasion of the host by particles or organisms—helminths, protozoa, bacteria and viruses. You must agree with me that it is a wonderful thing for all of us to come together to tear down unnecessary frontier barriers. May this unitarian principle of searching jointly for new knowledge have a further stimulus through this meeting.

REFERENCE

BROWN, G. L., 1962. *Nature, Lond.*, **193,** 724.

Session 1: Helminthic Infections

CHAIRMAN: N. R. Stoll

CHAIRMAN'S INTRODUCTION

N. R. STOLL

The Rockefeller Institute, New York

IN thanking you for the honour of being here let me make a bow to an Organizing Committee with the temerity to invite as contributors, as well as a chairman of one of these half-day sessions, outlanders from a sometime British Colony. The presence of foreigners I interpret as recognition that in the study of the scientific problems we face there are no national boundaries. For helminthiases in her own people, of course, Britain scarcely needs to be interested in chemotherapy. It is rather as a centre of increasing technological competence in this field, that added perspective should come from viewing anthelmintic possibilities, especially in tropical medicine, at a distance several degrees of latitude away from the equatorial zone.

The fact that a half-day's session on chemotherapeutic drugs is being devoted to helminthic infections has an added interpretation for me. It is a simple one and a serious one, namely, that we have a long, long way to go before we can bathe ourselves in a sense of satisfied achievement. Hall (1928) in his De Lamar lecture noted "that developments in anthelmintic medication comprise three epochs, as follows: First, centuries of uncritical empiricism; second, less than half a century of critical empiricism; and, third, a decade of critical experimental testing." In another place he went on to say "more definite information has been acquired ... in the past ten years than had been acquired in the previous centuries."

That was in 1928. Despite the considerable progress made since that time, particularly in the period after World War II, we are not yet in possession of a single drug against the worms of man that adequately fulfils professional requirements.

What are these requirements? In somewhat oversimplified statement I would say the anthelmintic for the intestinal nematodes of man, for instance, should at one and the same time be safe, be effective, be dispensable without individual prescription, and be cheap.

You will not make the mistake, nor did the Organizing Committee in inviting the speakers of this morning, nor did any of us in accepting (I hope I speak the truth),—you will not make the mistake of assuming we are so full of bright ideas that all that's needed beginning the day after tomorrow is to go home and rub an Aladdin's lamp. We may all agree, nevertheless, that in broaching even apparently unlikely or improbable solutions, as well as in exploring orthodox lines further, it is not impossible that some catalysis for the eventually successful effort could develop.

At this point may I emphasize that my own interest in anthelmintics is primarily with those designed for use against the worms of man; and among those worms it is the intestinal nematodes, and among the latter, particularly hookworm that demand attention. Why? Let me give a little of its dimension.

With malaria receding, hookworm comes into rank as the great unconquered infection in man in the warm moist tropical and subtropical regions of the earth. In my view it outranks in its toll all other worm infections of man combined. If a qualification is attached to such a statement it must be only for *Ascaris*; but the two are more often together than not, so measures against one must be measures against both.

In a recent extrapolation of prevalence (Stoll, 1947) over a fifth of the inhabitants of the planet were estimated to carry hookworms. There is no evidence that this ratio is decreasing, and one has legitimate suspicions it is increasing. Even as it stands, with a world population reaching by United Nations estimate three thousand millions in 1962, something over 600 million people now bear *Ancylostoma duodenale* (Dubini, 1843), or *Necator americanus* (Stiles, 1902), or both.

Hookworms are bloodletting. Irrespective of any other status concerning this infection something has been learned in recent years of the net blood loss in individuals inhabitated by hookworms. While there are some discrepancies in the data, it seems allowable to say this may average 0·1 ml. blood/worm/day. Something also has been learned over the years, directly by worm counts and indirectly in terms of egg counts, of the burdens carried by infested persons. The comprehensive studies of Keller, Leathers and Densen (1940) in several southern states of the U.S.A. may be taken as one evaluation of an average intensity of infestation for *Necator*. For 34,000 people, they being 17·7% of 192,000 examined, that average intensity was 2600 eggs/g. This is doubtless close to a minimum figure for hookworm-infected populations.

If we carry this a step further and assume as an index that 26 eggs/g. may represent a resident hookworm, then these average infections represent about 100 worms each, with a presumed blood-loss of 10 ml. per day. Tasker (1961), after worm counts, recently made determinations of about 8 ml. at this level of infection. For the infected moiety of the world population, 10 ml. daily blood loss is of the magnitude of the total blood volume of 1,500,000 persons. Thus the blood-sucking hookworms in man appear to be causing the loss each day, from the bodies of the infected, of a volume of blood equivalent to the sum of the blood volumes of the people of a city as large as Madras, or Istanbul, or Caracas; or a daily loss equivalent to the combined blood volumes of all the people in an entire country with the population, say of Albania, or of Nicaragua, or of the Togo Republic.

If this gives one graphic dimension of this extraordinary world problem, how can it be reached? This is not the platform from which to discuss its various aspects, but in summary I might quote an earlier expressed opinion (Stoll, 1961) that immunities, and nutrition, and anthelmintics, and genetics all have a contribution "although none of these, in present view, can *alone* take over control of worm-host systems, for the total protection of the host". One may with confidence predict that in the forseeable future the problem cannot be brought under control without the assistance of anthelmintics.

Accepting this as *a priori* to further discussion, let me return to the four requirements noted earlier for the anthelmintic we desire, and mention them now in reverse order: it, or they, must be cheap, be dispensable without prescription, be effective, and be safe.

Be cheap. Presently the two anthelmintics apparently most useful in the hookworm field differ in cost by a factor of about 10. How much advantage in dispensability, in effectiveness, and in safety must the expensive alternative possess to deserve survival in a world public health market? If it has no great advantage, aren't we faced with a problem primarily in chemical engineering to make the expensive drug approach the cheaper drug in price at the consumer level, in order that it become accessible to more millions of people?

Be dispensable without prescription. Like aspirin. Or perhaps dispensable in minute amounts wholesale, as is iodine in salt in areas of simple goitre. For the eventual anthelmintic these are self-evident necessities. Perhaps bearing on dispensability is the question of palatability. Here there are two schools of thought; one holds that unless drugs taste badly they do no good, the other that attractive flavour widens their use. I notice that drugs sold over the counter emphasize an appeal to their market by being of attractive flavour. Anthelmintics for tropical indigenes might also be flavoured to their tastes.

Be effective. An orthodox view was expressed recently as follows: "There are three criteria of the ideal anthelmintic. Firstly, it must have no toxic effects on the host. Secondly, it must remove or kill all the worms swiftly; and thirdly, it must be effective in small and easily administered single dose" (Hurly, 1960).

While I would give full approval to the "firstly", and have mentioned a potentially wholesale use as qualification of the single dose "thirdly", there are reasons for believing that the "secondly" is not the best expression of our goal. Is that goal necessarily the immediate and total annihilation of all the invaders in the host and at one treatment? Literal extirpation of the parasitic accumulation may seem at first thought logical, and it has long dominated our thinking, but it seems increasingly unrealistic biologically.

We have reached a point where we need to take a fresh look at our problem. The parasitism of man by hookworm, for instance, has been a long standing association indeed. Many are doubtless familiar with some words of Theobald Smith (1934): "Parasitism is in a sense a compromise or truce between two living things, accompanied by predatory processes whenever opportunity is offered by one or the other party. ... The pathological manifestations are only incidents in a developing parasitism". One cannot have observed over the years the manifestations of immunities that have become familiar in many comparative worm-host systems, without realizing that they must apply also, although to an as yet imperfectly defined degree, to hookworm in man (Stoll, 1962).

I trust at this point I am not intruding too much on the subject area of Dr. Soulsby in this programme. But if this view means what it appears to do, we need to revise our ideas of hookworm (and I think, of *Ascaris*, whipworm, and others) to the extent that under endemic conditions we come to regard it as capable of being a self-limiting infection, and as causing a self-limiting disease. Certain factors, it is true, condition that this will be the state of affairs. But the classic cases of profound anaemia are not to be regarded as the inevitable extrapolation of every exposure to endemic reinfection. Perhaps instead we should regard the classic cases as having the same relation to the worm-host problem that paralytic polio cases have to the presence of poliomyelitis virus infection moving in a population.

We need to restudy our therapeutic approach as one dealing not with a wholly susceptible population, but with a mixture of susceptibles and immunes of various degree.

There are ramifications arising from this position that I cannot well go into here. However, a few additional points may be brought forward. For instance, there is emerging from the study of comparative worm-host systems under conditions of reinfection this indication: that the host which shows a capacity to resist, to be immune, depends upon the continued presence and continued incoming of some worms for the development and maintenance of such resistance. This is probably no more mysterious than the necessity of a continuous feed-back of worm antigen of sorts into the host's protective mechanism. As I have emphasized in another place (Stoll, 1961), this is an assumption applicable widely for infectious agents, or parasites, of quite different character from worms.

It is of interest that saving a residue of worms in the host to act as incitement to development of its immune mechanism brings us to something of a parallelism with antibiotic intervention in infection with *Rickettsia tsutsugamushi*. Smadel *et al.* (1949) have noted that "the drug does not sterilize the tissues of mice and must be given for a long enough time to allow the animal to develop its immune processes sufficiently to control infection at the time when the inhibiting agent is discontinued".

If at this point we are on firm ground, we must conclude that complete dis-infestation by anthelmintic of individuals harbouring hookworms and living under endemic conditions is not a well-founded objective. What is needed is a knock-down of the individual infestation to bring it to smaller size. Unless worm-host systems of which man is a part differ from those among his biological relatives—and what evidence can be brought to bear indicates similarity instead—it is to be considered a disservice to the host exposed to reinfection to remove or kill all of his worms swiftly. One might suggest that against worm infestations the effective drug should achieve not mass murder but mayhem.

There will be little permanent progress against the worms of man in endemic areas through single treatment campaigns. Insofar as reliance for control is on anthelmintics they must be used again and again and again in the same area. The more to be desired then the cheap, dispensable, safe drug that reduces the size of infestation, than sacrifice of any of those three desirable criteria for the sake of a better killer.

With this, insofar as we are thinking of the effective antihookworm drug, must go the necessary postscript, that it should operate in parallel fashion in relation to the habitually associated *Ascaris*, and, ideally, also in relation to the whipworm.

Be safe. Hall and Shillinger (1925) pointed out long ago that "The question of the safety of the drug is naturally one of major importance". This was true then, and is now, as witness the testing for toxicity of the preparations furnished by the chemist as the first step in defining their possible usefulness.

I have neither wish nor competence to raise suggestions on the chemical formulation of drugs in this field. My only published association with anthelmintics is as joint author thirty-five years ago, of one of the early reports on the use of tetrachlorethylene in man (Schapiro and Stoll, 1927). As a spectator of the current scene I am enormously impressed when I see an array of hundreds and hundreds of dark bottles that have come from the chemist's laboratory, each with a few milligrams or grams of precious white powder, brought to this point at a cost of 500 to 750 pounds sterling each, and awaiting screening first for host toxicity, and, if favourable, for selective toxicity as between parasite and host. This has been the path, most of it unexciting and laborious, that has produced progress in this field.

Contrariwise, as a biologist one may wonder sometimes whether the exploring isn't too restricted; whether we shouldn't graduate from such basic philosophy as that phrased by Hall (1928) over 30 years ago, namely that "the medical man should always keep in mind that the anthelmintics are poisons intended for administration in such doses and in such a way as to most effectively destroy the worms with the minimum amount of damage to the patient".

Selective poisoning, as such, in view of the limited knowledge so far available as to the biochemical targets within the parasite, raises a question. It is as to whether ways should not be found to encourage more investigation for selection of such targets. I realize that this may not be appropriate for the pharmaceutical industry to undertake in its own laboratories. Might there not be gains in stimulating a very considerable research outside them?

If such investigations are stimulated, I make bold to offer two suggestions. They each arise from the enormous fecundity of the parasites. *N. americanus* females appear capable, when uncrowded, of laying about 9,000 eggs each day, *A. duodenale* two or three times that and *Ascaris* over twenty times that. Yet the odds against the parasite getting another parasite back to the host are equally enormous.

In a study of sheep infections for such an analysis it appeared that under almost ideal reinfection conditions, while the female parasite, *Haemonchus contortus*, oviposited at the rate of 8,000 eggs a day, on the average only one of those eggs resulted in another worm being established in the host while that host was fully susceptible (Stoll, 1932). One may assume that similar conditions obtain for the worm-host systems of man. If then interference with, or depression of, egg-laying of the female worms were achieved, decrease in reinfection would follow as the day the night. We are already aware that several of our known anthelmintics interfere temporarily with egg-laying by surviving female worms—a factor incidentally that has frequently introduced error in post-treatment examinations, with resulting spurious evaluations.

Perhaps a more direct hormonal interference, as in another area of human interest, with a progestin or its nemic equivalent, represents a productive approach.

In another direction, attack on the problem of worm infestations in man has made little use of a finding that has turned out to be of value in another area. I refer to the inability of strongyloid worms to grow during their free life in the dung of animals receiving phenothiazine in small daily doses (Habermann and Shorb, 1942). This is not a suggestion for the rehabilitation of phenothiazine in our armamentarium against worms in man, but it is doubtful whether this is the only drug producing such deleterious effects in faeces. As Harwood (1953) also points out "this proven activity of phenothiazine against pre-infective larvae offers an unique opportunity to study action of an anthelmintic outside of the host". Hall (1928) mentions that Perroncito's recommendation in 1880 of ethereal extract of male fern was based on tests on hookworm larvae *in vitro*.

Moreover, besides clinging to the orthodox approach of a single rapidly acting dose, should not consideration be given to devices permitting long-drawn-out effects? One thinks of parenteral preparations administered by needle with adjuvants and the pharmaceutical art has devised other methods of approach to secure prolonged action.

It is not my purpose to make inroads, real or implied, on the contributions scheduled for this morning but there is one general point that my interest as a biologist causes me to re-emphasize.

On a broad biological basis, we are under the necessity of remembering that with such forms as hookworms and related roundworms, we are dealing with one of the most resourceful of parasite groups. They demonstrate this, for instance, in the number of individuals they infect. Thus nematodes have established themselves in human hosts in approximately ten times the number of people as are parasitized by all the flatworm species, trematodes *plus* cestodes. "This is doubtless a tribute to the variety and comparative biological efficiency of nematode life cycles. All cestodes reach man by the host's own act, albeit at times not consciously, through ingestion by man of egg or larval forms; trematodes similarly reach him passively, through ingestion of larval forms, but in addition actively through the parasites' own efforts, as witness schistosome cercariae. It is, however, the nematodes that exhibit the most varied methods. They reach man by his own act of ingesting ova that have been recently passed, and ova that have had to ripen externally for days or weeks; by his own act of ingesting larval forms in water, and larval forms in food. They also reach him not through his own act but on the initiative of the parasites themselves, infective larvae actively penetrating his bare skin in contact with moist soil, and actively penetrating his skin in contact with the mouthparts of blood-sucking insects which reached him by air-borne tactics. Each of five helminthic species, illustrating four of these nemic life-history styles, registers more human infections than either all the cestodiases or all the trematodiases. Only two in the classification, namely *Dracunculus* and *Trichinella*, which come in by water and food, show so few parasitisms as do the food-transported flatworm species" (Stoll, 1947).

This biological resiliency of nematodes as parasites must reflect a long, long association with man as a host. *A. duodenale* didn't begin with Dubini in 1843 nor *N. americanus* with Stiles in 1902. It was just our awareness that was new. While the direct evidence is lacking, we may assume hookworms, for instance, have been in man for at least the three thousand generations that take us back to early cultures. I myself am convinced, seeing their nemic cousins are present in almost every mammalian species, that hookworms have been with the genus *Homo* since the nearly 1 million years allotted to it by Le Gros Clark (1959), if indeed they have not been in the antecedent primates for nearly another 74 million years.

If this is only remotely true, both hookworm and human species must have evolved a method for getting on with one another so that in civilizations that were cradled in the moist warm areas of the

earth, both hookworm and human species survived, forcing selection, so to speak, on one another. In the epic way of Nature, this
involved among other things selection of genetic strains of man
capable of living and associating with those genetic strains of the
parasites being selected as capable of adaptation to changing man.

As much should be said of *Ascaris* and of each of the other
familiar nematodes of man.

We may thus be well advised to remember that in worm-host
associations which we wish to interrupt with anthelmintics, we
are dealing with biological entities that have been a long time
forming, and represent no opportunity for easy and permanent
separation.

To quote again from an old friend, who died too young, but
who remains one of the most distinguished contributors to this
field, Maurice C. Hall (1928) once said:

"There must be reasons for the specificity of anthelmintics for
worms, and perhaps these reasons can be ascertained. ... As in all
other fields of human knowledge, what we know is much less than
what we do not know, and the general subject of anthelmintics is
and will long remain a problem for investigation".

REFERENCES

CLARK, W. E. LE G. (1959). The Antecedents of Man. Edinburgh: Edinburgh
Univ. Press.
DUBINI, A. (1843). *Ann. Univ. Med., Milano*, **106**, 5.
HABERMANN, R. T. and SHORB, D. A. (1942). *N. Amer. Vet.*, **23**, 318.
HALL, M. C. (1928). *In*, De Lamar Lectures 1927–28, Johns Hopkins Univ.
School of Hygiene and Public Health, Baltimore: Williams and Wilkins
Press, pp. 1–23.
HALL, M. C. and SHILLINGER, J. E. (1925). *Amer. J. trop Med.* **5**, 229.
HARWOOD, P. D. (1953). *Exp. Parasitol.*, **2**, 428.
HURLY, M. G. D. (1960). *Cent. Afr. J. Med.*, **6**, 348.
KELLER, A. E., LEATHERS, W. S. and DENSEN, P. M. (1940). *Amer. J. trop. Med.*, **20**, 493.
SCHAPIRO, L. and STOLL, N. R. (1927). *Amer. J. trop. Med.*, **7**, 193.
SMADEL, J. E., TRAUB, R., LEY, H. L., PHILIP, C. B., WOODWARD, T. E. and
LEWTHWAITE, R. (1949). *Amer. J. Hyg.*, **50**, 75.

SMITH, T. (1934). Parasitism and Disease. Princeton: Princeton Univ. Press.
STILES, C. W. (1902). *Amer. Med.*, **3,** 777.
STOLL, N. R. (1932). *Amer. J. Hyg.*, **16,** 783.
STOLL, N. R. (1947). *J. Parasitol.*, **33,** 1.
STOLL, N. R. (1961). *Amer. J. trop. Med. Hyg.*, **10,** 293.
STOLL, N. R. (1962). *Exp. Parasitol.*, **12,** in press.
TASKER, P. W. G. (1961). *Trans. R. Soc. trop. Med. Hyg.*, **55,** 36.

MODE OF ACTION OF ANTHELMINTICS

E. BUEDING

*Department of Pathobiology, School of Hygiene and Public Health,
Johns Hopkins University, Baltimore*

ALTHOUGH anthelmintics are among the oldest group of drugs used by man, little, if any, knowledge about their mode of action was available as recently as fifteen years ago. Perhaps it is no coincidence that lack of information about this subject at that time was associated with the relatively unsatisfactory status of anthelmintic agents, both from the standpoint of effectiveness and of absence of untoward side effects.

The first group of compounds which yielded some information about the mechanisms of their anthelmintic action and about the comparative biochemistry of parasitic worms were the cyanine dyes. Cyanines contain the resonating amidinium ion system in which a quaternary nitrogen is linked to a tertiary nitrogen by a conjugated chain of an uneven number of carbon atoms (Brooker, 1945, 1954):

$$>\overset{+}{N}=C-C-(-C=C-)_n-N< \quad \Longleftrightarrow \quad >N-C=(=C-C=)_n=\overset{+}{N}<$$

In the course of investigations initiated by Brooker and Sweet (1947), and designed to determine the biological properties of cyanine dyes, it was found that they have high activity *in vivo* and *in vitro* against a filarial worm, *Litomosoides carinii*, a parasite invading the pleural cavity of the cotton rat (Welch *et al.*, 1947; Wright *et al.*, 1948; Peters *et al.*, 1949). This activity is not restricted to any particular ring; the structural property conferring this activity is the amidinium ion resonance. Low concentrations of a large number of cyanines produce an inhibition of the oxygen

15

uptake of adult *Litomosoides* (Welch *et al.*, 1947; Peters *et al.*, 1949; Bueding, 1949*a*). This respiratory inhibition is associated with an increase in aerobic glycolysis. The metabolic effects of cyanines are not limited to conditions *in vitro* because the oxygen uptake of filariae of cotton rats to whom subcurative doses of cyanines has been administered is decreased also and aerobic glycolysis of these worms is increased (Bueding, 1949*a*). Therefore, it appears that these compounds exert their chemotherapeutic effect through inhibition of enzyme systems concerned with oxidative metabolism. Again, any structural modification which eliminates amidinium ion resonance abolishes the inhibitory effect on filarial respiration (Peters *et al.*, 1949). Concentrations of cyanine dyes a thousand times higher than those inhibiting the oxygen uptake of *Litomosoides* have no effect on the respiration of slices or homogenates of mammalian tissues or on the activities of cytochrome *c* or of cytochrome oxidase. Neither of the latter two respiratory enzymes could be detected in *Litomosoides* (Bueding, 1949*a*). Therefore, it appears that cyanines interfere in these worms with respiratory enzyme systems which play no rôle, or only a minor one, in mammalian tissues.

In contrast, cyanines have no chemotherapeutic activity *in vivo* against a filarial worm of man, *Wuchereria bancrofti* (Santiago-Stevenson, Welch, Oliver-González and Peters, unpublished observations) and against the trematode, *Schistosoma mansoni* (Bueding *et al.*, 1953). Yet, cyanines depress the respiration of schistosomes *in vitro* and *in vivo* (Bueding, 1950; Bueding *et al.*, 1953). For example, after repeated administrations of a cyanine dye to schistosome-infected hamsters, the oxygen uptake of the worms removed from these animals is inhibited markedly. Yet, under these conditions schistosomes continue to survive and to produce viable eggs (Bueding *et al.*, 1953). In spite of the relatively high oxygen tension of their natural habitat, and in contrast to *L. carinii*, oxidative metabolism does not supply a major portion of the energy required for survival and egg production of schistosomes.

This is also borne out by the fact that the rate of glycolysis of schistosomes is not affected by oxidative metabolism (Bueding, 1950). If this parasite were dependent on aerobic metabolism, inhibition of oxidative reactions by cyanine dyes should result in a compensatory increase in the rate of carbohydrate utilization and of glycolysis. The complete lack of chemotherapeutic activity of cyanines against *W. bancrofti* suggests that this filarial worm, unlike *Litomosoides*, does not depend on aerobic metabolism.

While these initial studies indicated that cyanines are of no value in the treatment of human filariasis or schistosomiasis, they provided some insight into the physiology of parasitic helminths. Furthermore they demonstrated that, despite the close morphological relationship between *L. carinii* and *W. bancrofti*, biochemical differences must exist between these two filarial worms. The chemotherapeutic actions of cyanines against *Litomosoides* and their lack of activity against *Wuchereria* demonstrate that the sensitivity of a parasitic worm to anthelmintic agents is determined to a much greater degree by biochemical, than by morphological or taxonomic characteristics.

In subsequent investigations of Hales and Welch (1953) and of Weston *et al.* (1953), it was found that cyanines have chemotherapeutic activity against a number of intestinal nematodes of dogs, rats, and mice. These observations led to the development of a cyanine dye, pyrvinium chloride (I), which proved highly effective in the treatment of human pinworm infections (Royer, 1956; Sawitz and Karpinski, 1956). Another cyanine dye, dithiazanine (II), was found to have marked activity in human infections caused by four intestinal nematodes, *Ascaris, Oxyuris, Trichuris trichura,* and *Strongyloides stercoralis* (Swartzwelder *et al.*, 1957; Bueding and Swartzwelder, 1957). Although this dye, in contrast to pyrvinium, is not devoid of toxic side effects, some structural modifications of dithiazanine might provide opportunities for the development of a cyanine with similar anthelmintic activities, but devoid of untoward actions on the host.

The oxygen tension of the habitat of the intestinal nematodes against which pyrvinium and dithiazanine are effective is extremely low. Furthermore, these parasites depend for survival on anaerobic rather than on aerobic metabolism (Bueding, 1949b; Von Brand, 1952). Therefore, it would appear that the chemotherapeutic actions of these two cyanine dyes are brought about by a mechanism other than inhibition of oxidative reactions.

Biochemical effects of dithiazanine

An attempt has been made to study this problem by determining the biochemical effects of dithiazanine on *Trichuris vulpis,* the canine whip-worm which is highly susceptible to the chemotherapeutic actions of this cyanine dye. In a synthetic medium this worm survives for significantly longer periods of time in an atmosphere containing 5% CO_2 in nitrogen than in 5% CO_2 in air or oxygen. Therefore, *T. vulpis* does not depend on oxidative metabolism for survival (Bueding *et al.*, 1960).

Concentrations of dithiazanine *lower* than those which affect the motility of the worms significantly inhibit their rate of glucose uptake. Therefore, dithiazanine has a direct effect upon the carbo-hydrate metabolism of *T. vulpis* and this biochemical change is not secondary to a reduction in the motility of the worm. When the organisms are exposed for 24 hours to concentrations ranging from 0·1 to 0·2 μg. of the drug/ml. and are then transferred into a dithiazanine-free medium, the inhibition of glucose uptake per-sists and becomes even more pronounced. Therefore, this meta-bolic effect of dithiazanine is irreversible. Exposure of the worms to concentrations of dithiazanine which produce a reduction in glucose uptake results in a marked decrease in the concentrations of free glucose, of ATP, and of glycogen in the worms (Bueding *et al.*, 1960). If the decrease in glucose uptake were due to an inhibition of one or of several enzymes concerned with the intra-cellular metabolism of carbohydrate, there would be an accumula-tion of glucose within the worm. However, the reduction of glucose uptake produced by dithiazanine is associated with a marked decrease in the concentration of free glucose in the parasite. Therefore, it is apparent that dithiazanine interferes with the uptake of glucose from the medium, rather than with its utilisation. Reduced availability of exogenous glucose, due to an inhibition of the transport of this sugar into the parasite, should increase the utilization of endogenous carbohydrate reserves. This is consistent with the observed marked decrease in the concentration of glyco-gen in worms which had been incubated with dithiazanine, indica-ting again that dithiazanine does not interfere with the intracellular utilization of carbohydrate. Furthermore, even high concentrations of dithiazanine have no inhibitory effect on the activity of hexokin-ase of *T. vulpis*; therefore, the cyanine dye does not inhibit the phosphorylation of glucose present in the parasite. It is concluded that the depletion of the carbohydrate reserves is secondary to the decreased availability of exogenous glucose, due to interference by dithiazanine with the transport of this sugar into the worm. This circumstance, in turn, leads to a decrease in the rate at which energy-rich phosphate bonds are generated, and accounts for the reduction in the concentration of ATP in the parasite. Owing to these changes in carbohydrate metabolism, brought about by dithiazanine, the supply of energy required for survival is decreased and eventually should become inadequate, resulting in the death of the worms.

Other cyanine dyes which are potent inhibitors of the oxidative metabolism of *L. carinii* have biochemical effects on *T. vulpis* similar to those of dithiazanine. However, considerably higher concentrations are required; also these actions are reversible (Bueding *et al.*, 1960). Among individual cyanines there is no parallelism between their potency with respect to their inhibitory effects on respiration on the one hand, and on glucose transport on the other. Thus, it appears that two unrelated mechanisms are involved.

Antimony and schistosomiasis

The failure of cyanines as chemotherapeutic agents in experimental schistosomiasis has revealed that schistosomes depend primarily on anaerobic metabolism for their survival and reproduction. Subsequently it was found that anaerobic utilization of carbohydrate to lactic acid, *via* the Embden-Meyerhof scheme of phosphorylating glycolysis represents the major source of energy for these parasites (Bueding, 1950; Bueding and Peters, 1951). Therefore, it is of interest that trivalent organic antimonials such as potassium antimonyl tartrate and stibophen, which have chemotherapeutic activity in schistosomiasis, inhibit the rate of glycolysis of schistosomes. By the use of cell-free extracts of these organisms it was found that antimonials interfere with a single step in glycolysis, the phosphorylation of fructose-6-phosphate by adenosine triphosphate resulting in the formation of fructose-1,6-diphosphate and adenosine diphosphate (Mansour and Bueding, 1954). This reaction is catalyzed by phosphofructokinase, and direct measurements of the effects of antimonials on schistosome phosphofructokinase confirmed that these compounds markedly inhibit the activity of this enzyme. By contrast, mammalian phosphofructokinases have a much lower sensitivity towards antimonials and at least 80 times higher concentrations of antimonials are required to inhibit the mammalian enzyme to the same extent (Mansour and Bueding, 1954). This selective effect of antimonials demonstrates that enzymes which have the same catalytic function in the parasite and in the host are not necessarily identical. Such differences not only account for the selective inhibitory effect of antimonials on schistosome phosphofructokinase, but also provide additional opportunities for interfering by means of chemical agents with the functional integrity of an enzyme of the parasite without affecting the enzyme which catalyses the same reaction in the host. Kinetic and immunological differences of other homologous enzymes of *S. mansoni* and of mammalian tissues have been demonstrated in three other glycolytic enzymes, hexokinase (Bueding and Mac-Kinnon, 1955a), phosphoglucose isomerase (Bueding and Mac-Kinnon, 1955b), and lactic dehydrogenase (Mansour, Bueding and Stavitsky, 1954; Henion, Mansour and Bueding, 1955).

The inhibitory effect of antimonials on the production of lactic acid from glucose by schistosome extracts is abolished by the addition of purified mammalian phosphofructokinase (Bueding and Mansour, 1957). Therefore, inhibition of schistosome phosphofructokinase activity by antimonials accounts for the inhibitory effects of these compounds on the rate of glycolysis catalysed by schistosome extracts. Inhibition of phosphofructokinase activity of schistosomes brings about decreased formation, and thus a lower concentration, of fructose-1,6-diphosphate; this in turn results in a decrease in the activity of aldolase which limits the rate of glycolysis of schistosomes.

The selective action of antimonials on phosphofructokinase activity of schistosomes can be demonstrated not only in cell-free extracts and isolated enzyme preparations of the worms, but also in the intact parasite after exposure to subeffective concentrations of an antimonial *in vitro* or *in vivo*. For example, after administration of subcurative dosage schedules of stibophen to schistosome-infected mice, the substrate of the phosphofructokinase reaction in the worms, fructose-6-phosphate, accumulates while there is a marked reduction in the concentration of the product, hexosediphosphate (Bueding and Mansour, 1957). Thus, under these conditions, the activity of the enzyme is inhibited in the intact worm and inhibition of phosphofructokinase activity can account for the chemotherapeutic actions of antimonials in schistosomiasis.

Alkyldibenzylamines

While antimonials have a marked inhibitory effect on a glycolytic enzyme of schistosomes, another group of antischistosomal compounds exert their action through a different mechanism. Although their activity appears to be limited to conditions *in vitro*, they have been useful in uncovering another phase of carbohydrate metabolism, inhibition of which has a deleterious effect on the parasite. As reported by McCowen *et al.* (1954), low concentrations of a number of symmetrical alkyldibenzylamines have amoebicidal properties. Some of these compounds exhibit antischistosomal activity *in vitro*. The most active compound in this respect was found to be 1,6 bis-[*p*-(*N*-methylaminomethyl)-phenoxy]-hexane (III)(Bueding, 1962):

$$H_3C \cdot HN \cdot H_2C \text{—} \langle \text{—} \rangle \text{—} O \cdot [CH_2]_6 \cdot O \text{—} \langle \text{—} \rangle \text{—} CH_2 \cdot NH \cdot CH_3$$

III

In the presence of subeffective concentrations of this diamine, glucose utilization of intact schistosomes is reduced significantly, but lactic acid formation is inhibited to a much lesser degree. Therefore, under these conditions, some lactic acid must have been produced from endogenous sources. This was confirmed by the observation that changes in the motility, produced by the diamine, were preceded by a marked increase in the rate of glycogenolysis of the worms. In contrast to these effects of the diamine on the carbohydrate metabolism of *intact* schistosomes, even ten times higher concentrations of this compound did not affect the rate of glycolysis of cell-free extracts of the parasites. Also, under these conditions the activities of hexokinase, of phosphorylase, of adenosine triphosphatase or of phosphoglucomutase were not altered (Bueding, 1962). Because of the absence of any direct effect of diamines on enzymes involved in the carbohydrate metabolism of the parasite, it appears that these compounds interfere with the active transport of glucose into the worm and that increased glycogenolysis is secondary to a reduced availability of exogenous glucose.

During the exposure of schistosomes to low concentrations of both a diamine and of stibophen, survival of the parasite is reduced

$$\underset{R_2}{\overset{R_1}{N}}-\text{<benzene ring>}-O\cdot[CH_2]_n\cdot O-\text{<benzene ring>}-N\underset{R_2}{\overset{R_1}{}}$$

IV

to a much greater degree in the presence of both these compounds than with the same concentration of each compound alone (Bueding, 1962). Therefore, schistosomes are more vulnerable to *simultaneous* inhibition of phosphofructokinase activity and of glucose transport than to interference with only one of these phases of carbohydrate utilisation. Also, this phenomenon suggests that reduction of the dosage of antimonials below the presently used effective but toxic levels, without reduction of their chemotherapeutic activity, might be possible if inhibition of glucose transport into schistosomes within their host could be accomplished.

Structurally, alkyldibenzylamines are related to a group of diaminophenoxyalkanes (IV) which have been studied extensively by Standen and Walls (1956) and which have high antischistosomal activity *in vivo*. The mode of action of these aniline derivatives differs from that of the benzylic diamines; they produce marked, morphologically demonstrable, destructive changes in the cuticle of the worms (Standen, 1955a).

Piperazine

Perhaps the most significant advance in the field of anthelmintics during the past decade has been the introduction of piperazine for the treatment of roundworm and threadworm infections. Piperazine paralyzes *Ascaris* muscle (Standen, 1955b); this results in the expulsion of the worm through the peristalsis of the host's intestine. The mechanism of this paralyzing action of piperazine has been elucidated by Norton and deBeer (1957). They found that low concentrations of acetylcholine produce a contraction of *Ascaris* muscle and that piperazine blocks this response. The blocking action of piperazine can be reversed competitively by acetylcholine. Therefore, in *Ascaris*, piperazine acts as a myoneural blocking agent. In comparison with piperazine, *d*-tubocurarine has relatively weak neuromuscular blocking effects on *Ascaris* muscle. Conversely, piperazine exerts virtually no myoneural blocking action on mammalian skeletal muscle (Norton and deBeer, 1957). This, in part, explains the lack of toxicity of this anthelmintic to the host. It is of interest that frog muscle occupies a somewhat intermediate position in this respect because its response to acetylcholine is blocked readily both by *d*-tubocurarine and by piperazine (S. Norton, personal communication). In any case, the anthelmintic activity and the low host toxicity of piperazine must be based on differences in the nature of the myoneural receptors between the host and the parasite. This supplies another example for the differences in the nature of biological systems which have similar functions and responses in the parasite and its host.

Ascaris produces large quantities of succinic acid under aerobic and anaerobic conditions (Bueding and Farrow, 1956; Bueding, Saz and Farrow, 1959). During incubation of *Ascaris* with paralysing concentrations of piperazine, succinate formation is reduced (Bueding *et al.*, 1959). As shown by Standen (1955b), the paralysing effect of piperzine on *Ascaris* is reversible and on transfer of the paralysed mematodes into a piperazine-free medium, motility is resumed. This is associated with an increase in succinate production to its original control level (Bueding *et al.*, 1959). It should be noted that there is a high degree of parallelism between the paralysing action of piperazine and the inhibition of succinate production. This brings up the question about the causal relationship between the reduced formation of succinate and the neuromuscular blocking action of piperazine. Using ^{14}C-labelled lactate, Saz and Vidrine (1959) have shown that *Ascaris* muscle strips produce succinate by CO_2 fixation into pyruvate, giving rise to malate. Interconversion of malate to fumarate is catalysed by a fumarase (Saz and Hubbard, 1957). Fumarate, in turn, is reduced to succinate. Since paralysing concentrations of piperazine have no effect on this series of reactions (Bueding *et al.*, 1959), the inhibition of succinate production by this drug is the result rather than the cause of the myoneural blockade. In skeletal muscle of vertebrates the energy from the anaerobic conversion of carbohydrate to lactic acid is utilized ultimately for muscular contraction through resynthesis of energy-rich phosphate compounds, such as adenosine triphosphate and creatine phosphate. On the other hand, lactic acid production by *Ascaris* is insignificant, despite the occurrence in *Ascaris* muscle of systems catalysing the formation of pyruvate *via* the Embden-Meyerhof scheme of phosphorylating glycolysis (Bueding and Yale, 1951). While in the host tissues pyruvate is converted to lactate, in *Ascaris* muscle CO_2 fixation into pyruvate eventually results in the formation of succinate (Saz and Vidrine, 1959). The last step in this series of reactions is catalysed by a mitochondrial system of *Ascaris* muscle. In this system, electrons from reduced coenzyme (DPNH) may be directed either to oxygen or, under the anaerobic conditions of the physiological habitat of *Ascaris*, to fumarate (Kmetec and Bueding, 1961). Evidence has been obtained indicating that in this system transfer of electrons from DPNH is coupled with phosphorylations under both aerobic and anaerobic

2

conditions (Chin and Bueding, 1954; Seidman and Entner, 1961). Succinate production could therefore supply energy-rich phosphate bonds for the contraction of *Ascaris* muscle. Reduction or suppression of muscular contraction by piperazine lowers the energy requirement of *Ascaris* muscle and thus can account for a decrease in succinate production.

According to observations of Broome (1961), acetylcholine does not antagonize the paralysis of *Ascaris* muscle produced by another anthelmintic, 2-(β-methoxyethyl) pyridine (see p. 47), whose mode of action appears to be comparable with the depolarizing effects of decamethonium on the myoneural junction.

p-*Rosaniline salts*

Recently, reduction of muscular activity of a parasitic worm has been observed as a result of the action of another anthelmintic agent. The chemotherapeutic activity of tris(p-aminophenyl) carbonium salts in experimental schistosomiasis was reported by Elslager *et al.* (1961), and by Thompson, Meisenhelder and Najarian (1962). Worms removed from mice which had received sub-curative doses of this compound exhibited no demonstrable changes in their carbohydrate and protein metabolism. On the other hand, a localized paralysis of the acetabulum and of the oral sucker was observed in these parasites. This functional defect was reversed consistently by low concentrations of the ganglionic blocking agent mecamylamine (Bueding, Schiller and Timms, unpublished observations). Since cholinergic agents reduce the muscular activity of schistosomes and since mecamylamine is blocking this effect (Bueding, 1962), it appears that administration of the carbonium derivative to the host brings about a localized accumulation of acetylcholine in the parasite. Using histochemical methods, it was observed that, following administration of the carbonium compound, there is a pronounced decrease in the cholinesterase activity in the central ganglia of the worms (Douglas, Ansari and Bueding, 1962, unpublished). Inhibition of cholines terase activity resulting in an accumulation of acetylcholine could impair the co-ordinated movements of the acetabulum and of the oral sucker. This in turn could bring about the loss of attachment of the worms to the mesenteric veins, as well as the development of nutritional deficiences of the parasites and thereby could account for the chemotherapeutic effect of the carbonium derivative.

This review of recent studies dealing with the mode of action of anthelmintics suggests that such investigations are not without reward to the physiologist and to the biochemist because they uncover basic mechanisms essential for that functional integrity of the organism which is affected by the antiparasitic agent. In addition, such an approach should reveal, within the parasite, more and more vulnerable points susceptible to inhibition by chemical agents and thereby eventually contribute to a more rational development of effective chemotherapeutic compounds.

Acknowledgements

The investigations of the author quoted in this review were supported by research grants from the National Institutes of Health (E-3515), U. S. Public Health Service, from Eli Lilly and from Burroughs Wellcome.

[Discussion on this paper was postponed until after the following paper by R. Gönnert and H. Kölling; see p. 40.]

REFERENCES

BROOKER, L. G. S. (1945). Frontiers in Chemistry, ed. Burk, R. E. and Grummit, O. New York: Interscience Publ., **3**, 63.

BROOKER, L. G. S. (1954). Theory of the photographic process, ed. Mees, C. E. K. New York: McMillan Co., p. 371.

BROOKER, L. G. S. and SWEET, L. A. (1947). *Science*, **105**, 496.

BROOME, A. W. J. (1961). *Brit. J. Pharmacol.*, **17**, 327.

BUEDING, E. (1949a). *J. exp. Med.*, **89**, 107.

BUEDING, E. (1949b). *Physiol. Rev.*, **29**, 195.

BUEDING, E. (1950). *J. gen. Physiol.*, **33**, 475.

BUEDING, E. (1962). *Biochem. Pharmacol.*, **11**, 17.

BUEDING, E. and FARROW, G.W. (1956). *Exp. Parasitol.*, **5**, 345.

BUEDING, E., KMETEC, E., SWARTZWELDER, C., ABADIE, S. and SAZ, H. J. (1960). *Biochem. Pharmacol.*, **5**, 311.

BUEDING, E. and MACKINNON, J. A. (1955a). *J. biol. Chem.*, **215**, 495.
BUEDING, E. and MACKINNON, J. A. (1955b). *J. biol. Chem.*, **215**, 507.
BUEDING, E. and MANSOUR, J. M. (1957). *Brit. J. Pharmacol.*, **12**, 159.
BUEDING, E. and PETERS, L. (1951). *J. Pharmacol.*, **101**, 210.
BUEDING, E., PETERS, L., KOLETSKY, S. and MOORE, D. (1953). *Brit. J. Pharmacol.*, **8**, 15.
BUEDING, E., SAZ, H. J. and FARROW, G. W. (1959). *Brit. J. Pharmacol.*, **14**, 497.
BUEDING, E. and SWARTZWELDER, J. (1957). *Pharmacol. Rev.*, **9**, 329.
BUEDING, E. and YALE, H. W. (1951). *J. biol. Chem.*, **193**, 411.
CHIN, C. H. and BUEDING, E. (1954). *Biochim. biophys. Acta*, **13**, 331.
ELSLAGER, E. F., SHORT, F. W., WORTH, D. F., MEISENHELDER, J. E., NAJARIAN, H. and THOMPSON, P. E. (1961). *Nature, Lond.*, **190**, 628.
HALES, D. H. and WELCH, A. D. (1953). *J. Pharmacol.*, **107**, 310.
HENION, W. E., MANSOUR, T. E. and BUEDING, E. (1955). *Exp. Parasitol.*, **4**, 40.
KMETEC, E. and BUEDING, E. (1961). *J. biol. Chem.*, **236**, 584.
MANSOUR, T. E. and BUEDING, E. (1954). *Brit. J. Pharmacol.*, **9**, 459.
MANSOUR, T. E., BUEDING, E. and STAVITSKY, A. B. (1954). *Brit. J. Pharmacol.*, **9**, 182.
MCCOWEN, M. C., CALLENDER, M. E., RENNELL, T. and LAWLIS, J. F. (1954). *Antibiot. Chemother.*, **4**, 753.
NORTON, S. and DEBEER, E. J. (1957). *Amer. J. trop. Med. Hyg.*, **6**, 898.
PETERS, L., BUEDING, E., VALK, A., HIGASHI, A. and WELCH, A. D. (1949). *J. Pharmacol.*, **95**, 212.
ROYER, A. (1956). *Canad. med. Assn. J.*, **74**, 297.
SAWITZ, W. G., and KARPINSKI, F. E. (1956). *Amer. J. trop. Med. Hyg.*, **5**, 538.
SAZ, H. J. and HUBBARD, J. A. (1957). *J. biol. Chem.*, **225**, 921.
SAZ, H. J. and VIDRINE, A., JR. (1959). *J. biol. Chem.*, **234**, 2001.
SEIDMAN, I. and ENTNER, N. (1961). *J. biol. Chem.*, **236**, 915.
STANDEN, O. D. (1955a). *Trans. R. Soc. trop. Med. Hyg.*, **49**, 416.
STANDEN, O. D. (1955b). *Brit. med. J.*, **2**, 20.
STANDEN, O. D. and WALLS, L. P. (1956). *Brit. J. Pharmacol.*, **11**, 375.
SWARTZWELDER, J. C., FRYE, W. W., MUHLEISEN, P. J., MILLER, J. H., LAMPERT, R., ANTHONY, S. O., PENA-CHAVARRIA, A., ABADIE, S. H. and SAPPENFIELD, R. W. (1957). *J. Amer. med. Assn.*, **165**, 2063.
THOMPSON, P. E., MEISENHELDER, J. E. and NAJARIAN, H. (1962). *Amer. J. trop. Med. Hyg.* **11**, 31.
VON BRAND, T. (1952). Chemical physiology of endoparasitic animals. New York: Academic Press.
WELCH, A. D., PETERS, L., BUEDING, E., VALK, A. and HIGASHI, A. (1947). *Science*, **105**, 486.
WESTON, J. K., THOMPSON, P. E., REINERTON, J. W., FISKEN, R. A. and REUTNER, T. F. (1953). *J. Pharmacol.*, **107**, 315.
WRIGHT, H. N., BIETER, E. H., CRANSTON, E. H., CUCKLER, D. C., LICHFIELD, J. T. and BREY, T. (1948). *Ann. N.Y. Acad. Sci.*, **50**, 109.

THIOXANTHONES AND RELATED COMPOUNDS IN EXPERIMENTAL SCHISTOSOMIASIS

R. Gönnert and H. Kölling

Farbenfabriken Bayer, AG., Wuppertal—Elberfeld

For the chemotherapist one of the most interesting problems is the clarification of relationships between the chemical constitution and biological activity of drugs. In spite of intensive work carried out over decades, especially in the research laboratories of the pharmaceutical industry, our knowledge of these relationships is still poor. Chemotherapy therefore is a predominantly empirical

science and with few exceptions it must be admitted that the connections between constitution and efficacy can only be understood and analysed in retrospect. It would be a considerable gain for pharmaceutical research if, from a given constitution, conclusions as to a particular activity might be drawn with greater accuracy. This goal, however, is difficult to attain because the efficacy of drugs can be influenced by numerous factors such as the route of application, the species and strain of both the causative agent and the host.

The work on xanthones, thioxanthones and other chemical classes and the testing of these compounds in experimental schistosomiasis in mice has led to the introduction of lucanthone (I; miracil D) for the treatment of human schistosomiasis and has given us a good insight into the connection between constitution and biological activity. A wealth of material is available, but a detailed representation is out of the question. We therefore shall restrict ourselves mainly to *Schistosoma mansoni* (Liberian strain) infections in the mouse. Methods of investigation, and the evaluation of results are described by Kikuth and Gönnert (1948, 1949) who were the first to develop a schistosomiasis test for screening purposes. Data on the schistosomicidal efficacy of the compounds are presented by means of diagrams. This type of presentation has the advantage of being more instructive and permits the demonstration of the graded effectiveness of individual doses together with the toxicity of the compound in question. In addition, the gradual transition from toxic to tolerated and from effective to ineffective doses becomes evident.

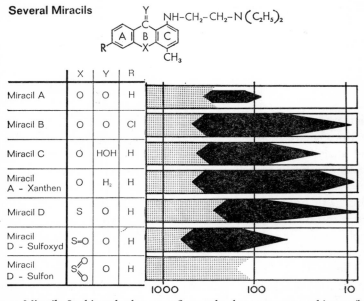

FIG. I. Miracils. In this and subsequent figures the doses are expressed in mg./kg. The clear area on the right covers the ineffective dose range, the black area indicates the schistosomicidal range and the stippled area the toxic range for each drug in mice.

Xanthones

A xanthone derivative, synthesized in 1938 by Mauss (1948) for testing against malaria was found to have slight schistosomicidal activity. This compound, 1-dimethylaminoethylamino-4-methylxanthone, was later designated miracil A (Fig. 1).

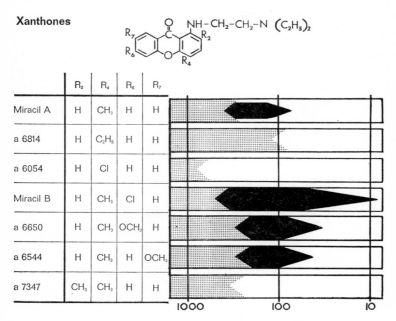

FIG. 2. Xanthone derivatives; variations in ring substituents

Systematic investigation of this chemical class led to the finding that schistosomicidal activity may be expected only if a basic side chain was present in position 1 of the molecule and a methyl group in position 4. Transposition of the two substituents, the introduction of a higher alkyl, of a methoxy group or of a halogen atom instead of the methyl group in position 4 of the molecule, led to a loss of activity (Fig. 2). Introduction of additional substituents into ring "C" also caused a loss of activity. Additional substituents in position 5, 6, 7 or 8 of ring "A" proved to be advantageous and resulted in some increase in efficiency. The introduction of a chlorine atom or a methoxy group in position 6 or 7 of the xanthone molecule is especially worth noting, for the 6-chloro-

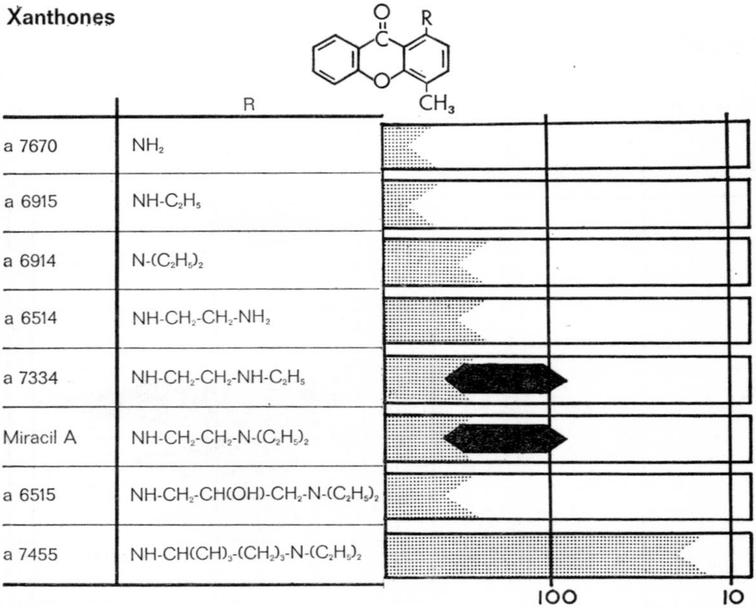

Xanthones

	R		
a 7670	NH_2		
a 6915	$NH\text{-}C_2H_5$		
a 6914	$N\text{-}(C_2H_5)_2$		
a 6514	$NH\text{-}CH_2\text{-}CH_2\text{-}NH_2$		
a 7334	$NH\text{-}CH_2\text{-}CH_2\text{-}NH\text{-}C_2H_5$		
Miracil A	$NH\text{-}CH_2\text{-}CH_2\text{-}N\text{-}(C_2H_5)_2$		
a 6515	$NH\text{-}CH_2\text{-}CH(OH)\text{-}CH_2\text{-}N\text{-}(C_4H_9)_2$		
a 7455	$NH\text{-}CH(CH)_3\text{-}(CH_2)_3\text{-}N\text{-}(C_2H_5)_2$		
		100	10

FIG. 3. Xanthone derivatives; variations in the side-chain

derivative of miracil A proved to be the most effective compound in mice. This compound is called miracil B.

Besides the introduction of substituents into the ring system, particular attention was paid to variation of the basic side chain in position 1. An optimum of efficiency was obtained when the two amino-groups were separated by an alkyl chain of 2 or 3 carbon atoms. Moreover, a terminal mono- or diethylamino group proved to be especially favourable (Fig. 3). Other changes in the molecule involved the carbonyl group. Reduction of the carbonyl group of miracil A to xanthydrol (miracil C), and to the corresponding xanthene compound increased activity considerably.

Thioxanthones

Substitution of the ring oxygen atom by a sulphur atom in most cases led to an increase of efficacy. This was especially true for the thioxanthone analogue of miracil A (Fig. 1) which was called miracil D (Kikuth, Gönnert and Mauss, 1946) and is now known by the official name of lucanthone hydrochloride.

Lucanthone was found to be active against human schistosomiasis when given by mouth (Blair, Hawking and Ross, 1947; Azim, Halawani and Watson, 1948). Intensive chemical investigation then took place in many laboratories. Variation of the basic side chain included the introduction of an alkoxy group into the terminal tertiary amino group (Archer and Suter, 1952; Berberian, Dennis and Freele, 1953), the replacement of the terminal ethyl groups by *n*-butyl groups (Archer, 1953; Gailliot and Gaudechon, 1953*b*) or by piperazinyl residues (Gailliot and Gaudechon, 1953*a*) and replacement of the entire aliphatic side chain with a N_1-substituted piperazine nucleus (Kushner, 1953).

Variation of the ring system caused a modification of the redox potential. 5-Azamiracils were made by introducing a nitrogen atom into position 5 of the ring system (Coombs and Gray, 1953; Newsome, 1953, 1954) and mono- and dialkyl groups were substituted in ring "A" (Druey and Maier, 1958; Brener and Pellegrino, 1958; Sankale, Rivoalen, Milhade and Le Viguelloux, 1957; Shafei, 1958). Compounds were also prepared in which the ring sulphur atom of lucanthone was oxidized to the sulphoxide (Strufe; Kölling, unpublished) or the sulphone (Mauss, 1948).

Most of these compounds were tested under standard conditions and their activity in mice was equal to or less than that of lucanthone Only the sulphone was completely inactive. The sulphoxide has been isolated from the urine of a patient treated with lucanthone, by Strufe (Gönnert, 1962; Strufe, 1963), and is nearly as effective as the original lucanthone. Other metabolites isolated from the blood or urine of treated patients were inactive (Newsome and Robinson, 1960). Postulated metabolites of the miracils, derived from the splitting of ring "B" either at the carbonyl group or at the ring sulphur or oxygen atom, have been synthesized by Kölling (unpublished) and Gönnert (1961). None of these had any schistosomicidal activity in mice.

In the course of our work on the xanthones and thioxanthones, a very clear relationship between constitution and effectiveness came to light; the positioning of the basic side chain *para* to the methyl substituent was recognized as being imperative for schistosomicidal activity. It seemed logical to apply this substitution relationship to other chemical classes and as early as 1940 Mauss had started this work. The idea of synthesizing moieties of the xanthone and thioxanthone nuclei led to the preparation of derivatives of chromone and thiochromone through removal of ring "A". Further removal of ring "B" led to derivatives of 4-aminotoluene, and 4-aminoxylene and to the subsequent development of tetrahydroquinolines.

Thiochromones

Syntheses in the thiochromone and chromone series were begun by Mauss and, after his death, continued by Bossert (Bossert and Gönnert, 1956; Bossert, Henecka and Gönnert, 1958). While the chromone class yielded no compound with increased effectiveness a continuation of studies on thiochromones proved to be interesting (Fig. 4). As with the thioxanthones, a basic side chain in position 5 and a methyl group in the 8 (*para*) position are prerequisites for schistosomicidal activity. The introduction of another substituent in the thiopyrone ring is here imperative. Substitution at R_2 (Fig.4) yields compounds of higher activity than does substitution at R_3. Compounds were also prepared in which a third ring was formed by a polymethylene bridge. A *n*-butane residue formed a compound analogous to miracil D, unsaturated in ring "A".

Thiochromones

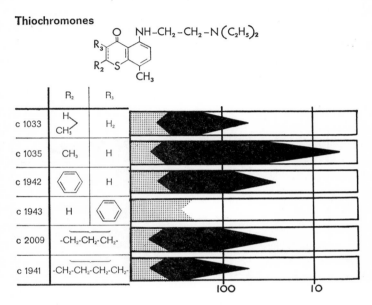

FIG. 4. Thiochromone derivatives.

Toluenes and xylenes

These two chemical classes were investigated by Mauss and Kölling (Mauss, Kölling and Gönnert, 1956). Here too the now recognized principle of substitution proved to be effective and led to numerous active compounds; some of these were more active than lucanthone. To arrive at effective compounds, however, it was found necessary to introduce an additional substituent in position 3 of the benzene ring. This substituent (Fig. 5) may be a halogen atom, a nitro- or a cyano-group. Substitution with chlorine gave optimal results, and the resulting compound has been named mirasan. Here

also replacement of the methyl group in position 4 by another substituent results in completely ineffective compounds. The possibilities of variations in the basic side chain correspond to those
already known from other classes.

Toluenes

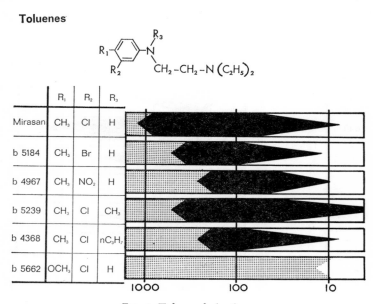

FIG. 5. Toluene derivatives.

Replacement of the basic side chain of mirasan with a methyl-
piperazyl group, interestingly enough, led to a compound (Farb-
werke Hoechst S 688) with prophylactic properties in mice; introduction of additional methyl groups in positions 2 and 6 of the
benzene ring (S 616) resulted in the same prophylactic effect
(Ruschig *et al.*, 1957, 1958; Lämmler, 1958; de Meillon, England
and Lämmler, 1956; Luttermoser, Bruce and McMullen, 1960).
Ruschig *et al.* (1958, 1959) also arrived at effective substances by
inducing reactions of these compounds with esters and anhydrides
of carboxylic acids.

Regarding further possibilities of variation in the basic side chain the introduction of a second aliphatic group into the ring nitrogen atom of mirasan (Mauss, Kölling and Gönnert, 1956) remains to be mentioned. Such compounds also had considerable schisto-somicidal properties (Fig. 5).

Tetrahydrochinolines

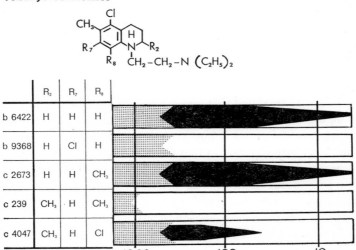

FIG. 6. Tetrahydroquinoline derivatives.

Tetrahydroquinolines

Starting from mirasans with a second basic group Mauss, Kölling and Gönnert (1956) arrived at a group of active tetrahydroquino-lines and quinaldines (Fig. 6). As with mirasans, these two new series required a chlorine atom *ortho* to the methyl group to make them effective against *S. mansoni*. Introduction of an additional substituent into position 8 of the tetrahydroquinoline, however, caused a decrease of activity.

Other chemical classes

Work on the chemical classes so far discussed clearly demonstrated that a basic side chain, a methyl group *para* to it and, in some instances, additional substituents are prerequisites for schistosomicidal activity in mice. The question naturally arose as to whether or not this principle of substitution could be applied to other chemical classes. Preliminary results have already been obtained with indolines, quinolines, carbazoles, tetra- and hexahydrocarbazoles, phenanthridines, phenoxazines, benzimidazoles, benzotriazoles, acridines, acridones and anthraquinones (see also Archer, Rochester and Jackmann, 1954), diphenylsulphides, diphenylbenzoquinones and diphenylamines. Summarizing this work, it may be stated that one can indeed synthesize compounds belonging to one or the other of these classes and possessing schistosomicidal activity but in no case has it been possible to achieve activity superior to that of lucanthone.

It was mentioned initially that the efficacy of a drug may depend upon species and strain of both host and parasite. This also applies to lucanthone (Gönnert and Vogel, 1955) and points to the close relationship between the efficacy of a drug and its fate *in vivo* (by absorption and metabolism) within the host and parasite.

But the physicochemical properties of compounds are also of importance. Scholtan and Gönnert (1956), for instance, showed that there exists, for certain compounds of the lucanthone series, a direct relationship between degree of association (micellar molecular weight) and biological effectiveness. Extent of association in itself, however, is no indication of schistosomicidal activity. Munro (1961), who also investigated some of the physicochemical properties of miracil D as well as of some of its homologues, measured basicity and surface activity as well as affinity for proteins and lipids. He arrived at the conclusion that activity was predominantly dependent upon lipid solubility.

An extensive knowledge of the schistosomicidal compounds

under discussion, however, should not blind us to the fact that we are largely ignorant of their mechanism of action. The hope remains that extended and continued research in this field will some day present us with the key to the development of an ideal drug against schistosomiasis, a disease which continues to spread in many parts of the world and against which no really promising new drug is available.

REFERENCES

ARCHER, S. (1953). U.S. Patent Spec., 2, 653, 949.
ARCHER, S., ROCHESTER, L. B. and JACKMANN, M. (1954). J. Amer. chem. Soc., 76, 588.
ARCHER, S. and SUTER, C. M. (1952). J. Amer. chem. Soc., 74, 4296.
AZIM, M. A., HALAWANI, A. and WATSON, J. M. (1948). Lancet, i, 712.
BERBERIAN, D. A., DENNIS, E. W. and FREELE, H. W. (1953). Proc. V Int. Congr. trop. Med. Malaria, Istanbul, 2, 292.
BLAIR, D. M., HAWKING, F. and ROSS, W. F. (1947) Lancet, ii, 911.
BOSSERT, F. and GÖNNERT, R. (1956). W. German Patent Spec., 954, 599.
BOSSERT, F., HENECKA, H. and GÖNNERT, R. (1958). W. German Patent Spec., 1,024, 980.
BRENER, Z. and PELLEGRINO, J. (1958). J. Parasit., 44, 659.
COOMBS, M. M. and GRAY, W. H. (1953). Brit. Patent Spec., 700, 124.
DRUEY, J. and MAIER, K. (1958). W. German Patent Spec., 1,037,458
GAILLIOT, P. and GAUDECHON, J. (1953a). French Patent Spec, 1,041,572.
GAILLIOT, P. and GAUDECHON, J. (1953b). French Patent Spec., 1,041,573.
GÖNNERT, R. (1961). Bull., W.H.O., 25, 702.
GÖNNERT, R. and VOGEL, H. (1955). Tropenmed. u. Parasit., 6, 193.
KIKUTH, W. and GÖNNERT, R. (1948). Ann. trop. Med. Parasit., 42, 256.
KIKUTH, W., and GÖNNERT, R. (1949). Tropenmed. u. Parasit., 1, 234.
KIKUTH, W., GÖNNERT, R. and MAUSS, H. (1946). Naturwiss., 33, 253.
KUSHNER, S. (1953). U. S. Patent Spec. 2,656,357.
LÄMMLER, G. (1958). Tropenmed. u. Parasit., 9, 294.
LUTTERMOSER, G. W., BRUCE, J. I. and McMULLEN, D. B. (1960). Amer. J. trop. Med., 9, 39.
MAUSS, H. (1948). Chem. Ber., 81, 19.
MAUSS, H., KÖLLING, H. and GÖNNERT, R. (1956). Med. u. Chemie, 5, 185.
MEILLON, DE B., ENGLAND, E. C. and LÄMMLER, G. (1956). S. Afr. med. J., 30, 611.
MUNRO, D. C. (1961). J. chem. Soc., 5381.
NEWSOME, J. (1953). Trans. R. Soc. trop. Med. Hyg., 47, 428.
NEWSOME, J. (1954). Trans. R. Soc. trop. Med. Hyg., 48, 342.

NEWSOME, J. and ROBINSON, D. L. H. (1960). *Trans. R. Soc. trop. Med. Hyg.*, **54,** 582.

RUSCHIG, H., SCHMIDT-BARBO, D. M., LEDITSCHKE, H., SCHORR, M. and LÄMM-LER, G. (1957). W. German Patent Spec., 1,019,308.

RUSCHIG, H., SIEDEL, W., LEDITSCHKE, H., SCHMIDT-BARBO, D. N. and LÄMM-LER, G. (1959) W. German Patent Spec., 1,057,120.

RUSCHIG, H., SIEDEL, W., LEDITSCHKE, H., SCHMIDT-BARBO, D. M., SCHORR, M. and LÄMMLER, G. (1958). W. German Patent Spec., 1,042,595.

RUSCHIG, H., SIEDEL, W., SCHORR, M., LEDITSCHKE, H., SCHMIDT-BARBO, D. M. (1957). W. German Patent Spec., 1,001,275.

SANKALE, M., RIVOALEN, A., MILHADE, J. and LE VIGUELLOUX, J. (1957). *Bull. Soc. Path., exot.*, **50,** 917.

SCHOLTAN, W. and GÖNNERT, R. (1956). *Med. u. Chemie*, **5,** 314.

SHAFEI, A. Z. (1958). *J. trop. Med. Hyg.*, **61,** 12.

STRUFE, R. (1963). *Med. u. Chemie*, **7,** in press.

DISCUSSION

F. L. Rose (Imperial Chemical Industries): Cyanine compounds: I have always been intrigued by the fact that cyanine compounds, like many of the trypanocidal drugs, are substances which can bind to cellulose. They have an affinity for cellulose, and they probably attach themselves to the cellulose molecules through a sort of polyhydrogen bonding. Cellulose is built up of cellobiose units and, of course, cellobiose units are glucose units or two glucose units at any rate. I should like to ask whether any experiments have ever been made to determine whether cyanine compounds associate with glucose molecules, perhaps in aqueous solution. It might be a point worth looking into.

Bueding: To my knowledge this has not been studied. However, in mammalian tissues carbohydrate metabolism is not affected by cyanine dyes. Cyanines also affect the oxygen uptake of *Litomosoides* in the absence of exogenous glucose and after depletion of endogenous carbohydrate (glycogen) stores.

A. Shulman (Department of Physiology, Melbourne): Could I ask Dr. Bueding what is the effect of potassium ion, atropine and anti-cholinesterase drugs on the neuromuscular paralysis in worms produced by piperazine? If you have an effect on the acetylcholine activation of muscle, you should have an effect on muscles of this sort.

Bueding: I have no knowledge about potassium ions. Regarding schistosome cholinesterases, anticholinesterase compounds fairly closely parallel their cholinesterase inhibitory effects on mammalian cholinesterases. As far as we know, there are no clear-cut differences. As far as the blocking agents are concerned, we have data in schistosomes. Neither atropine nor d-tubocurarine nor the quaternary ganglionic blocking agents of the hexamethonium series have any effect on the worms. The only effective cholinergic blocking agent in schistosomes proved to be mecamylamine which is a tertiary ganglion blocking agent. Pempidine and piperazine have qualitatively the same effect but are less potent. I believe that this would indicate, analogous to the observations with *Ascaris* muscle, that the neuromuscular junction in these two parasites is much more sensitive to blocking agents of the tertiary amine series, as already has been shown clearly by the experiments of Norton and de Beer. This, I believe, is a significant difference between the myoneural junction of the parasite and that of the host.

E. F. Gale (Medical Research Council Unit for Chemical Microbiology, Cambridge): Can Dr. Bueding tell us anything about the possible mode of action of the xanthones or any of the compounds about which Dr. Gönnert has been talking?

Bueding: I am afraid I cannot, because *in vitro* these thioxanthones are inactive. However, if worms are incubated in serum of animals which have received thioxanthones, these sera are active. Therefore, the thioxanthone must be converted by the host into some active schistosomicidal agent. The active metabolite has, to my knowledge, not been isolated, but I should like to take this opportunity to make a plea that in view of the activity of the thioxanthones *in vivo*, perhaps some attention should be directed towards isolating this material from plasma or serum of animals which have received these compounds. This might prove very interesting because it might help to elucidate the mode of action of these compounds.

Rose: Does this mean postulating an active metabolite for every one of these compounds? It is a little bit far-fetched really, is it not?

Bueding: I can only speak of miracil D with which numerous attempts have been made to detect some *in vitro* activity and none has been found. Some of the metabolites which were tested, particularly the ones which were isolated from the urine, such as the sulphoxide derivative, had no *in vitro* activity either. Therefore, I can only say that those thioxanthone derivatives which were tested have no direct *in vitro* activity.

L. G. Goodwin (The Wellcome Laboratories of Tropical Medicine): I was just wondering if Dr. Gönnert had any evidence of the activity or inactivity of the different thioxanthone metabolites produced by different species of animal.

Gönnert: We isolated several metabolic compounds from the urine of men and animals, and the only compound active in mouse schistosomiasis was the sulphoxide of miracil D. The other products were ineffective, and we agree here with Newsome's observations. The sulphoxide of miracil D accounted for more than half of all the compounds excreted in the urine, so we suppose it to be the active metabolite. If this is oxidized to the sulphone you will not get any activity. Further, the compound in blood must be bound to protein. My colleague Strufe showed that sulphoxide excreted in the urine is associated with a protein and that the amino acid composition of the protein derivative varies from man to man. That is all we know.

MECHANISMS OF ANTHELMINTIC ACTION WITH PARTICULAR REFERENCE TO DRUGS AFFECTING NEUROMUSCULAR ACTIVITY

A. W. J. BROOME

Imperial Chemical Industries Ltd., Pharmaceuticals Division, Alderley Park

BEFORE discussing the ways in which certain drugs remove nematodes of the alimentary canal it is desirable to consider the host–parasite complex. The adult parasites do not actually reside in the animal body but exist in a variety of micro-habitats along the whole length of the gut. Immature forms are often embedded in the gut mucosa. Drugs possessing broad spectra of anthelmintic activity must therefore be capable of reaching and entering the nematodes under a wide range of conditions. Since most of the parasites are outside the animal body it should be possible to design drugs which are preferentially absorbed by nematode tissues. Unfortunately, the evidence suggests that the factors which govern absorption of drugs by hosts are similar to those controlling absorption by parasites (Trim, 1949). However, there may be considerable differences in the ability of parasitic nematodes and of their hosts to metabolize and excrete drugs and this may allow the concentration of drugs in parasite tissues.

Presumably nematodes of the alimentary canal possess some method of orientation which enables them to retain their position in the gut in the face of peristalsis and other gut movements. It is not necessary to kill such parasites in order to ensure their removal, because any factor which impairs their activity or "sense of direction" may render them susceptible to expulsion. Since drugs which affect neuromuscular activity produce just this effect, it is not surprising that they may be associated with anthelmintic action. A full understanding of the way in which drugs achieve their action helps to identify susceptible parasite systems and to show the properties of drugs necessary to affect them. It is with this end in view that the activity of the following drugs has been considered.

Phenothiazine

A completely satisfactory explanation of the mechanism by which phenothiazine eliminates parasitic nematodes has defied research workers for over twenty years. The features of its action which have proved most difficult to understand have been the need for extremely large doses of drug for full activity, the greater efficiency of phenothiazine against parasites of the abomasum, caecum and colon, compared with those of the small intestine and the precise mechanism by which the parasites are eliminated. Up to 40% of a dose of phenothiazine is excreted unchanged in the faeces of treated sheep and cattle and this focussed attention on the apparent wastage of much of the administered drug. Available evidence suggests that the drug is not converted into an active anthelmintic by metabolism (Esserman, 1952), and it must therefore be assumed that the large dose is needed to ensure that the parasites absorb toxic amounts of unchanged drug. Although phenothiazine has very low solubility in water it is considered to enter parasitic nematodes through the cuticle (Lazarus and Rogers, 1951) and presumably must be in solution before absorption can occur. The amount of drug in solution in the host's gut depends on the balance between the rate of solution from the solid state on the one hand, and the rate of removal by absorption by the host on the other. Phenothiazine is readily absorbed from the gut and therefore rate of solution is likely to be the major factor controlling its concentration in solution in the gut. Rate of solution will depend on the available surface area of drug and if this falls below a critical level the concentration of phenothiazine in solution will be too low to remove parasites, even though solid phenothiazine may still be present. This hypothesis is supported by observations (Forsyth, Scott and Bainbridge, 1961) showing that the anthelmintic efficiency of a given dose of phenothiazine is related to its total surface area. Similarly, the effect of chemical purity on the anthelmintic efficiency of phenothiazine is likely to be mediated through an effect on solution rate.

It seems feasible that the anthelmintic spectrum of phenothiazine is related to differences in the drug concentration and the time for which it persists in various parts of the gut. Since the small intestine is the region of the gut most highly specialized for absorption, it is to be expected that the balance between absorption by the host and solution from the solid state will be most unfavourable for anthelmintic action in this area.

The next point of interest is the way in which phenothiazine eliminates parasitic nematodes without affecting the host. Studies of the drug concentration in parasite and host tissues (Lazarus and Rogers, 1951) showed that the tissues of the parasite always contained more phenothiazine than those of the host. This led to the conclusion that the uptake of drug by the host was less than the uptake by parasitic nematodes. However, it must be remembered that the concentration of drug in the host's intestinal tissues is probably kept low by rapid transport to the liver followed by metabolism and excretion. Similar metabolism and excretion by parasitic nematodes does not seem to occur; the phenothiazine content of nematodes taken from treated animals did not fall when the worms were maintained in drug-free media for periods of up to 24 hours. As a result the phenothiazine entering parasitic worms accumulates to produce toxic concentrations whilst that entering the host is rapidly metabolized and excreted before toxic concentrations are reached.

It is clear that phenothiazine does not exert a lethal action on parasitic nematodes. Worms eliminated from treated animals are alive and can be maintained *in vitro* for just as long as parasites from untreated animals. The only definite effect of phenothiazine yet demonstrated in nematodes appears to be an inhibition of egg-laying which occurs both *in vivo* and *in vitro*. This is probably not related to a specific drug action on the nematode reproductive system because egg-laying is likely to be reduced by any change in the well-being of the adult.

Studies on the metabolism of phenothiazine have indicated its ability to form redox systems and it has been postulated that such

systems may be related to its anthelmintic action. Thus phenothiazine and some of its metabolites are capable of forming free radicals or semiquinones which could prevent the operation of an oxygen transfer system essential to helminth metabolism. Circumstantial evidence for this view comes from the structure/activity studies of Craig, Tate and Warwick (1960) showing that phenothiazine derivatives with substituents in both the 3- and 7-positions which preclude the formation of such redox systems are devoid of activity. Only a limited number of compounds with substituents in position 3 showed any activity and they required the presence of a hydrogen atom at the ring nitrogen. Further examination of these compounds appeared to reveal a definite association between anthelmintic activity and the ability to form resonance stabilized semiquinones with oxidation potentials in the region of 550 to 850 millivolts. Despite much theoretical reasoning that such systems may play a role in the action of phenothiazine, nobody has demonstrated an action of the drug or of a metabolite on any nematode redox system which could account for the anthelmintic effect.

Another action of phenothiazine which has aroused interest is its ability to inhibit horse serum cholinesterase (Collier and Allen, 1942). Although small amounts of both acetylcholine (Mellanby, 1955) and of acetylcholinesterase (Bueding, 1952) have been isolated from ascarid tissue it is not certain that the acetylcholine-cholinesterase system is important in nematode physiology. Attempts to demonstrate an effect of phenothiazine on exposed neuromuscular preparations of *Ascaris* were unsuccessful (Baldwin and Moyle, 1949). It is perhaps significant that some of the organic phosphorus compounds have recently been shown to potentiate the anthelmintic action of phenothiazine (Kingsbury, 1961).

In addition to these actions, phenothiazine has also been shown to affect a wide variety of mammalian enzyme systems. Unfortunately the significance of these actions cannot be assessed because so little is known about the importance of such enzymes in nematode metabolism. Nevertheless, these varied actions of phenothiazine emphasize that it is a very toxic compound capable of affecting a wide variety of animal life. The precise lesion by which parasitic nematodes are eliminated still remains to be identified.

Methyridine (2-β-methoxyethylpyridine)

Methyridine (promintic) is a drug whose properties present a complete contrast to those of phenothiazine; it is a liquid which is miscible with water in all proportions and which is effective when administered by the oral, subcutaneous or intraperitoneal routes.

In order to understand how such a compound can eliminate nematodes from all regions of the gut it is necessary to consider its distribution in the animal body. Blood and gut contents of sheep killed at various intervals after the administration of therapeutic doses of the drug subcutaneously are shown in Fig. 1 (Broome, 1961).

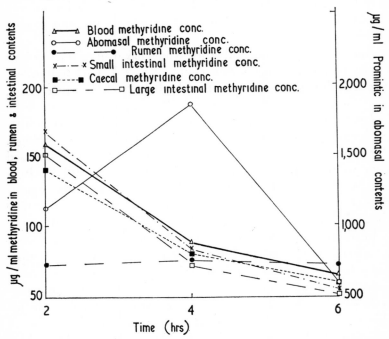

FIG. 1. Analysis of blood and gut contents from sheep given methyridine 200 mg./kg. subcutaneously. (Broome, A. W. J. (1961). *Brit. J. Pharmacol.* **17,** 327.)

It is clear that methyridine is able to reach all regions of the alimentary canal and that the peak concentration of 80 to 100 μg./ml. is only present for 1 to 2 hours. Further studies revealed that these concentrations were sufficiently high and prolonged to paralyse a variety of nematode species *in vitro*, and that the paralysis could not be reversed by transferring the worms to drug-free media. Fig. 1

also shows a close relationship between concentrations of drug in the blood and in the contents of all regions of the alimentary canal except the abomasum. This suggests that the concentration of methyridine in the intestinal region of the gut is a function of the level in the blood and that the drug can pass readily from the blood to the gut and *vice versa*. This idea was confirmed in studies on gut absorption of methyridine in rats. It is therefore evident that the drug has an unusual way of passing into the gut and that this enables it to contact all worm species irrespective of their varying habitats. The concentration of methyridine in the abomasum is extremely high and bears little or no relation to the blood and intestinal levels. This result is not surprising in view of Schanker's (1960) observation that the gastric epithelium is selectively permeable to the undissociated form of a drug, with the result that basic drugs such as methyridine become concentrated in the gastric juice.

Although there is a high drug concentration in the abomasum, Walley (1961) has shown methyridine to be less effective against abomasal than against intestinal parasites. We were unable to detect differences in the sensitivity of various species of nematode to the drug and therefore examined the effect of pH on its action *in vitro*. Results indicated that the anthelmintic action of methyridine decreased as acidity increased until at pH 3·0 it was ineffective at usual concentrations. The nematode cuticle, like the gastric epithelium, appears to be selectively permeable to the undissociated form of a drug. Support for this hypothesis was obtained by measuring the uptake of methyridine by ascarids placed in drug solutions buffered at various pH values. Results showed (Fig. 2) that significantly more methyridine was removed by the ascarids from solutions at pH 8 than at either pH 5 or pH 3. Since ascarids do not appear to metabolize methyridine *in vitro* it is considered that the results in Fig. 2 demonstrate the effect of pH on the ability of methyridine to enter the nematodes.

Another interesting aspect of methyridine is the nature of the paralysis noted in *in vitro* studies. This was investigated using exposed neuromuscular prepartions of *Ascaris* similar to those employed by Norton and De Beer (1957) in their work on piperazine. Figure 3 shows the tracing from an experiment in which the action of methyridine and acetylcholine were compared. Although acetylcholine is obviously more active than methyridine

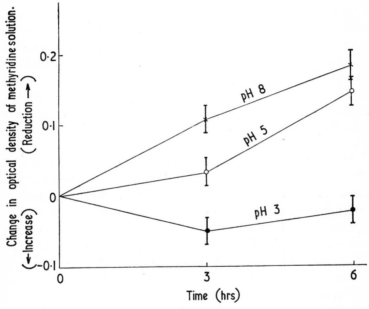

FIG. 2. Uptake of methyridine from solutions of differing *p*H by *Ascaris* from pigs. (Broome, A. W. J. (1961). *Brit. J. Pharmacol.*, **17**, 327.)

both compounds appear to produce a similar contracture of nematode muscle. The effect of acetylcholine can be completely eliminated by washing the preparation, but methyridine exerts a paralysing action on the muscle long after the contracture has been reversed by washing. Addition of *d*-tubocurarine reverses the paralysis and also blocks the response of the preparation to additional acetylcholine or methyridine. In the same way piperazine (250 μg./ml.) blocks the muscle response to acetylcholine and to methyridine.

These observations suggest that methyridine produces a depolarizing effect on nematode muscle closely resembling that of acetylcholine. A similar action has also been demonstrated in mammals

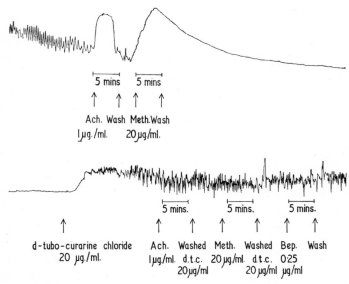

Fig. 3. Effect of drugs on exposed neuromuscular preparation of *Ascaris* from pigs. Ach., acetylcholine; Meth., methyridine; Bep., bephenium.

given excessive doses of drug. Since similar amounts of methyridine appear to reach the tissues of both host and parasite it seems possible that the therapeutic usefulness of this compound may depend on a differential sensitivity of nematode and mammalian systems to its action. Evidence that this may be the case is available because levels of 10 to 20 μg./ml. affect nematodes whilst blood concentrations of up to 100 μg./ml. do not kill mice, rats or sheep.

It is interesting to examine the methyridine molecule in order to correlate its structure with its pharmacological properties.

I   II

In vitro and *in vivo* studies have shown that the feature of the methyridine (I) molecule which is essential for activity is the unhindered pyridine nitrogen atom and the β-alkoxyethyl grouping in the 2-position. This portion of the molecule bears an obvious resemblance to one of the essential features of the acetylcholine molecule (II) and it does not appear unreasonable to suggest that both are acting on the same site at the neuromuscular junction. Methyridine is less active than acetylcholine, which might be expected because it only contains a tertiary nitrogen atom, although some ionization is likely to occur at physiological pH (pKa of methyridine is approximately $5 \cdot 5$). In addition, the distance between the pyridine nitrogen atom and the ether oxygen atom does not appear to be optimal so that the affinity of the drug for the receptor site might be expected to be less than that of acetylcholine. This makes it difficult to understand why the effect of methyridine cannot be readily reversed by washing. Irreversible paralysis appears to be rather specific to the methyridine molecule and is undoubtedly one of the major factors determining the drug's activity, because effective drug concentrations are present in the gut for limited time intervals.

Bephenium salts

The bephenium salts provide another series of safe, broadspectrum anthelmintics which are particularly effective against nematodes dwelling in association with the mucosa. Unlike methy-ridine, these compounds appear to be poorly absorbed from the gut probably because they possess a quaternary nitrogen atom. Rogers, (1958*b*) recovered less than 1% of a dose of bephenium in the urine during the 24 hours following administration to man. Such poor gut absorption coupled with metabolism and excretion by the host, readily explains the lack of mammalian toxicity. Solubility of the various bephenium salts affects their anthelmintic efficiency, which is optimal in the hydroxynaphthoate. It is interesting to speculate that the high activity against mucus-dwelling nematodes may be associated with the formation of drug-mucus complexes such as those described for other quaternary ammonium compounds by Levine, Blair and Clark (1955).

Poor absorption from the gut, coupled with the presence of a quaternary nitrogen atom, naturally leads to the conclusion that these compounds do not readily pass through the nematode cuticle. Thus it is not surprising that the bephenium salts are rela-tively inactive against intact *Ascaris in vitro*. However, they might be expected to show high activity against the susceptible nematode system. This conclusion has been verified by a study of their action on exposed neuromuscular preparations. A tracing is shown in Fig. 4 and indicates that bephenium at 0·25 μg./ml. (base) produces a contracture of nematode muscle similar to that produced by acetylcholine at 1 μg./ml. This indicates that be-phenium is more than five times as active as acetylcholine on a molar basis.

Though it is not apparent from this particular tracing, bephenium does not produce a long lasting paralysis of the methyridine type. A more persistent concentration of drug in the gut is probably needed to remove the worms. Fig. 4 shows that the action of bephenium can be blocked with piperazine; a similar effect was obtained with *d*-tubocurarine (Fig. 3). Once again the action appears to resemble that of acetylcholine.

A consideration of the structure of bephenium (III) and of the related thienyl compound (IV) reveals a striking resemblance to acetylcholine.

III   IV

Both possess the $>$N$^+$—CH$_2$.CH$_2$.O— system in a position likely to be free from steric hindrance. No structure/activity data are available for these anthelmintics but it seems likely that the two heterocyclic groupings may be needed to provide sufficient fat solubility to allow the quaternary nitrogen to pass through the nematode cuticle. The greater molar activity of bephenium compared with acetylcholine could be related to the phenyl-group attached to the ether oxygen atom. The "nicotine-like" action of many phenyl ethers of choline is known to be much greater than that of acetylcholine in vertebrates and appears to be related to the electron-activating effects of the substituents. Thus substituents leading to the accumulation of a positive charge on the ether oxygen atom improve activity (Barlow, 1955). Theoretically then, it might be expected that the activity of bephenium could be increased by certain substituents in the phenyl ring.

Organophosphorus compounds

Following their use as systemic insecticides, some of the organophosphorus compounds have been examined for anthelmintic activity in sheep and cattle. The most widely tested compounds have been O,O-dimethyl-1-hydroxy-2-trichloromethyl phosphonate (Bayer L13/59; Neguvon; Dipterex), 3-chloro-4-methyl-umbelliferone-O,O-diethyl thiophosphate (Bayer 21/199; Coral; Asuntol), O,O-diethyl-O-(2,4,5-trichlorophenyl) phosphorothiate

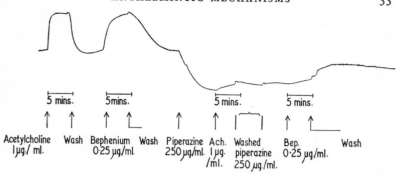

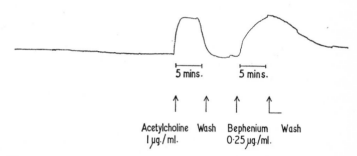

Fig. 4. Effect of bephenium on exposed neuromuscular preparation of *Ascaris* from pigs.

(Dow, E. T. 57; Trolene; Etrolene), and 4-*tert*-butyl-2-chloro-phenyl dimethylphosphoramidate (Ruelene). All compounds possess anthelmintic activity but this is usually characterized by a narrow and sometimes unpredictable margin of safety.

The activity of the organophosphorus compounds as insecti-cides is well known and is related to their ability to act as as cho-linesterase inhibitors. A consideration of the structure of the above compound indicates that they should be capable of functioning as cholinesterase inhibitors by virtue of their ready cleavage to give phosphorylating systems capable of nucleophilic attack on enzymes such as cholinesterase. Whether or not these compounds function as anthelmintics through a similar mechanism has not been determined. Small amounts of acetylcholine and acetylcholinesterase have been demonstrated in nematode tissue but Baldwin and Moyle (1949) were unable to show any effect of eserine in experiments with exposed ascarid neuromuscular preparations. They therefore concluded that there was no functional acetylcholinesterase in their preparations. Later, Norton and De Beer (1957) claimed that eserine potentiated the action of acetylcholine on exposed neuromuscular preparations of *Ascaris* by about 50%. This potentiation is small compared with that on leech muscle, but it indicates that small amounts of functional acetylcholinesterase may be present in nematode tissue. A similar conclusion arises from the work of Krotov (1957) who showed that the depolarizing activity of acetylcholine is destroyed by incubation with extracts of ascarid tissue. It therefore seems likely that the organophosphorus compounds act by inhibiting cholinesterase but no direct experiments to test this hypothesis appear to have been reported.

Piperazines

Piperazines form another series of anthelmintics which appear to owe their activity to an effect on neuromuscular transmission. The various salts of the simple piperazines are very safe drugs, most valuable for the removal of nematodes such as *Ascaris* and *Enterobius* which live freely in the alimentary canal. Their action against mucus-dwelling forms is of a lower order but the reason for this is not apparent and does not appear to have been studied. Piperazine is known to produce a flaccid paralysis of nematode muscle which blocks the response to acetylcholine, methyridine, and bephenium (Fig. 4). Norton and De Beer (1957) showed that nematode muscle paralysed by piperazine was capable of responding to electrical stimuli; they therefore concluded that the action was on the neuromuscular junction rather than directly on the muscle. These authors also showed that piperazine was relatively much less active at mammalian neuromuscular junctions. This was thought to account for the therapeutic usefulness of the drug because piperazine is absorbed from the gut in considerable quantities. About 30% of a dose may be recovered from the urine (Rogers, 1958a). The action of piperazine on the nematode neuromuscular junction appears to be that of a competitive inhibitor and is rather like that conventionally associated with d-tubocurarine in mammalian physiology. However, a comparison of the actions of piperazine and d-tubocurarine in nematode neuromuscular preparations reveals certain differences, particularly in respect to their effect on spontaneous rythm. Thus, the concentration of piperazine which is needed to block a given amount of acetylcholine causes an immediate and sustained relaxation of ascarid preparations. When d-tubocurarine is applied in concentrations needed to block the response to similar amounts of acetylcholine, it has little effect on spontaneous activity or muscle tone. A further demonstration of this difference was encountered in studies on the effect of diethylcarbamazine (hetrazan) in nematode neuromuscular activity. This is illustrated in Fig. 5, which shows that the drug increased the muscle tone and spontaneous activity of the preparation. Diethylcarbamazine had no significant effect on the muscle response to acetylcholine, even with concentrations of 250 μg./ml. When d-tubocurarine was added it did not block the action of diethylcarbamazine and sometimes potentiated it.

These differences suggest that piperazine and d-tubocurarine do not act on the nematode neuromuscular system in precisely the same way. One possible explanation may be that there is more than one site at which the activity of these neuromuscular preparations can be influenced. This might be related to the anatomical structure of the nematode muscle cell. The sarcoplasm of each muscle cell gives rise to an "innervation process" which ensheaths the neurofibrils as they pass from the somatic nerve to the muscle fibres (Chitwood and Chitwood, 1937). The presence of intracellular electric potentials with coordinated depolarization spikes has also

3

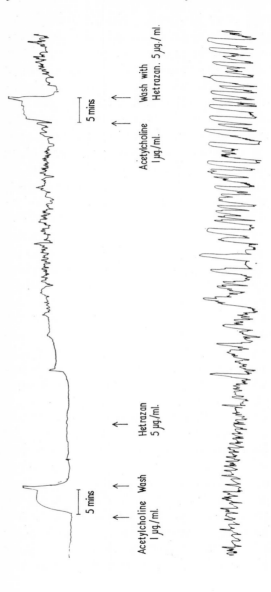

FIG. 5. Effect of acetylcholine and *d*-tubocurarine on the response to diethylcarbamazine (hetrazan) in *Ascaris* neuromuscular preparations.

been demonstrated (Jarman, 1959) and it seems possible that the normal transfer of impulses from nerve to muscle fibre may occur within the nematode muscle cell. Such actions might be unaffected by externally applied drugs if the drugs could not pass readily through the cell membrane; many of the quaternary ammonium compounds would probably fall into this category. It is difficult in terms of this explanation to account for the observation that piperazine is more effective against nematode than against mammalian neuromuscular transmission. The further possibility that the neurotransmitter/receptor complex of nematodes may differ from that of mammals, particularly in its relative sensitivity to piperazine and to d-tubocurarine, thus seems worthy of consideration.

An examination of the structure/activity relationships of various piperazine derivatives might be expected to throw some light on the the nature of the neurotransmitter/receptor complex. Many studies of this type have been made and have recently been reviewed by Craig and Tate (1961). Unfortunately, the criterion for assessing activity has usually been an *in vivo* anthelmintic test. Such results measure the end product of a series of events involving the whole host-parasite complex and are of little value in helping to identify the effect of structural modifications on the action of compounds on the nematode neuromuscular system. Results of these tests indicate that substitution in the piperazine ring generally reduces anthelmintic activity (Brown, Chan and Hussey, 1954). However, the activity of some higher alkyl-substituted monoquaternary piperazine derivatives has been reported (Harfenist, 1957). There is no guarantee that the activity of quaternary compounds on the nematode is similar to the action of piperazine.

It has been suggested that the action of piperazine is associated with its ability to inhibit reversibly the production of succinic acid by ascarid worms. However, later work by the same authors (Bueding, Saz and Farrow, 1959) showed that the incorporation of $2\text{-}^{14}\text{C}$-labelled lactate into muscle strips of *Ascaris* was not affected by piperazine. This seems to indicate that reduction of succinic acid production in piperazine-paralysed worms is the result, and not the cause, of the paralysis.

A stimulatory action of diethylcarbamazine on the nematode neuromuscular system could account for the anthelmintic action of the compound. It might well be sufficient to interfere with the mechanisms by which the parasite orientates itself. A similar mechanism may account for the antifilarial properties of diethyl-carbamazine, for it is known that microfilariae are rendered susceptible to the host's defence system by drug treatment.

It is evident that the nematode neuromuscular system is particularly sensitive to the action of many anthelmintic drugs. Compounds which possess structural features associated with the depolarizing action of acetylcholine cause effects which may result in the elimination of parasites.

Such compounds also affect the neuromuscular activity of the host, but are capable of exerting useful action in spite of the fact that similar concentrations of drug reach both host and parasite tissues. Possibly this indicates that the nematode neuromuscular system is more sensitive to these drugs than the vertebrate system. This could be related to the comparatively small amounts of acetylcholine and acetylcholinesterase present in nematode tissue. Alternatively, it could indicate that a slight, but non-fatal, impairment of nematode neuromuscular activity is sufficient to allow the host's defence mechanisms to remove the parasites. Large safety margins are possible with this type of drug if high concentrations in the tissues of the host can be avoided.

The nematode neuromuscular system also appears to be sensitive to certain drugs which competitively inhibit the action of depolarizing compounds. Their action suggests that there may be a difference in the organization of mammalian and nematode neuromuscular transmission, but the nature of this difference is not known. If the mechanism by which the simple piperazines block neuromuscular activity could be elucidated new light might be thrown on this aspect of nematode physiology.

[Discussion of this paper was postponed until after the following paper by E. J. L. Soulsby; see p. 76.]

REFERENCES

BALDWIN, E. and MOYLE V. (1949). *Brit. J. Pharmacol.*, **4**, 145.
BARLOW, R. B. (1955). Introduction to Chemical Pharmacology, London: Methuen.
BUEDING, E. (1952). *Brit. J. Pharmacol.*, **7**, 563.
BUEDING, E., SAZ, H. J. and FARROW, G. W. (1959). *Brit. J. Pharmacol.*, **14**, 497.
BROOME, A. W. J. (1961). *Brit. J. Pharmacol.*, **17**, 327.
BROWN, H. W., CHAN, K. F. and HUSSEY, K. L. (1954). *Amer. J. trop. Med. Hyg.*, **3**, 504.
CHITWOOD, B. G. and CHITWOOD, M. B. (1937). Introduction to Nematology, Baltimore: Monumental Printing Co.
COLLIER, H. B. and ALLEN, D. E. (1942). *Canad. J. Res.*, **20B**, 189.
CRAIG, J. C. and TATE, M. E. (1961). Progress in Drug Research, **3**, 76.
CRAIG, J. C., TATE, M. E. and WARWICK, G. P. (1960). *J. med. pharm. Chem.*, **2**, 659.
ESSERMAN, M. B. (1952). *Aust. J. sci. Res., Series. B.*, **5**, 485.
FORSYTH, B. A., SCOTT, M. T. and BAINBRIDGE, J. R. (1961). *Vet. Rec.*, **73**, 67.
HARFENIST, M. (1957). *J. Amer. chem. Soc.*, **79**, 2211.
JARMAN, M. (1959). *Nature, Lond.*, **184**, 1244.
KINGSBURY, P. A. (1961). *Res. vet. Sci.* **2**, 265.
KROTOV, A. I. (1957). *Bull. exp. Biol. Med., U.S.S.R.*, **43**, 227.
LAZARUS, M. and ROGERS, W. P. (1951). *Aust. J. sci. Res., Series B*, **4**, 163.
LEVINE, R. M., BLAIR, M. R. and CLARK, B. B. (1955). *J. Pharmacol.*, **114**, 78.
MELLANBY, H. (1955). *Parasitol.*, **45**, 287.
NORTON, S. and DE BEER, E. J. (1957). *Amer. J. trop. Med. Hyg.*, **6**, 898.
ROGERS, E. W., (1958a). *Brit. Med. J.*, **i**, 136.
ROGERS, E. W., (1958b). *Brit. Med. J.*, **ii**, 1576.
SCHANKER, L. S. (1960). *J. med. pharm. Chem.*, **2**, 343.
TRIM, A. R. (1949). *Parasitol.*, **39**, 281.
WALLEY, J. K. (1961). *Vet. Rec.*, **73**, 159.

THE RELATION OF IMMUNITY IN HELMINTH INFECTIONS TO ANTHELMINTIC TREATMENT

E. J. L. SOULSBY

Department of Animal Pathology,
University of Cambridge

IN a country such as Great Britain where the incidence of parasitic disease in the human population is low, little or no account need be taken of the importance of immunity in the control of helminth infections. However, this is not the case with domestic animals in which parasitic helminths abound and frequently are the cause of great loss to the agricultural industry. In the tropical and sub-tropical areas of the world parasitic helminths of man are all too common, causing ill-health and stagnation of morale over wide areas of the globe. The position is no better in the animal population.

Present means of control of the helminth diseases of man and animals depend mainly on hygiene, husbandry and therapy, with particular emphasis on therapy. A start has been made on the use of vaccines in the control of helminth diseases as with the X-irradiated lungworm vaccine for parasitic bronchitis of cattle (Jarrett, Jennings, McIntyre, Mulligan, Sharp and Urquhart, 1958). With increasing knowledge of the immunological mechanisms against helminth infections it becomes clear that in the none too distant future other vaccines will be available for control not only of animal but also of human pathogenic helminths.

It has also been realized that under natural conditions the seasonal incidence of helminths in animals is markedly influenced by their immunological mechanisms, and modern thought tends to regard anthelmintic drugs as part of the supportive armament for control of helminth infections as well as agents for treatment of clinical helminthiasis. Many instances arise where the best and indeed the only method of control is the use of appropriate anthelmintics. In outbreaks of clinical disease no one would doubt the value of therapy, but the question arises as to whether repeated use of anthelmintics in the absence of clinical disease, often on an empirical basis, will interfere with the development of a satisfactory level of immunity to helminths in a population of animals. When the only anthelmintic drugs available were those which affected the adult stage of the parasite this problem was not too serious, since in many cases the larval stages of the helminth are responsible for inducing the immune response. However, with the development of anthelmintics which are effective against both adult and larval stages the question becomes of more than academic interest. Caecal coccidiosis in poultry is a good example of a disease which is controlled by the judicious use of antiparasite drugs. If anticoccidial drugs are given in doses which will allow some development of the parasite to take place, yet will control the pathogenic phase of the infection, a satisfactory level of immunity develops and protects the bird from subsequent infections. If the drugs are given at too high a dose rate all development of the parasite is inhibited and no immunity results, thus leaving the bird susceptible to re-infection after therapy is ended. It is this sort of danger that may exist in the use of larvicidal anthelmintics. Whether this presents a real danger remains to be seen, but an attempt will be made to give consideration to both sides of the question.

It should be stressed that where information is available on the relationship between therapy and immunity in any particular helminth infection, it applies to that helminth alone. It is very unwise to attempt to extrapolate such information to helminths in general. There are instances where, under natural conditions, helminth infections do not induce any degree of immunity and where therapy is thus essential for the control of disease. This is the case with *Fasciola hepatica* infection in sheep, and in areas where this infection is serious repeated treatments are necessary for control. The same situation may well apply to schistosomiasis in man where, though immunity is considered to occur in infected persons and has been shown experimentally in monkeys, it is slow to develop and anthelmintic therapy may be necessary to prevent heavy burdens of worms being acquired by persons in endemic areas. Both these examples are of trematode infections where the most serious pathogenic effects are produced by the adult stage of the organism. In nematode infections too, it is usually the adult stages which are the most pathogenic and this is particularly so in the hookworms of man and in the large stomach worm of sheep, *Haemonchus contortus*, both of which are voracious blood-suckers. Unlike the two trematodes, hookworms and stomach worms do produce a satisfactory degree of immunity and, provided the pathogenic adult phase can be controlled, the animal will become resistant to these parasites.

The relationship of anthelmintic treatment to the acquisition of immunity has two aspects. First that where the judicious use of anthelmintics can be beneficial to the development of immunity, and second that where treatment can be disadvantageous to the acquisition of immunity.

The advantages of the use of anthelmintics in the acquisition of immunity

In many helminths it is chiefly the larval phases of the infection which produce immunity, whereas the adult form is pathogenic. Consequently if a good antigenic stimulus can be provided by the larval stages and the pathogenic adult stage can be avoided, it should be possible to provide a human or an animal with a satis-factory degree of immunity. Otto (1941) studied the development of immunity to hookworm infection and showed that the induc-tion of immunity over a given time bears a direct relationship to the number of infective larvae administered. Otto found that the removal, with an anthelmintic, of successive crops of hookworms shortly after their arrival in the intestine did not prevent or retard the development of immunity in the animal but did prevent the development of anaemia. He concluded from this work that the effective use of drugs for the control of hookworms in humans would neither increase nor decrease but leave essentially unchanged the patient's immunological capacity to cope with successive hookworm infections.

With the abomasal parasite of sheep *H. contortus* it has been demonstrated that larval stages of the helminth are particularly important in stimulating the immune response. This is particularly so in the "self cure" mechanism when an existing burden of parasites is spontaneously eliminated, the reaction being initiated by antigens produced by the moulting phase from the third to the fourth larval stage (Soulsby and Stewart, 1960). In the acquisition of protective immunity to a *H. contortus* infection Jarrett *et al.* (1959) have demonstrated that the larval stages of the parasite are necessary for the immune response which can develop in the absence of mature worms. Since this particular parasite is a voracious blood-sucker and produces anaemia comparable with that induced by hookworm infection in man, the control of the adult phase by anthelmintic drugs, whilst allowing the larval stages to develop and exert their immunizing capacity, should be of value in the long-term control of this infection. Indeed, in such countries as Australia where *H. contortus* is of outstanding importance in the sheep industry, this pattern of management is followed and anthelmintic drugs are used for strategic as well as tactical control. At one time it was thought that the anaemia which developed in hookworm disease seriously retarded the development of immunity. However, Otto (1941) showed this not to be so; acute blood loss did not materially affect the development of immunity. The importance of the anaemia was that since the induction of immunity was directly related to the number of larvae administered, the period of immunization could be shortened only if extensive blood loss could be prevented. Hence the problem becomes one of providing enough of the immunizing antigen without increasing the debt of gross pathological change. The latter can be avoided by the use of drugs which will eliminate the adult helminths.

A possible extension of the use of anthelmintics to control helminth infection but at the same time allowing the host to acquire a satisfactory degree of immunity can be envisaged with the newer drugs which affect both the larval and adult stages of helminths. In order to become satisfactorily immune to a helminth the host must have presented to it metabolic products of the living parasite. The parasite must live and develop in the host. One of the important times for the release of protective antigens is the moulting period of larvae, the time when they metamorphose from one larval stage to the next (Soulsby, 1959). Attentuated larval vaccines such as that used in *Dictyocaulus* infection of cattle, are attenuated by X-irradiation to a point where larval development, including moulting periods, still occurs, but where full adult development does not take place. Since some of the new anthelmintics are also larvicidal it can be envisaged that an alternative method of vaccination might consist in allowing larvae to develop normally and to undergo the necessary moulting periods, and terminating the infection by a larvicidal anthelmintic before full patency is reached. Thus a scheme could be proposed whereby a measured dose of normal infective larvae would be given and the infection terminated after, say, two moulting phases; in the case of *H. contortus* this would be after the tenth day of infection. Such a scheme would be fraught with some danger in that if the vaccinated animal for any reason did not receive the curative dose of anthelmintic, clinical disease might supervene. In addition such a scheme would require a trustworthy anthelmintic which would kill larvae at any stage of development. In the young animal the control or even the elimination of helminth infections by appropriate drugs probably has much wider implications than the limited prevention of the pathogenic effects associated with the adult worm. This is particularly so in sheep. Taylor (1934) has shown that immunity to gastro-intestinal worms in lambs is acquired slowly and does not appear to become firmly established for 18 weeks. Under natural conditions some considerable time elapses before any evidence of an immune response occurs, and though some lambs in a flock may show an immune response at four months of age, in many cases the immune response may not appear before the age of 6 to 8 months (Soulsby, unpublished). Under natural conditions, therefore, lambs are unable to protect themselves against any marked challenge of infective larvae from the pasture and it becomes necessary to prevent severe burdens being acquired. This is necessary not only to avoid the pathogenic phase of the infection but also to prepare the animal in a satisfactory manner for the immune response which it will ultimately make. It has been shown by Gibson (1952) with *Trichostrongylus axei* infection that if lambs are given small doses of infective larvae when young an increased resistance is evident later in life, but if large doses of such larvae are given at an early age they are detrimental to the acquisition of resistance later.

It may be possible to equate this with the observations on other immunological systems such as that reported by Barr (1951) who found that it was important to prepare an animal adequately to get a good immunological response later in life. If too much antigen was administered at an early age the immune response was poor and the avidity of the antibody produced was of a low order. No evidence exists at present to show that the avidity of antibody plays a part in resistance or susceptibility to helminth infections but there is every reason to think that it might. Taliaferro, Taliaferro and Pizzi (1960) have indicated that where antibody mechanisms are complement-dependent a strongly avid antibody may be a disadvantage to the host, but that where such responses are not dependent on complement the presence of a strongly avid antibody may be of great benefit. In recent work concerned with the adhesion of apparent antibody-producing cells to the cuticle of nematodes the reaction was dependent on the presence of antibody on the cuticle but was independent of the presence of complement (Soulsby, unpublished). It is suspected that the avidity of antibody will play an important role in the reaction. In lambs which do not respond well until they are of considerable age, regulation of the intake of infective larval stages of helminths may be of great importance, since too large an intake of larvae may produce an antibody response of poor quality.

Recent work in this laboratory has suggested that the prevention of helminth infection of the young is of importance not only for the production of good quality antibody but also in determining the ability of the animal to produce an antibody response at all. It has been found in two helminth infections at least, that if animals are infected at, or shortly after, birth a degree of immunological unresponsiveness may be induced which puts such animals at a disadvantage later in life should they meet a serious infective challenge. In *Cysticercus bovis* infection of cattle (the intermediate stage of the human tapeworm *Taenia saginata*) animals infected when they are a month or more of age show a good immune response; cysts produced by the infection are usually destroyed within nine months and the animal is immune to re-infection. If, however, calves are infected at birth a very poor antibody response is seen; cysts are still viable after ten months and animals are susceptible to re-infection. This parasite is widespread in Africa and it is suspected that immunological unresponsiveness may be a factor in its widespread incidence (Urquhart, 1958). The use of an anthelmintic to control infections in newborn calves and allow them to remain free of infection until they are immunologically competent would be a great advantage in control measures.

In a similar manner calves infected at birth with the stomach parasite *Mecistocirrus digitatus* showed little or no antibody response and when challenged with infective larvae at a later date were quite susceptible to the infection, in contrast to other calves which had been previously infected when they were immunologically competent to respond. Experiments are now in progress to see if this phenomenon is widespread in helminth infections. Certainly in areas of endemic helminth infection the induction of a condition of immunological unresponsiveness as a result of infection in the early days of life may have far-reaching implication in control measures. Measures which can eliminate or greatly reduce the chance of infection in the early stages of life will avoid this situation and allow a host to make a satisfactory immune response at a later date. It may well be that drugs which affect only the adult stage of a helminth will not be satisfactory for this purpose. Since the main immunizing antigens are associated with the larval stages of helminths, immunological unresponsiveness may develop towards functional antigens which are produced by these larval stages and against which it is desired to immunize the animals at a later stage. Consequently the use of larvicidal anthelmintics in the early stages of the life of an animal may be of great value.

Most information available on the relationship between the chemotherapeutic control of helminths and the acquisition of immunity has been acquired from stages of gastrointestinal nematodes in domestic animals. There is relatively little information regarding this aspect in humans.

Disadvantages of anthelmintic therapy in the acquisition of immunity to helminths

In natural conditions the acquisition of parasites is essential for the development of an immune response. The behaviour of parasite populations in sheep in Great Britain illustrates this well. The course of events in the development and waning of immunity in different age-groups of sheep can be followed quite clearly since there occurs every year, with apparently unfailing regularity, a phenomenon which has been designated "the spring rise". Morgan and Sloan (1947) originally described this in Scottish hill sheep and found a marked increase in strongyle egg output during spring. This was associated with an increase in the number of adult and larval stages of the parasites responsible. The spring rise reaches its peak about four to six weeks after lambing (Crofton, 1954) to be followed by a rapid elimination of the infections, the egg counts then falling to a very low level. During summer and autumn, despite an increase in pasture burdens of infective larvae at this time, egg counts and worm burdens remain low. Such is the situation with the older members of the flock. The lambs behave in a similar manner but reach a peak of infection during summer and autumn and finally discard their burdens by an immunological curative mechanism similar to that seen in the ewes (Crofton, 1955). Studies of this phenomenon in ewes (Soulsby, 1956, 1957) have shown that the termination of the spring rise has an immunological basis and that the period of low egg counts during the rest of the year is a function of the immunity which has been acquired by the sheep having undergone the immunological mechanism which terminates the spring rise. The curative mechanism has all the attributes of the self-cure phenomenon which was originally described by Stoll (1929) in respect of *H. contortus*, but it is also seen in infections with other helminths such as hookworm (McCoy, 1931). Stoll demonstrated that high faecal egg counts in grazing lambs infected with *H. contortus* suddenly fell about 10 weeks after infection and thereafter lambs which had shown this change were resistant to challenge doses of infective larvae.

Though there is general agreement that the spring rise period is terminated by a self-cure mechanism several reasons have been advanced as to why the spring rise occurs. These suggestions have included an increased egg production by existing worms (Cushnie and White, 1948), adverse weather conditions and reduced food intake causing a general reduction of resistance (Paver, Parnell and Morgan, 1955), and a general depression of the immune status of the flock due essentially to a lack of antigenic stimulation as the result of the reduction of larval intake during mid and late winter (Soulsby, 1957). Though depression of the immune state of the host during mid and late winter is generally accepted as an adequate reason for the initiation of the spring rise, some doubts still exist as to the origin of the larvae which become the adult worms which take part in the increased egg laying during the spring rise. Several workers (Spedding and Brown, 1956; Field, Brambell and Campbell, 1960) have shown that the spring rise in egg counts may be observed in sheep which have been housed during the winter and which have thus not had access to infective larvae for several months. In such cases it is considered that the spring rise is derived from larvae that have persisted in a latent form in the mucosa of the host over winter. Further support for this, and evidence against an increased egg production by existing worms, is that the conventional anthelmintics (that is, those affecting the adult stages only) are of little use in preventing the spring rise which occurs despite previous anthelmintic treatment (Hawkins, Cole, Kline and Drudge, 1944; Naerland, 1952). It would appear that the spring rise in nematode populations in sheep is an annual event which not only is the source of a substantial pasture burden of infective larvae for their lambs but also produces a substantial degree of immunity in the adult members of the flock. On balance it seems better to allow the natural course of events to occur at least until efficient vaccines are available to maintain a high level of immunity throughout the year. In fact, Crofton (1955) produced evidence that lambs receiving repeated anthelmintic treatment did not develop the same degree of immunity as those which had remained untreated. Thus, while repeated anthelmintic treatment may reduce the total worm burden, the acquisition of immunity is not as complete as it might otherwise be, which in certain circumstances might lead to danger. The advent of larvicidal anthelmintics may greatly alter the seasonal behaviour of helminths in sheep. Studies are in progress to determine whether this is so and what the implications of such altered behaviour might be.

Though the larval stages appear to be the most important stages of infection for the induction of a satisfactory degree of immunity, the adult phase appears to play a part in its maintenance. There are instances where adult helminths appear to exert a profound influence on the development of larval stages and removal of the adult worms by appropriate treatment allows the development of larvae which has been inhibited by the presence of relatively few worms. In the case of the spring rise phenomenon, some evidence exists to show that the treatment of animals with an anthelmintic prior to the spring rise not only fails to eliminate the spring rise but may be followed by a higher level of egg output and a weaker curative mechanism at the end of the spring rise than if anthelmintic treatment had not been given. Furthermore, the use of anthelmintics at a time when the main immunological response is taking place (Fig. 1) may temporarily retard the development of immunity and lead to increased activity on the part of the helminths (Soulsby, unpublished). These results would suggest that the adult stage of the gastrointestinal nematodes of sheep play a substantial part in the maintenance of immunity and may be analogous to the phenomenon seen with *Haemonchus placei* of the abomasum of cattle.

Roberts and Keith (1959) showed that a firm immunity to *H. placei* was established in cattle by spaced doses of infective larvae. If, however, animals were given repeated treatments of phenothiazine during the immunization period, some degree of immunity did develop but animals were often left with a heavy worm burden, which at times was pathogenic. The authors considered that treatment had prevented the development of immunity to levels which were apparent in its absence. Furthermore it appeared that the mature worms, which are highly susceptible to phenothiazine, were responsible for inhibiting the development of the larval stages, which are resistant to phenothiazine. Removal of the adult worms had permitted the phenothiazine-resistant survivors to resume development. Regular use of the drug may lead to a much heavier worm population than would have become established in its absence. It seems ironical that a drug destined for the elimination of helminths may in this particular instance lead to severe helminth disease.

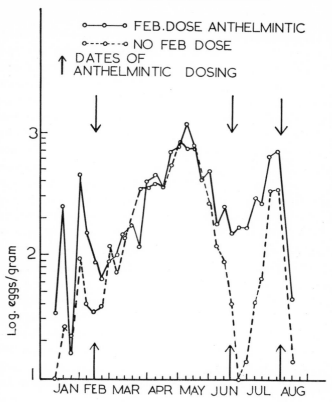

FIG. I. Mean faecal strongyle egg count in two groups of sheep undergoing the "Spring Rise" phenomenon. Only one group (solid line) was given a dose of anthelmintic (phenothiazine) before lambing (Feb.). This group showed a higher spring rise and also a poorer curative mechanism. Both groups of sheep were given phenothiazine in June and August, the June treatment being followed by a rise in egg counts.

Gibson (1953) has shown that the larval stages of *Trichonema* of the large intestine of the horse may remain dormant in the mucosa for some considerable time, being inhibited by the presence of adult worms in the lumen. Following removal of the adult worms by an anthelmintic, groups of dormant larvae emerge from the mucosa and become mature. This procedure can be repeated several times, larvae continuing to emerge from the mucosa after each anthelmintic treatment. It is difficult to see what immunological mechanisms are concerned in this inhibition of larval stages by adult worms. Elimination of the adult worms usually allows the larvae to develop quite quickly, indicating a very rapid waning of the retarding influence. In *Hymenolepis nana* var. *fraterna* in mice the ability to inhibit development of other stages is very rapid indeed; when the larval stages (cysticercoids) of this parasite develop in the villi of infected mice, resistance is apparent in 12 hours (Hearin, 1941). This phenomenon is seen not only in higher vertebrates but also in fish infected with monogenetic trematodes. Recent work in Poland has shown that a phenomenon of "resistance to super-infection" is present in fish which have an existing infection of the gills with monogenetic trematodes; in this state they are incapable of being super-infected with other monogenetic trematodes. The elimination of the existing burden of trematodes results in the gills becoming completely susceptible to re-infection within 24 hours (Dr. Maria Prost, personal communication). In these various phenomena it is not clear whether an antigen–antibody reaction is responsible for the suppression of development of a super-infection, although adult worm infections, created by transplantation techniques, do induce antibody formation. Where acquisition and loss of the inhibitory influence is very rapid, possibly some sort of interference phenomenon on an organ or tissue basis is in operation.

If interference by adults with the development of larval stages is widespread in helminths, and if by virtue of this a reasonable state of health is maintained in infected animals, the removal of the inhibitory influence may be disadvantageous to the host.

There are instances where the prolonged use of anthelmintic drugs may lead to a drug-resistant population of parasites. Where low-level dosing of phenothiazine has been used extensively for the control of *H. contortus* a population of *Haemonchus* has developed which is resistant to phenothiazine. No information exists to show whether phenothiazine-resistant *Haemonchus* will induce immunity to phenothiazine-susceptible *Haemonchus* or *vice-versa*, but fortunately there is a low incidence of helminths with acquired resistance to a frequently-used anthelmintic.

When anthelmintics possessing larvicidal properties come into general use they can be used for either tactical or strategic control of helminths. Obviously, attempts will be made by repeated use of such drugs to eliminate helminths from populations of animals. By so doing it is fairly certain that the general level of immunity of the population to helminth infection will fall, thus placing the animals at risk should the anthelmintic treatment cease. A tactical approach would be to reserve the newer and more effective drugs for defined outbreaks of helminth disease. Certainly with good husbandry the sheep population of Great Britain can look after itself adequately from the point of view of helminth infection. In fact it becomes immunized in a very satisfactory manner against the helminth parasites that beset it. On the other hand the susceptible lambs, though they may be at risk to helminth infection for a period of four to five months, thereafter also undergo an immunological curative process which endows them with an adequate protection which generally lasts for the rest of their lives. It would seem unwise to alter a system such as nature has ordained and which she operates with such effectiveness.

With the newer larvicidal anthelmintics becoming available and the era of vaccines for the control of helminth disease at hand, a new epidemiological picture of helminth infections will probably emerge, and the old dictum *festina lente* may well be sound advice for the long-term strategic control of helminth disease in man and his domestic animals.

REFERENCES

BARR, M. (1951). *J. Path. Bact.*, **63**, 557.
CROFTON, H. D. (1954). *Parasitology*, **44**, 465.
CROFTON, H. D. (1955). *Parasitology*, **45**, 99.
CUSHNIE, G. H. and WHITE, E. G. (1948). *Vet. Rec.*, **60**, 105.
FIELD, A. C., BRAMBELL, M. R. and CAMPBELL, J. A. (1960), *Parasitology*, **50**, 387.
GIBSON, T. E. (1952). *J. Helminth.*, **26**, 43.
GIBSON, T. E. (1953). *J. Helminth.*, **27**, 29.
HAWKINS, W. T., COLE, C. L., KLINE, E. E. and DRUDGE, J. H. (1944). *Vet. Med.*, **39**, 154.
HEARIN, J. T. (1941). *Amer. J. Hyg.*, **33** (Sect. D), 71.
JARRETT, W. F. H., JENNINGS, F. W., McINTYRE, W. I. M., MULLIGAN, W., SHARP, N. C. C. and URQUHART, G. M. (1958). *Vet. Rec.* **70**, 451.
JARRETT, W. F. H., JENNINGS, F. W., McINTYRE, W. I. M., MULLIGAN, W., SHARP, N. C. C. and URQUHART, G. M. (1959). *Amer. J. vet. Res.*, **20**, 527.
McCOY, O. R. (1931). *Amer. J. Hyg.*, **14**, 268.
MORGAN, D. O. and SLOAN, J. E. N. (1947). *Scot. Agric.*, **27**, 28.
NAERLAND, G. (1952). *XIV Int. Vet. Congr.*, *Madrid*, **2**, 65.
OTTO, G. F. (1941). *Amer. J. Hyg.*, **33**, 39.
PAVER, H., PARNELL, I. W. and MORGAN, D. O. (1955). *J. comp. Path.*, **65**, 220.
ROBERTS, F. H. S. and KEITH, R. K. (1959). *Aust. vet. J.*, **35**, 409.
SOULSBY, E. J. L. (1956). *J. Helminth.*, **30**, 129.
SOULSBY, E. J. L. (1957). *J. Helminth.*, **31**, 143.
SOULSBY, E. J. L. (1959.) *XVI Int. Vet. Congr.*, *Madrid*, **2**, 571.
SOULSBY, E. J. L. and STEWART, D. F. (1960). *Aust. J. agric. Res.*, **11**, 595.
SPEDDING, C. R. W. and BROWN, T. H. (1956). *J. Helminth.*,**31**, 171.
STOLL, N. R. (1929). *Amer. J. Hyg.*, **10**, 384.
TALIAFERRO, W. H., TALIAFERRO, L. G. and PIZZI, A. K. (1960). *J. infect. Dis.*, **87**, 37.
TAYLOR, E. L. (1934). *J. Helminth.*, **12**, 143.
URQUHART, G. M. (1958). *Bull. epizoot. Dis. Africa*, **6**, 385.

DISCUSSION

R. Gönnert (Farbenfabriken Bayer): Dr. Soulsby has considered the development of immunity and the influence of chemotherapy on the development of immunity. I would like to know whether he has any experience of the influence of immunity on the action of any anthelmintic. Survival of the parasites will depend to some degree on the species of the parasite and on the antibody reaction of the host. Therefore, it could be possible that the activity of an anthelmintic may be quite different when it acts against a parasite in an immune host, a semi-immune host or a host which has not developed any antibodies. Can he tell me anything about this?

Soulsby: I personally have had no experience of the effect of immunity on the action of an anthelmintic, and I know of no direct work on the problem. However, to some extent I can envisage how this could operate. In many cases immunity appears to inhibit larval development, resulting in, at times, a large population of dormant larvae in the bowel or stomach mucosa of an infected animal. Consequently, an anthelmintic which had action solely against adults or late larval stages might well clear these susceptible stages out, yet leave unaffected the other, unsusceptible, larval stages. This would result in an apparent clinical cure which at a later stage would prove not to be a cure.

There is also the situation, discovered by Gibson (1953) that in *Trichonema* species in the bowel of the horse, the removal by anthelmintics of the adult members of the population will result in dormant larval stages coming out of the mucosa and developing.

M. R. Pollock (National Institute for Medical Research): I should like to ask what is probably a very ignorant question. I was rather surprised not to hear any reference to the possible development of *immunity in the parasite.* I do not know whether this has been observed or whether so far it is difficult to devise experiments for testing it, but in view of Professor Stoll's remark about the possible inadvisability of mass murder of the parasite this seems to be rather relevant. I think many bacteriologists are now coming to believe—it is possible that they are incorrect—that one of the best ways of stopping the development of drug resistance in bacterial infections is to get rid of all or as many as possible of the parasites immediately with one big dose, and to avoid repeated dosing in order to prevent the possible emergence of resistance in the few survivors. This does seem to be relevant to the general problem of worm infestation.

N. R. Stoll (The Rockefeller Institute): I do not know of any evidence for drug resistance occurring in parasitic worms. This is a problem which needs to be considered in relation to the general direction of emphasis which I raised. It is just possible that some of the helminths will fall into the pattern with which you people are familiar; it is also possible that they may not. As far as I know there is no evidence either way.

Soulsby: I believe there is a strain of the sheep parasite, *Haemonchus contortus,* in the southern United States which is resistant to phenothiazine. As far as I am aware this has developed over the prolonged use of low doses of phenothiazine, of about 1 g. a day. This has taken, I think, about nine to ten years to develop. Of course, the situation in helminths is slightly different from that in bacteria, the generation time is so much longer, you have to have the drug present for a very long time to allow (presumably) selection to take place to sort out the resistant forms from the non-resistant forms.

A. C. Cuckler (Merck Institute for Therapeutic Research, Rahway): I should just like to expand on Dr. Soulsby's point. Dr. Drudge, who I believe reported one of these cases of phenothiazine-resistance in the sheep stomach worm (Drudge, Leland and Wyant, 1957), has also reported phenothiazine-resistance in *Strongyles* in horses. In fact, last year at a parasitology meeting in the U.S. we had a paper on this subject.

Stoll: We come all the way over here to be educated!

B. Weitz (The Lister Institute of Preventive Medicine): I wonder if Dr. Soulsby would tell us what sort of immunity develops in animals. Is it a humoral immunity? If that is the case, how does the antibody affect the parasite in the lumen of the gut?

Soulsby: The evidence which we have at present would indicate that the immunity to a helminth is not solely mediated by humoral agencies. For example, it is not comparable with the type of immunity which develops against a toxin where the giving of immune serum to a host will protect the recipient from a challenge of the toxin. It has been possible to demonstrate a degree of passive transfer of immunity but this is always of a fairly low order or, alternatively, one has to give a tremendous amount of immune serum in order to get any obvious effect.

Histological studies of immune reactions indicate that the white cells play an important part in the immune process. Recent work which we have been doing suggests that the antibody may play an important part as an opsonin, attracting antibody-producing cells (transitional macrophages) to either the body of the parasite or to the area nearby. Probably the whole immune process is based on antibody, but an antibody produced locally. However, I think the build-up of the immune mechanism to produce the final effect is a combination of antibody and white cells.

It used to be thought that the main effects of immunity was to produce precipitation of metabolites at the various natural orifices of the parasite. This possibly is an important mechanism but we think that in addition the antibody gets into the parasite and inhibits various essential processes. What processes are inhibited are not known. In summary, immunity to helminths is a combination of locally-produced antibody and white cell activity with other white cells coming in at a later stage to phagocytose the "debris" which is left behind when the antibodies have done their work.

A. Bishop (*The Molteno Institute of Biology and Parasitology*): Does the removal of the spleen have any effect upon the immune reactions of these animals, or is that not a possible thing to try?

Soulsby: The removal of the spleen does reduce the immune response to the animal. We have not examined the effect of splenectomy on the opsonic ability of antibody.

H. M. Adam (*Pharmacology Department, Edinburgh University*): When Dr. Soulsby says "white cells", does he mean eosinophils? Is it true that there is a concentration of eosinophils in the gut in the course of these helminthic infections?

Soulsby: Yes there is. On histological examination helminth infections are particularly characterized by a vast accumulation of eosinophils. *In vitro* studies and certain *in vivo* studies suggest that there is a combination of cells which are attracted to a parasite. The initial attraction is to the eosinophil followed very closely by the attraction of transitional macrophages with a lot of RNA in their cytoplasm. The more we look at this, the more this seems to follow the postulates of Spiers (1958) on his eosinophil work and the production of antibodies.

F. Bergel (*Chester Beatty Research Institute*): I should like to ask Dr. Broome whether organophosphates which he described have been investigated for that very unfortunate side-effect some insecticides have, namely, the demyelination of nerves, because if that were so, then you have chronic toxicities which you cannot discover until after you have started your treatment.

Broome: As far as I know none of these compounds has been investigated in this way although most of them are used as systemic insecticides so they may have received attention from people interested in insecticides. I do not think anyone has been too worried about the toxic effect in animals. This is the point. When you treat an animal you do not really mind if you make it a little sick as long as it is better tomorrow. When you are dealing with humans you are a lot more worried about the long-term effects.

R. B. Barlow (Department of Pharmacology, Edinburgh University): I should like to ask Dr. Broome whether there is any direct evidence that substances like methyridine depolarize membranes in *Ascaris*.

Broome: There is no evidence. I think Prof. Paton at Oxford has shown that it does depolarize the muscle membrane in mammals but we have no evidence in *Ascaris*.

L. G. Goodwin (The Wellcome Laboratories of Tropical Medicine): I am delighted that this morning's talk has emphasized one of the theories which I have always held, which is that animals besides guinea-pigs and rabbits have pharmacology! I have a question on which both Dr. Broome and Dr. Bueding may like to comment because they both mentioned anticholinesterases. Dr. Bueding's work with *para*-rosaniline was most interesting and so were some of Dr. Broome's remarks. What sort of cholinesterases are these? Do the worms have pseudo- and true cholinesterases or do they not?

Broome: I cannot answer this because we have never examined them. There are no detailed reports in the literature.

E. Bueding (The Johns Hopkins University): I can mainly talk about schistosomes. Schistosomes have at least two types of cholinesterase. One is specific for acetylcholine and does not split butyrylcholine. This cholinesterase is found in the insoluble fraction of schistosome homogenates. In addition, there is a soluble non-specific cholinesterase which acts more rapidly on butyrylcholine than on acetylcholine, and there is some evidence that there are other even less specific esterases.

With regard to the effect of *p*-rosaniline. Using the histochemical method of Koelle (1951) as modified by Gomori (1952), one finds that after treatment with *p*-rosaniline there is a marked inhibition of acetylcholinesterase activity in the two lateral ganglia and their commissure. Plate I illustrates the difference between control worms and worms from animals treated with *p*-rosaniline.

I might add also that the acetylcholinesterase activity of schistosomes is at least as high as that of grey matter of mammalian brain and also that the worms contain a very active choline acetylase, a system which

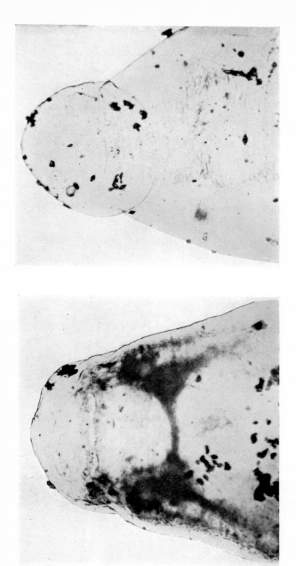

PLATE I. On the left an adult male specimen of *Schistosoma mansoni* from a non-treated mouse, fixed in formalin and incubated fifteen minutes with acetylthiocholine for demonstration of cholinesterase. Ganglia and nerve trunks are visible. Posterior to the central ganglia and commissure is a mass of hematin and a few crystals of sodium sulphate. On the right a male worm from a mouse fed a diet containing 1% *p*-rosaniline. Since this specimen was devoid completely of colour, the substage diaphragm was stopped down slightly to obtain better refraction.

To face p. 80

catalyses the synthesis of acetylcholine from acetyl CoA and choline at a rapid rate.

A. Shulman (*Department of Physiology, Melbourne*): I should like to bring up a few points on some work which has been done in Australia which could provide a basis for discussion and which arises from comments made by Dr. Bueding and Dr. Broome. The points of importance in the action of the drugs mentioned this morning are that the substance needs to be lipophilic, for example a tertiary base. It needs to be a blocking agent and to have anticholinesterase activity. Substances which have an effect in altering DPNH transport in providing energy to these worms are also very important in their anthelmintic action. It has been shown by Koch and Gallagher (1959) that heliotrope alkaloids and *d*-tubocurarine are very effective in blocking the neuromuscular junction of mammalian tissue. It has been shown that these two substances have an equivalent effect in inhibiting oxidations in isolated liver mitochondria, and they appear to do this by increasing the permeability of the mitochondria to DPNH.

It is also of interest that a ruthenium complex of 1,10-phenanthroline, which is very stable and cannot be metabolized, does exactly the same sort of thing. It has been postulated that an essential process both in blocking neuromuscular transmission and in depressing mitochondrial oxidation, is an alteration in membrane permeability.

The other point is that these ruthenium complexes are very powerful neuromuscular blocking agents of mammalian tissue (Dwyer *et al.*, 1957) and they are also very powerful anticholinesterases. They are effective at a concentration of about 10^{-6} M.

The final point I should like to make is that Baldwin in about 1943 and Arundel (unpublished work) in Melbourne have shown that chelating agents of the 2,2′-dipyridyl and 1,10-phenanthroline types are fairly effective anthelmintics. These are tertiary bases and as such will penetrate the worm, and inside the worm they may chelate with a metal and form a neuromuscular blocking agent. These points I raise are consistent with the fact that substances of this sort may act on membrane permeability and that the substance will be a neuromuscular blocking agent. They are tertiary and quaternary substances which are stable.

REFERENCES

DRUDGE, J. H., LELAND, S. E. and WYANT, Z. N. (1957). *Amer. J. vet. Res.*, **18**, 317.
DWYER, F. P., GYARFAS, E. C., WRIGHT, R. D. and SHULMAN, A. (1957). *Nature, Lond.*, **179**, 425.
GIBSON, T. E. (1953). *J. Helminth.*, **27**, 29.
GOMORI, G. (1952). Microscopic Histochemistry, Chicago: University Press.
KOCH, J. H. and GALLAGHER (1959). *Nature, Lond.*, **184**, 1039.
KOELLE, G. B. (1951). *J. Pharmacol.*, **103**, 153.
SPIERS, R. S. (1958). *Nature, Lond.*, **181**, 681.

Session 2: Protozoal Infections

CHAIRMAN: L. G. Goodwin

MALARIA, 8-AMINOQUINOLINES AND HAEMOLYSIS

A. S. ALVING, R. D. POWELL, G. J. BREWER
and J. D. ARNOLD

Department of Medicine, University of Chicago

THE 6-methoxy-8-aminoquinoline antimalarials, of which pamaquine was the first to be synthesized, are the only compounds with sufficient activity against the late exoerythrocytic (fixed tissue) stages of *Plasmodium vivax* malaria (Fig. 1) to be of practical value in the radical cure of this infection. In some individuals these drugs have profound toxic effects upon erythrocytes, causing, for example, methaemoglobin formation and haemolysis. We wish to present evidence suggesting that the erythrocyte toxicity and the antimalarial properties of these compounds are intimately related. This hypothesis is not new (Blanchard, 1946; Brodie and Udenfriend, 1950). Examination of its validity in man has been possible only recently. We believe that both the erythrocyte toxicity and the antimalarial activity of these drugs depends upon their conversion, during oxidative degradation in the host, to reversible oxidation-reduction (redox) intermediates.

The therapeutic studies of Sinton and Bird (1928) demonstrated that pamaquine could prevent relapses of *vivax* malaria. James and coworkers (James, 1931; James, Nicol and Shute, 1931) showed that pamaquine had true causal prophylactic effect in both *falciparum* and *vivax* malaria. Because of its toxicity, however, pamaquine had been relegated, by the time of World War II, for use as a gametocytocidal and sporontocidal drug. For these purposes, it was employed in short courses, in small doses, and in conjunction with an effective blood schizonticidal agent.

During World War II, interest in the 8-aminoquinolines reawakened because the highly active suppressive antimalarials,

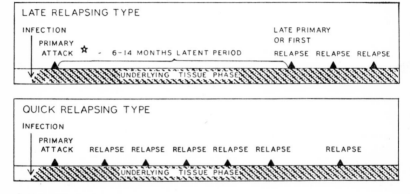

Fig. 1. *P. vivax* infections, unlike *P. falciparum* infections, develop a late exoerythrocytic stage. These secondary tissue schizonts, unless eradicated or prevented, give rise to relapses. Chesson Southwest Pacific strain of *P. vivax* is an example of a quick relapsing type of malaria. The underlying tissue phases represent a main locus of action of the therapeutically active 6-methoxy-8-aminoquinoline antimalarials.

such as mepacrine and chloroquine, proved unable to prevent relapses of *vivax* malaria. The antimalarial and toxic properties of more than fifty 8-aminoquinolines and related compounds were studied in volunteers at the University of Chicago, Army Medical Research Unit, at Stateville Penitentiary, Joliet, Illinois. Drugs exhibiting plasmocide type toxicity in monkeys (irreversible central nervous system damage; Schmidt, 1946) were eliminated from clinical study.

Compounds having high chemotherapeutic indices were charac-terized by: (1) a methoxy substituent at the 6-position in the quino-line nucleus; (2) separation of the two nitrogen atoms in the aliphatic side chain by four or five methylene groups; and (3)

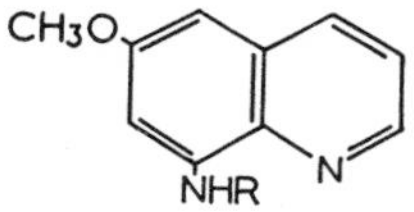

Drug	R	Chemotherapeutic index
Pamaquine	$-\overset{CH_3}{\underset{\mid}{CH}}[CH_2]_3 \cdot N(C_2H_5)_2$	< 1
Pentaquine	$-[CH_2]_5 \cdot NH \cdot CH(CH_3)_2$	1
Isopentaquine	$-\overset{CH_3}{\underset{\mid}{CH}}[CH_2]_3 \cdot NH \cdot CH(CH_3)_2$	2
SN-3883	$-[CH_2]_4 \cdot NH_2$	> 2
Quinocide	$-[CH_2]_3 \cdot CH \cdot NH_2$	—
Primaquine	$-\overset{CH_3}{\underset{\mid}{CH}}[CH_2]_3 \cdot NH_2$	6

FIG. 2. In Caucasians, the chemotherapeutic index of primaquine is at least 6 times that of pamaquine. The chemotherapeutic index of SN 3883 is greater than that of isopentaquine. The chemotherapeutic indices of SN 3883 and quinocide do not appear as great as that of primaquine, but studies of SN 3883 and quinocide are not extensive enough to enable evaluation of their relative chemotherapeutic indices.

presence of a primary amine terminally on the aliphatic side chain in the 8-position. Several 5,6-dimethoxy compounds, as predicted by Schönhöfer in 1942, had antimalarial activity greater than that of their 6-methoxy analogues, but proved impractical antimalarials because of severe bone marrow toxicity, expressed as granulocyto-penia or agranulocytosis. Of the compounds studied, primaquine was the safest; its chemotherapeutic index in Caucasians was at least 6 times that of pamaquine (Fig. 2). For practical purposes, primaquine has now replaced the other 8-aminoquinolines for the radical cure of the relapsing human malarias. In most *vivax* infections, primaquine is effective when given in daily doses of 15 mg. For radical cure of the Chesson strain of Southwest Pacific *vivax*, twice this dose is necessary.

Tests of primaquine toxicity in American Negroes who had sustained haemolysis following pamaquine administration were disappointing: 30 mg. of primaquine base proved severely haemolytic. When comparisons were based upon erythrocyte toxicity in these individuals, only a two-fold gain in chemotherapeutic index was achieved (pamaquine's chemotherapeutic index was 0·3; primaquine's was 0·6). A daily primaquine regimen can be used safely for the cure of Korean *vivax*, but not for *vivax* acquired in the Southwest Pacific area.

Before discussing further the relationship between the haemolytic and antimalarial properties of the 8-aminoquinolines, we wish to review certain features of the biodegradation of these drugs.

The metabolic fate of the 6-methoxy-8-aminoquinoline antimalarials

The therapeutically active 6-methoxy-8-aminoquinolines are rapidly catabolized in man. Clinical investigations indicate that the antimalarial, as well as the methaemoglobin-forming and haemolytic, properties of these drugs are caused by metabolites. The level of "undegraded drug" in the plasma correlates poorly, if at all, with antimalarial activity. The causal prophylactic effect of a single dose of primaquine in mosquito-induced Chesson *vivax* malaria is maximal when the drug is administered 12 hours before volunteers are infected (Fig. 3). The peak concentration of "undegraded drug" in the plasma occurs 4 to 6 hours after drug administration; in drug-sensitive subjects, haemolysis begins only after a latent period of 24 hours or more.

Detailed studies of the biodegradation of the 8-aminoquino-lines have not been carried out in man, but important investigations have been completed in lower animals (Zubrod, Kennedy and

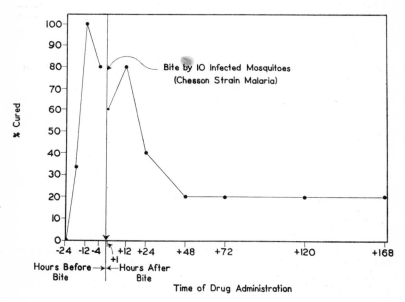

CAUSAL PROPHYLACTIC EFFECT
OF A SINGLE DOSE PRIMAQUINE BASE (180mg.)

Fig. 3. A single dose of 180 mg. primaquine base exerts a casual prophylactic effect (action against the pre-erythrocytic tissue schizonts) in mosquito-induced Chesson *vivax* malaria. This effect is maximal when drug is administered 12 hours before infection.

Shannon, 1948; Hughes and Schmidt, 1950; Brodie and Uden-friend, 1950; Josephson, Taylor, Greenberg and Ray, 1951*a* Josephson, Greenberg, Taylor and Bami, 1951*b*; Elderfield and Smith, 1953; Smith, 1956). Schönhöfer (1942) correlated chemi-cal structure with activity against the asexual erythrocyte forms of

Plasmodium relictum, an avian parasite, and postulated that the activity of 6-methoxy-8-aminoquinolines, including pamaquine, is related to the formation of quinonoid products in the host. *In vitro* studies reported by Drake and Pratt (1951) supported Schönhöfer's hypothesis. Additional supporting evidence was brought forth by

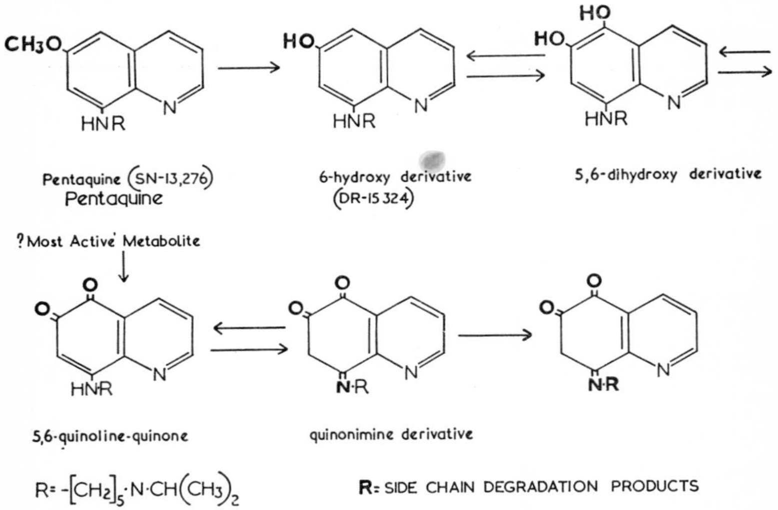

Pentaquine (SN-13,276)
Pentaquine

6-hydroxy derivative
(DR-15 324)

5,6-dihydroxy derivative

? Most Active Metabolite

5,6-quinoline-quinone

quinonimine derivative

$R = -[CH_2]_5 \cdot N \cdot CH(CH_3)_2$ **R =** SIDE CHAIN DEGRADATION PRODUCTS

FIG. 4. Suggested pathway of pentaquine biodegradation. Relatively little information is available regarding degradation of the aliphatic side chain in the 8-position (see Elderfield and Smith, 1953, and Smith, 1956); its terminal alkyl group is probably more resistant to cleavage and subsequent oxidation than is the nuclear 6-methoxyl group.

Josephson *et al.* (1951*b*) when they identified a highly active pamaquine metabolite as the 5,6-quinolinequinone derivative. *In vitro* tests showed that both the antimalarial activity against *P. gallinaceum* and the methaemoglobin-forming effect of the metabolite were about 16 times those of pamaquine (Josephson *et al.*, 1951*a*).

A compound analogous to the pamaquine metabolite appears to be a main degradation product of pentaquine in the rhesus monkey (Smith, 1956). Smith found that pentaquine, during biodegradation, is demethylated at the 6-position before oxidation (Fig. 4). The first metabolite is the 6-hydroxy derivative. The 5,6-dihydroxy derivative is formed next. The third step requires oxidation of the dihydroxy derivative to the 5,6-quinolinequinone. The available evidence indicates that the 5,6-quinolinequinone derivative is the active degradation product of the therapeutically effective 6-methoxy-8-aminoquinoline antimalarials.

The quinolinequinone intermediates are electron-carrying redox compounds capable of acting as oxidants. Emerson, Ham and Castle (1941, 1949) suggested such intermediates may cause methaemoglobin formation and haemolysis, but they were unable to correlate the severity of methaemoglobinaemia with red cell destruction. In man these toxic manifestations seemed to occur almost capriciously. It had been assumed that the haemolysis resulting from the administration of certain aromatic compounds, including the 8-aminoquinoline antimalarials represented an acquired condition. Recent studies have shown that hypersusceptibility to haemolysis occurs in individuals whose erythrocytes have a genetically determined enzyme efficiency.

Drug-induced haemolysis

Investigators in many countries have helped define the characteristics of the susceptibility to drug-induced haemolysis termed primaquine-sensitivity. Clinically, an acute, self-limited haemolytic anaemia follows the ingestion of primaquine or any of more than 40 other drugs and vegetable foods.

Primaquine-sensitivity is transmitted by a partially dominant gene on the X-chromosome. Its geographic distribution parallels, in general, the distribution of *falciparum* malaria. The incidence of primaquine-sensitivity is approximately 13 % in American Negro males. It is rare among Caucasians of Northern European stock, but occurs in more than 20 % of some peoples of the Mediterranean area. The clinical and biochemical characteristics of primaquine-sensitivity have been reviewed recently by Carson (1960), Larizza

4

(1960), Löhr and Waller (1961), Tarlov, Brewer, Carson and Alving (1962), and Kellermeyer, Tarlov, Brewer, Carson and Alving (1962). Discussion here will be limited to those features relevant to the relationship between erythrocyte toxicity and antimalarial activity.

Carson, Flanagan, Ickes and Alving (1956) showed that the most prominent, possibly the primary, defect in the erythrocytes of primaquine-sensitive individuals is a marked decrease in the activity of glucose-6-phosphate dehydrogenase (G-6-PD). This enzyme catalyses the initial oxidative step in the pentose phosphate pathway of glucose metabolism (Fig. 5). The first two enzymes of this pathway provide the only source of reduced triphosphopyridine nucleotide (TPNH) in the mature erythrocytes of humans.

TPNH is important in certain reductive processes in erythrocytes, for example, conversion of oxidized glutathione (GSSG) to its reduced form (GSH). In red cells of primaquine-sensitive persons, GSH is decreased in content and is unstable (Beutler, Dern, Flanagan and Alving, 1955; Beutler, 1957). One function of GSH is to protect sulphydryl groups of sulphydryl-dependent enzymes, haemoglobin, and other cellular proteins against oxidation. Glyceraldehyde-3-phosphate dehydrogenase is an example of a sulphyldry-dependent enzyme important in red cell metabolism. In erythrocytes, GSH is the main substance available to protect this enzyme's sulphydryl groups against oxidation. In haemolysates the activity of glyceraldehyde-3-phosphate dehydrogenase can be shown to vary markedly depending upon the concentration of GSH. The decreased content and the instability of GSH in erythrocytes of drug-sensitive individuals appear to render certain components of these cells unusually susceptible to oxidative damage or inactivation

Carson and his coworkers (Carson, Brewer and Ickes, 1961) studied haemolysates from an individual whose erythrocytes showed a substantial decrease in glutathione reductase activity. Although G-6-PD activity was normal in haemolysates of this individual's erythrocytes, an acute haemolytic anaemia developed

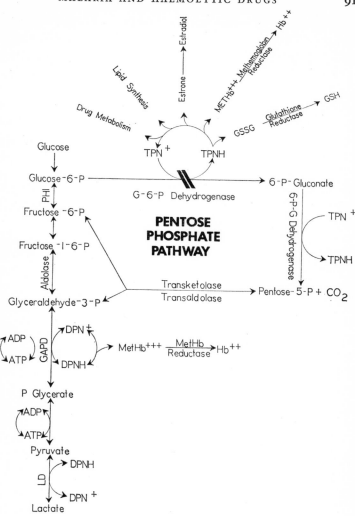

FIG. 5. Diagram of the pentose phosphate and Embden–Meyerhof pathways of glucose metabolism. A diagonal mark indicates the G-6-P dehydrogenase abnormality. Abbreviations: phosphate (P); glutathione (GSSG); reduced glutathione (GSH); methaemoglobin (Methb+++); haemoglobin (Hb++); phosphohexose isomerase (PHI); glyceraldehyde-3-phosphate dehydrogenase (GAPD); adenosine diphosphate (ADP); adenosine triphosphate (ATP); lactic dehydrogenase (LD); oxidized diphosphopyridine nucleotide (DPN+) and its reduced form (DPNH); and oxidized triphosphopyridine nucleotide (TPN+) and its reduced form (TPNH).

following the administration of primaquine. These studies indicate that abnormalities involving not only G-6-PD, but also other enzymes and coenzymes related to the pentose phosphate pathway, may render erythrocytes hypersusceptible to haemolysis.

TPNH is also of importance, in certain circumstances, in the reduction of methaemoglobin. Methaemoglobin formed under physiological conditions in erythrocytes is reduced enzymically to haemoglobin chiefly by a system linked to reduced diphospho-pyridine nucleotide; the role of TPNH-linked methaemoglobin reduction appears to be relatively minor. In normal red cells, artificial electron carriers, such as the redox dye methylene blue or the degradation products of the 8-aminoquinoline antimalarials, can greatly accelerate TPNH-linked methaemoglobin reduction. The same is not true in erythrocytes of drug-sensitive persons. Erythrocytes of primaquine-sensitive individuals have an increased susceptibility to form methaemoglobin. Methaemoglobin formation, although potentially reversible, seems an essential prerequisite for the irreversible denaturation of haemoglobin. The mechanisms by which methaemoglobin is further oxidized and precipitated as irreversibly denatured proteins is complex, but appears intimately related to glutathione metabolism. Methaemoglobinaemia is often not apparent during drug-induced haemolysis. The most likely explanation for this is that the older erythrocytes, those most susceptible to methaemoglobin formation, are preferentially destroyed during haemolysis and are thus removed from the circulation (Brewer, Tarlov, Kellermeyer and Alving, 1962).

Methylene blue abolishes methaemoglobinaemia in both non-sensitive and primaquine-sensitive persons. In individuals not hypersusceptible to haemolysis, methylene blue reduces non-functioning methaemoglobin to functioning haemoglobin. The same mechanism does not occur in erythrocytes of drug-sensitive individuals; in these red cells, methylene blue cannot accelerate TPNH-linked methaemoglobin reduction. Methylene blue abolishes methaemoglobinemia in drug-sensitive persons (Brewer and

Tarlov, 1961) chiefly because, like primaquine, it causes acute haemolysis (Fig. 6.).

Studies of the antimalarial effect of methylene blue are of interest at this point because they provide evidence concerning the link

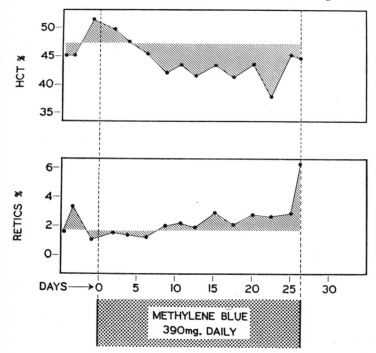

FIG. 6. A fall in haematocrit (HCT) level and a rise in reticulocyte count (RETICS) followed the administration of methylene blue to a primaquine-sensitive individual.

between erythrocyte toxicity of certain compounds and their antimalarial activity.

The antimalarial effect of methylene blue

Methylene blue was the first synthetic organic compound found to have antimalarial activity. Guttman and Ehrlich (1891) employed methylene blue to treat clinical relapses of what was probably *vivax* malaria. The drug was weakly active against the blood schizonts and gradually terminated clinical attacks. This discovery led eventually to the development of pamaquine.

The blood schizontocidal activity of methylene blue in mosquito-induced Chesson *vivax* malaria has been studied, essentially repeating, in non-immune volunteers, Guttman and Ehrlich's experiments. Five hundred mg. of methylene blue administered orally each day during clinical attacks had insufficient activity against the blood schizonts to terminate either parasitaemia or clinical symptoms. For this reason, in subsequent trials of methylene blue's anti-relapse effect, quinine was administered concurrently to obtain its blood schizontocidal action. Methylene blue failed to prevent relapses when used in treatment of primary attacks, but led to radical cure in 8 of 10 cases treated during clinical relapses. All individuals treated with quinine alone had subsequent attacks of malaria. Methylene blue has definite activity against the late exoerthrocytic (persisting tissue) stages of *vivax* malaria, a property similar qualitatively to the action of primaquine and its congeners. These experiments with the dye methylene blue strongly support the concept that the 6-methoxy-8-aminoquinolines owe their haemolytic and, at least in part, their radical curative effects to their conversion, during oxidative degradation, to redox intermediates, such as hydroxy derivatives which can be reversibly converted to quinonimines.

Relationship between the haemolytic and antimalarial properties of the 8-aminoquinolines and some nuclear substitutions

Modifications in the aliphatic side chain, as mentioned previously resulted in compounds that, compared with pamaquine, had greatly improved chemotherapeutic indices in individuals who were not hypersusceptible to haemolysis. However, only a slight gain was achieved in the chemotherapeutic index in drug-sensitive individuals. These findings support the view that similar, perhaps identical, mechanisms may be operative in effecting haemolytic and antimalarial activity. Additional support has been gained by studies of two compounds with other nuclear substitutions. Compound DR-15, 305 is analogous to pentaquine except that it has a methyl substituent in the 7-position and lacks the 6-methoxyl group. This compound has no antimalarial activity and no haemolytic effect when administered in a daily dose of 480 mg. (16 times the haemolytic dose of pentaquine). This supports Schönhöfer's (1942) hypothesis that only those 8-aminoquinolines capable of being transformed into quinonoid compounds are effective antimalarials. Substitution of the 7-methyl group for the 6-methoxy group may prevent degradation by way of the 6-hydroxy sequence to quinonimine derivatives.

The second drug, DR-15, 324, is probably the first degradation product of pentaquine. This drug is highly active *in vitro*. However, *in vivo*, it has only slight action against the late tissue stages of Chesson *vivax* malaria. DR-15, 324 led to radical cure of only 1 of 5 patients when 60 mg. (base) was administered, concurrently with quinine, daily for 14 days. Its radical curative activity was less than one fourth that of the parent compound. It showed no general toxic manifestations and no anaemia developed. However, ^{51}Cr labelling of the erythrocytes revealed that DR-15, 324 was mildly haemolytic in primaquine-sensitive individuals. Thus, both the therapeutic and haemolytic properties of DR-15, 324 are slight. This intrinsically more active metabolite, when administered orally, may be catabolized too rapidly to exert fully its potential haemolytic and therapeutic effect.

These studies stimulated a search for drugs possessing radical curative activity against *vivax* malaria among other compounds known to be haemolytic in primaquine-sensitive individuals. Nitrofurantoin is such a compound. Preliminary studies indicate it has some activity against the late tissue stages of *P. vivax*. The activity, however, is too slight for the drug to be of practical value as an antimalarial. The studies are of additional interest because of the report that nitrofurans, *in vitro*, can interfere with glutathione reductase activity (Buzard, Kopko and Paul, 1960), and because of the observation that an individual with decreased glutathione reductase activity developed haemolysis following administration of primaquine.

The results presented in this discussion indicate that an intimate relationship exists between the haemolytic and antimalarial properties of certain drugs. The findings suggest two ways in which the 6-methoxy-8-aminoquinolines may exert antimalarial activity: (1) The drug metabolites may unfavourably affect TPNH-linked reductive biosynthetic processes in those liver cells that are already stressed by the tissue schizonts they contain; the infected parenchymal cells may, under the additional stress of drugs, be unable to furnish nutrients essential for rapid growth of the parasites. (2) The tissue schizonts, compared with the blood schizonts, may have deficiencies involving enzymes of their pentose phosphate pathway, or involving its related cofactors, so that these forms of the parasites are unusually vulnerable to oxidative damage. We hope experiments to test the validity of these speculations can be devised in the near future.

[Discussion on this paper was postponed until after the following paper by A. Bishop; see p. 111.]

REFERENCES

BEUTLER, E., DERN, R. J., FLANAGAN, C. L. and ALVING, A. S. (1955). *J. Lab. clin. Med.*, **45**, 286.

BEUTLER, E. (1957). *J. Lab. clin. Med.*, **49**, 84.

BLANCHARD, K. C. (1946). *In* Wiselogle, F. Y., A Survey of Antimalarial Drugs 1941–1945, I, 129., Ann Arbor: J. W. Edwards.

BREWER, G. J. and TARLOV, A. R. (1961). *Clin. Res.*, **9**, 65.

BREWER, G. J., TARLOV, A. R., KELLERMEYER, R. W., and ALVING, A. S. (1962). *J. Lab. clin. Med.*, in press.

BRODIE, B. B. and UDENFRIEND, S. (1950). *Proc. Soc. exp. Biol., N.Y.*, **74**, 845.

BUZARD, J. A., KOPKO, F. and PAUL, M. F. (1960). *J. Lab. clin. Med.*, **56**, 884.

CARSON, P. E., (1960). *Fed. Proc.*, **19**, 995.

CARSON, P. E., BREWER, G. J. and ICKES, C. (1961). *J. Lab. clin. Med.*, **58**, 804.

CARSON, P. E., FLANAGAN, C. L. ICKES, C. E. and ALVING, A. S. (1956). *Science*, **124**, 484.

DRAKE, N. L. and PRATT, Y. T. (1951). *J. Amer. chem. Soc.*, **73**, 544.

ELDERFIELD, R. C. and SMITH, L. L. (1953). *J. Amer. chem. Soc.*, **75**, 1022.

EMERSON, C. P., HAM, T. H. and CASTLE, W. B. (1941). *J. Lab. clin. Med.*, **20**, 451.

EMERSON, C. P., HAM, T. H. and CASTLE, W. B. (1949). in Potthoff, C. P., The Preservation of the Formed Elements of the Blood., 114, Amer. Natl. Red Cross.

GUTTMAN, P. and EHRLICH, P. (1891). *Berl. klin.Wschr.*, **28**, 953.

HUGHES, H. B. and SCHMIDT, L. H. (1950). *Proc. Soc. exp. Biol. Med.*, *N.Y.*, **73**, 581.

JAMES, S. P. (1931). *Trans. R. Soc. trop. Med. Hyg.*, **24**, 477.

JAMES, S. P., NICOL, W. D., and SHUTE, P. G. (1931). *Lancet*, **ii**, 341.

JOSEPHSON, E. S., TAYLOR, D. J., GREENBERG, J. and RAY, A. P. (1951a). *Proc. Soc. exp. Biol.*, *N.Y.*, **76**, 700.

JOSEPHSON, E. S., GREENBERG, J., TAYLOR, D. J. and BAMI, H. L. (1951b). *J. Pharmacol.*, **103**, 7.

KELLERMEYER, R. W., TARLOV, A. R., BREWER, G. J. CARSON, P. E. and ALVING, A. S. (1962). *J. Amer. med. Assoc.*, In press.

LARIZZA, P. (1960). *Z. klin. Med.*, **156**, 287.

LÖHR, G. W., and WALLER, H. D. (1961). *Dtsch. med. Wschr.*, **86**, 27 and 87.

SCHMIDT, L. H. (1946), in Wiselogle, F. Y. A Survey of Antimalarial Drugs in 1941–1945, I, 106, Ann Arbor: J. W. Edwards.

SCHÖNHÖFER, F. (1942). *Z. physiol. Chem.*, **274**, 1.

SINTON J. A. and BIRD W. (1928). *Indian J. med. Res.*, **16**, 159.

SMITH, C. C. (1956). *J. Pharmacol.*, **116**, 67.

TARLOV, A. R., BREWER, G. J., CARSON, P. E. and ALVING, A. S. (1962). *Arch. intern. Med.*, **109**, 209.

ZUBROD, C. G., KENNEDY, T. J. and SHANNON, J. A. (1948). *J. clin. Invest.*, **27**, 114.

CHEMOTHERAPY AND DRUG RESISTANCE IN PROTOZOAL INFECTIONS

ANN BISHOP

Medical Research Council Chemotherapy Research Unit,
Molteno Institute, University of Cambridge

THE observation that micro-organisms, in the course of treatment of their hosts, can become resistant to drugs to which formerly they were sensitive, was first made upon trypanosomes in Ehrlich's laboratory early in the present century. More recently the problem has arisen in malaria parasites. As yet little is known of the biological changes which enable these organisms to withstand the action of the drugs. The protozoologist or biochemist who wishes to study the problem of drug-resistance in these parasitic protozoa is faced with a difficulty not encountered in similar studies in bacteria; it is not possible to cultivate trypanosomes or malaria parasites for any useful period in the stages of development which are present in the blood stream of their mammalian hosts. The blood-stream form of trypanosomes which are pathogenic to man and domestic animals in Africa can be kept alive *in vitro* for about 24 hours by a method devised by Yorke, Adams and Murgatroyd (1929) or by modifications of this method, but the only stage which can be cultivated at present is that which occurs in the gut of the tsetse fly. These culture forms differ physiologically from the blood-stream forms. Most of the work upon drug-resistance in trypanosomes has therefore been carried out either upon experimentally induced infections in animals or on suspensions of trypanosomes which rarely multiply and which remain viable for relatively short periods. However, the fact that trypanosomes can be kept alive for some hours outside the body of the host has made possible short-term metabolic studies of drug-resistant and normal trypanosomes, and comparative studies of the effect of inhibitors and the absorption of drugs. The intracellular habitat of the malaria parasite is an additional difficulty in physiological and biochemical work upon this parasite. Moreover, it is not possible to infect animals other than Primates with the species of *Plasmodium* which cause malaria in man; work upon drug-resistance in malaria has therefore to be carried out upon species of *Plasmodium* which are infective to laboratory animals or upon human volunteers.

The two methods most frequently used for inducing drug-resistance in trypanosomes are the relapse method and the short passage method. By the relapse method the infection is treated with subcurative doses of the drug and the subsequent series of relapses are treated with gradually increasing doses. The trypanosomes are therefore exposed not only to the action of the drug but to the antibodies produced by the host in its response to the infection and they may thus become resistant to antibody. By the short passage method the trypanosomes are passed through a series of drug-treated animals at frequent intervals, before any immunological changes have taken place in the host. Many years ago some evidence was produced that, in the case of suramin, the defence mechanism of the host plays an important part in the rate at which trypanosomes become resistant to the drug. Resistance to this compound developed more rapidly in animals which had been splenectomized and in which the reticuloendothelial system had been blockaded by the intravenous injection of electro-colloidal copper than in intact animals (Jancsó and Jancsó, 1935), an observation which was confirmed by Hawking (1939). More recently, it has been shown that a strain of *Trypanosoma brucei* which had become antibody-resistant was less sensitive to suramin and quinapyramine (antrycide) than a strain which had not been exposed to antibody (Soltys, 1959). This suggests that resistance to these drugs might develop more readily in a strain which is antibody-resistant and which is therefore not affected by the defence mechanism of the host than in a normal strain. The insensitivity to these drugs conferred by antibody-resistance is not, however, identical to suramin-resistance as produced by that drug in an antibody-sensitive strain, since such a strain proved to be sensitive to antrycide whereas the antibody-resistant strain had lost its sensitivity to both these compounds.

Resistance to trypanocidal compounds is not necessarily confined to the compound which produced it. Cross-resistance may occur between compounds differing in their chemical structure, for example, trypanosomes made resistant to the arsenical compounds atoxyl (the sodium salt of p-aminophenylarsonic acid) and tryparsamide (sodium N-phenyl-glycineamide-p-arsonate) are resistant to the acridine compound acriflavine and this cross-resistance is reciprocal (Yorke, Murgatroyd and Hawking, 1931a). A strain of T. $rhodesiense$ resistant to melarsen (disodium salt of 4-melaminylphenylarsonic acid) proved to be resistant also to a wide variety of trypanocidal compounds including some to which tryparsamide and atoxyl-resistant strains are sensitive (Rollo and Williamson, 1951). There is evidence that trypanosomes made resistant to organic arsenical compounds such as tryparsamide and to acriflavine by treatment with either of those compounds do not absorb the compounds to which they are resistant, though the compounds are readily absorbed and reach a high concentration in normal trypanosomes (Yorke, Murgatroyd and Hawking, 1931b; Hawking, 1934, 1937). In these experiments biological and chemical methods of measurement were employed; labelled compounds have not been used. Selective absorption of the drug does not appear to be the important factor in the development of resistance to other trypanocides. No significant difference was observed in the amount of suramin absorbed by normal and suramin-resistant trypanosomes (Hawking, 1939). Antrycide, stilbamidine (4,4'-diamidinostilbene) and 2-hydroxystilbamidine were able to penetrate into antrycide-resistant and normal trypanosomes, but the normal trypanosomes seemed to retain the drug in their substance, whereas it disappeared from the resistant trypanosomes (Ormerod, 1952). Antrycide-resistant trypanosomes were almost as sensitive as normal trypanosomes to the *in vitro* action of the drug, but the resistant trypanosomes remained infective to mice after *in vitro* exposure to a dose of antrycide which destroyed the infectivity of normal trypanosomes (Hawking and Thurston, 1955).

It has been postulated, in relation to the arsenical trypanocides, that the action of these drugs upon the parasite is effected in two stages, a preliminary stage in which the drug becomes fixed to or absorbed by the organism, followed by a stage in which the chemically reactive arsenoxide group combines with some essential constituent of the cell (King and Strangeways, 1942). It has been suggested that the important factor determining cross-resistance between compounds belonging to widely different chemical classes may be the ionizable groups in the compounds and that resistance may be due to a shift in the isoelectric point of some of the proteins in the trypanosome (Schueler, 1947). More recently, strains of *T. rhodesiense* made resistant to eight trypanocides belonging to different chemical groups have been examined for cross-resistance to nine trypanocidal compounds belonging to structurally dissimilar chemical groups. The compounds were classified as feebly ionized, ionized as cations and ionized as anions. From the results of these extensive tests it was concluded that to attempt to explain cross-resistance on an ionic basis was an oversimplification of the problem, but it was suggested that stereospecific structural changes associated with the initial uptake of the drug occur in resistant trypanosomes (Williamson and Rollo, 1959).

No difference in metabolism has been found between normal and drug-resistant trypanosomes of a degree which would account for the great change in sensitivity to the drug observed in some resistant trypanosomes (Bishop, 1959). This problem has recently been investigated in a stilbamidine-resistant strain of *T. rhodesiense* by the use of metabolic inhibitors. The strain showed a high degree of resistance to a wide range of trypanocidal compounds, but no change in intermediary metabolism of a degree comparable to the resistance developed could be demonstrated. Oxidation-reduction potential was shown to be important in trypanocidal activity, but there was no evidence that it was related to the development of stilbamidine-resistance. Evidence of the dependence of the trypanocidal action of ionizing trypanocides upon pH supported the hypothesis that the development of resistance to drugs involves physical changes in the cellular structures associated with the uptake of the drug (Williamson, 1959).

The rate with which resistance to trypanocidal drugs develops in experimentally induced infections varies with the compound; resistance to aromatic arsenicals and acriflavine develops relatively quickly in a matter of weeks, whereas it took 16 months of continuous treatment with stilbamidine to produce a strain of *T. rhodesiense* which was fully resistant to the drug (Fulton and Grant, 1955). A strain of *T. equiperdum* which had been passaged serially through mice treated with this drug, for 16 months, was still not fully resistant to it (Kaltenbach, 1959). The stability of resistance in the absence of the drug is also variable, varying with the strain and the compound; but one atoxyl-resistant strain of *T. rhodesiense* is known to have retained its resistance for 24 years (Fulton and Grant, 1955).

Many years ago a high degree of resistance to reduced tryparsamide was produced in *T. rhodesiense in vitro* by exposing suspensions of the flagellates to increasing concentrations of the drug in a nutrient medium, the trypanosomes being washed free of drug at the end of each course of treatment and inoculated into mice where they multiplied. Since a large proportion of the trypanosomes were killed during each course of treatment, the drug obviously had a selective action upon the population (Yorke, Murgatroyd and Hawking, 1931c). Recently, populations of *T. rhodesiense* have been analysed for resistance to reduced tryparsamide by the same method and a small proportion of the initial population were found to be resistant to the highest dose of drug to which resistance could be produced by prolonged treatment (Hawking, 1961). It is obvious, however, that when resistance to a drug only develops after many months of treatment it cannot be the result of the selection and multiplication of resistant individuals present in the original population; the resistant trypanosomes must have arisen later from sensitive individuals.

The stability of drug resistance in trypanosomes suggests that this character develops by mutation. Attempts have been made by Fulton (1961) to induce resistance to drugs in normal *T. rhodesiense* by incubating them with deoxyribonucleic acid (DNA) extracted from strains of this species resistant to arsenicals, stilbamidine and suramin. In these experiments mice were inoculated with the suspension of incubated trypanosomes and, when the infection had become patent, were treated with the appropriate drug in a dosage higher than that which would clear the blood of the normal strain of trypanosomes. The data obtained with DNA from an atoxyl-resistant strain suggested that transfer of resistance may have occurred.

Inoki and his co-workers in Japan (Inoki and Matsushiro, 1960; Inoki, Taniuchi, Sakamoto, Ono and Kubo, 1961) have described both intra- and interspecific transformation of drug resistance in trypanosomes. They observed that akinetoplastic forms of a *p*-rosaniline-resistant strain of *T. gambiense* maintained in mice did not increase in number, even when the drug was administered in a dosage which produced akinetoplastic trypanosomes in the normal strain. They therefore used the proportions of akinetoplastic trypanosomes present in a strain in drug-treated mice as an indicator of drug-resistance. Using this method of assessment it was claimed that resistance had been transferred from a *p*-rosaniline-resistant strain of *T. gambiense* to a sensitive strain by incubation with a lysate of the resistant strain. Transfer of resistance was prevented if the lysate was first incubated with deoxyribonuclease. Reciprocal transfer of *p*-rosaniline resistance between *T. gambiense* and *T. evansi* has also been described. Sensitivity of the growth rate of these strains in drug-treated mice was not assessed.

Quinine-resistance has never been a problem in the treatment of malaria, but resistance to two of the newer synthetic antimalarial compounds has been described from certain areas where these drugs have been in use. These compounds, proguanil (paludrine, IV) and pyrimethamine (daraprim, VI) produce resistance relatively readily in experimentally induced infections of *Plasmodium*,

whereas compounds such as the 8-aminoquinolines pamaquin (plasmoquine, I) and primaquine, the 4-aminoquinolines chloroquine (II) and amodiaquine, and the acridine compound mepacrine (III), do not.

Proguanil is metabolized in the body of the host into a more effective dihydrotriazine derivative, (V) which bears a striking resemblance to pyrimethamine in its chemical structure (Carrington, Crowther, Davey, Levi and Rose, 1951). Proguanil and pyrimethamine also resemble one another closely in their visible effect upon the parasite; they both inhibit nuclear division in the developing erythrocytic schizont. Further evidence of the relationship between these compounds comes from the study of strains of

Plasmodium made resistant to their action. It has been observed that strains made resistant to pyrimethamine are resistant to proguanil and that proguanil-resistant strains may be resistant to pyrimethamine, though this is not always the case. Cross-resistance tests have also shown that prognuail and pyrimethamine are related in their mode of action to the sulphonamide compounds sulphadiazine and sulphanilamide; but whereas sulphadiazine- and sulphanilamide-resistant strains have been shown to be resistant to proguanil and

pyrimethamine, the converse is not true; pyrimethamine-resistant strains are sensitive to sulphadiazine and so, in general, are proguanil-resistant strains. It is apparent therefore that though the mode of action of these drugs is related, they do not act upon the parasite in an identical way (Bishop, 1959).

p-Aminobenzoic acid (*p*-AB) and folic acid antagonize the antimalarial action of sulphadiazine, proguanil and pyrimethamine, though in the case of proguanil their antagonistic effect has been found to vary with the species of *Plasmodium* (Bishop, 1959). The inhibitory action of the sulphonamides upon malaria parasites is presumably due to interference with the utilization of *p*-AB, and it has been suggested that proguanil and pyrimethamine interfere with the conversion of folic to folinic acid (Rollo, 1955). There is evidence that folic acid or related substances are concerned with the metabolism of the malaria parasite. The survival of malaria parasites in the erythrocytes *in vitro* has been shown to be favoured by the presence of *p*-AB (Anfinsen, Geiman, McKee, Ormsbee and Ball, 1946) and folic acid in the medium (Glenn and Manwell, 1956); but when *P. lophurae* of ducks was removed from the erythrocytes and maintained free in a nutrient medium, their survival was favoured by folinic acid but not by folic acid (Trager, 1958). Erythrocytes of ducks infected with this parasite were found to contain more folic and folinic acid than those of uninfected ducks of the same age, and only a part of this increase could be accounted for in the parasites themselves (Trager, 1959). Sulphadiazine prevented the increase in folic and folinic acids, both in the erythrocytes of ducks infected with a normal strain of *P. lophurae* and in ducks infected with a sulphadiazine-resistant strain, though the latter multiplied in the presence of the drug; but if the birds infected with the resistant strain were treated with pyrimethamine, to which they were also resistant, only the increase in folinic acid was prevented. Thus, folinic acid production was affected at the point of synthesis characteristic of each drug. The observations suggest that in the parasite/erythrocyte complex folinic acid synthesis is carried out mainly in the erythrocytes and is therefore affected by the drugs irrespective of the strain of parasite which is present; they also suggest that resistant parasites require less folinic acid, or some product of it, than normal parasites (Trager, 1961).

A strain of *P. gallinaceum* has recently been made resistant to diaminodiphenyl sulphone (DDS), a compound used in the treatment of leprosy. Although, like sulphadiazine, the inhibitory action of DDS upon the parasite is antagonized by *p*-AB and folic acid, the DDS-resistant strain shows practically no enhancement of resistance to proguanil or pyrimethamine (Bishop, unpublished results). Also no enhancement of resistance to these compounds was observed in a strain of *P. cynomolgi* which had been made highly resistant to DDS (Ramakrishnan, personal communication). It must be concluded therefore that resistance to those sulphonamide compounds whose inhibitory action upon the parasite is directed against p-AB-folic-folinic acid metabolism, does not necessarily produce resistance to proguanil and pyrimethamine. The exact relationship of the mode of action of these compounds is still a matter for conjecture.

It has been suggested that inadequate dosing and a significant parasitaemia, as in the inadequately treated acute attack or smouldering infection, provide the conditions which lead to the development of drug resistance in malaria (Covell, Coatney, Field and Jaswant Singh, 1955). The problem of the effect of parasite numbers and of the size of dose of drug upon the rate of development of resistance has recently been studied in strains of a clone of *Plasmodium gallinaceum* (Bishop, 1962). The method was that used previously in the study of the development of resistance to metachloridine in this parasite (Bishop, 1958).

In strains treated with proguanil evidence was obtained that resistance developed more rapidly when large populations of parasites (10^9) were exposed to the drug than when the populations were relatively small (5×10^7), that is to say, the rate of development of resistance to the drug was related to the size of the population of parasites exposed to its action. No such relationship was observed in the experiments with pyrimethamine, but a greater variability in the rate of development of resistance to the drug was observed in strains maintained by relatively small populations of parasites, as compared with strains maintained with large populations. Thus, although resistance developed as rapidly in some strains maintained by small populations as in others maintained by large, in some of the former the rate of the development of resistance was much slower than in any of the strains maintained by the large populations.

The effect of the size of the dose of pyrimethamine upon the rate of development of resistance has also been studied, but there was no evidence that resistance developed more rapidly if the birds through which the strain was passed were treated with small doses (1μg./20g.) than if the doses were large (50μg./20g.). These observations upon pyrimethamine are in agreement with those of Williamson and Lourie (1947) who showed that resistance to proguanil developed as rapidly in a strain of *P. gallinaceum* treated with the maximum tolerated dose of proguanil as in a strain treated with a small but effective dose.

The suddenness with which resistance developed in many of the strains treated with proguanil or pyrimethamine, the sporadic nature of its development when small populations of parasites were exposed to the action of the drugs, and the relative stability of resistance to these drugs favour the hypothesis that resistance is due to the selection of mutants of low frequency; but although resistance persists through the sexual cycle of development in the mosquito nothing is known of the method by which it is inherited since, unfortunately, there is at present no means of cultivating individual zygotes and analysing the inheritance of drug-resistance in their progeny.

It has been shown that resistance to pyrimethamine can develop rapidly in the malaria parasites of man. Young (1957) has described its development in *P. malariae* in a neurosyphilitic patient who had been infected with the parasite for therapeutic reasons and who had received 100 mg. of the drug in two days, a dose greater than that recommended for suppression (Covell, Coatney, Field and Jaswant Singh, 1955). Similar observations were made upon patients infected with *P. vivax* and *P. falciparum* who had received single doses of the drug during the peak of parasitaemia (Young and Burgess, 1959; Burgess and Young, 1959).

Although resistance to proguanil and pyrimethamine can develop rapidly under experimental conditions, and although these drugs are widely used, the areas in which resistance has developed are restricted, and there are many widely separated countries in which the drugs have been used extensively without resistance being encountered (Anonymous, 1961; W.H.O., 1961). This suggests that the geographic strain of parasite may be of importance in determining whether resistance will develop. It was observed that, in an area in East Africa where resistance to pyrimethamine had developed, it did not spread very far beyond the district in which the drug had been used (Clyde and Shute, 1957). Since resistance to proguanil and pyrimethamine may develop as a result of their use in the treatment of malaria, it is fortunate that such infections respond to treatment with chloroquine and mepacrine.

The difficulty encountered in producing resistance to chloroquine under experimental conditions suggested that the probability of resistance developing when the drug was used in the treatment of malaria was slight; but the fact that a 200-fold enhancement of resistance to this drug has been developed in *P. berghei* (Ramakrishnan, Prakash and Choudhury, 1957) showed that the probability could not be ignored. In these experiments mice were treated with gradually increasing doses of the drug, but Sautet and his co-workers have reported that although they were unable to produce chloroquine-resistance in this species by this method, some resistance developed when large doses of the drug were used for short periods (Sautet, Aldighieri and Aldighieri, 1959). However, in spite of the difficulty in developing resistance to chloroquine in malaria parasites experimentally, two cases of chloroquine-resistant malaria have recently been reported from South America. Both were infections of *P. falciparum* acquired in Colombia, and both failed to respond to prolonged treatment with this drug (Moore and Lanier, 1961). Infections produced in neurosyphilitic patients by the injection of infected blood from one of these cases also failed to respond to treatment with chloroquine (Young and Moore, 1961) and with the 4-aminoquinoline compounds amodiaquine and hydroxychloroquine; but treatment with quinine and mepacrine was effective, though relapses occurred (Young, 1961). Pyrimethamine proved effective in the one case treated with this compound. Since chloroquine is used for treatment of malaria in the Magdalena valley where the primary cases occurred, it must be assumed that the local strain of *P. falciparum* responds to chloroquine treatment. There is thus no evidence that the failure of the two infections to respond to chloroquine was due to the natural insensitivity of a local strain of *P. falciparum*.

Recently, resistance to primaquine has been produced in infections of *P. vivax* in human volunteers but its development was slow (Arnold, Alving, Clayman and Hochwald, 1961).

Although drug resistance has not, up to the present, occurred on a scale large enough to form a serious problem either in the treatment of malaria or in malaria eradication programmes, the fact that malaria parasites are able to become highly resistant to such commonly used synthetic antimalarials as proguanil, pyrimethamine, and chloroquine calls for constant vigilance, particularly when such drugs are used in mass treatment.

REFERENCES

ANFINSEN, C. B., GEIMAN, Q. M., McKEE, R. W., ORMSBEE, R. A. and BALL, E. G. (1946). *J. exp. Med.*, **84**, 607.

ANONYMOUS (1961). COOPERATION ADMINISTRATION EXPERT PANEL ON MALARIA REPORT, *Amer. J. trop. Med. Hyg.*, **10**, 451.

ARNOLD, J., ALVING, A. S., CLAYMAN, C. B. and HOCHWALD, R. S. (1961). *Trans. R. Soc. trop. Med. Hyg.*, **55**, 345.

BISHOP, A. (1958). *Parasitology*, **48**, 210.

BISHOP, A. (1959). *Biol. Rev.*, **34**, 445.

BISHOP, A. (1962). *Parasitology*, **52** (in press)

BURGESS, R. W. and YOUNG, M. D. (1959). *Bull. Wld Hlth Org.*, **20**, 37.

CARRINGTON, H. C., CROWTHER, A. F., DAVEY, D. G., LEVI, A. A. and ROSE, F. L. (1951). *Nature, Lond.*, **168**, 1080.

CLYDE, D. F. and SHUTE, G. T. (1957). *Trans. R. Soc. trop. Med. Hyg.*, **51**, 505.

COVELL, G., COATNEY, G. R., FIELD, J. W. and JASWANT SINGH (1955). Chemotherapy of Malaria, p. 61. Geneva: *Wld Hlth Org.*

FULTON, J. D. (1961). *Ann. trop. Med. Parasit.*, **55**, 144.

FULTON, J. D. and GRANT, P. T. (1955). *Exp. Parasit.*, **4**, 377.

GLENN, S. and MANWELL, R. D. (1956). *Exp. Parasit.*, **5**, 22.

HAWKING, F. (1934). *Ann. trop. Med. Parasit.*, **28**, 67.

HAWKING, F. (1937). *J. Pharmacol.*, **59**, 123.

HAWKING, F. (1939). *Ann. trop. Med. Parasit.*, **33**, 13.

HAWKING, F. (1961). *Ann. trop. Med. Parasit.*, **55**, 139.

HAWKING, F. and THURSTON, J. P. (1955). *Brit. J. Pharmacol.*, **10**, 454.

INOKI, S. and MATSUSHIRO, A. (1960). *Biken's J.*, **3**, 101.

INOKI, S., TANIUCHI, Y., SAKAMOTO, H., ONO, T. and KUBO, R. (1961). *Biken's J.*, **4**, III.

JANCSÓ, N. VON and JANCSÓ, H. VON (1935). *Ann trop. Med. Parasit.*, **29**, 95.

KALTENBACH, A. (1959). *Wien tierärztl. Mschr.*, **46**, 639.

KING, H. and STRANGEWAYS, W. I. (1942). *Ann. trop. Med. Parasit.*, **36**, 47.

MOORE, D. V. and LANIER, J. E. (1961). *Amer. J. trop. Med. Hyg.*, **10**, 5.

ORMEROD, W. E. (1952). *Brit. J. Pharmacol.*, **7**, 674.

RAMAKRISHNAN, S. P., PRAKASH, S. and CHOUDHURY, D. S. (1957). *Ind. J. Malar.*, **11**, 213.

ROLLO, I. M. (1955). *Brit. J. Pharmacol.*, **10**, 208.

ROLLO, I. M. and WILLIAMSON, J. (1951). *Nature, Lond.*, **167**, 147.

SAUTET, J., ALDIGHIERI, J. and ALDIGHIERI, R. (1959). *Bull. Soc. Path. exot.*, **52**, 331.

SCHUELER, F. W. (1947). *J. infect. Dis.*, **81**, 139.

SOLTYS, M. A. (1959). *Parasitology*, **49**, 143.

TRAGER, W. (1958). *J. exp. Med.*, **108**, 753.

TRAGER, W. (1959). *Exp. Parasit.*, **8**, 265.

TRAGER, W. (1961). *Exp. Parasit.*, **11**, 298.

WILLIAMSON, J. (1959). *Brit. J. Pharmacol.*, **14**, 443.

WILLIAMSON, J. and LOURIE, E. M. (1947). *Ann. trop. Med. Parasit.*, **41**, 278.

WILLIAMSON, J. and ROLLO, I. M. (1959). *Brit. J. Pharmacol.*, **14**, 423.

W.H.O. REPORT (1961). Chemotherapy of Malaria p. 31. *Wld Hlth Org. techn. Rep. Ser.* 226.

YORK, W., ADAMS, A. R. D. and MURGATROYD, F. (1929). *Ann. trop. Med. Parasit.*, **23**, 501.

YORKE, W., MURGATROYD, F. and HAWKING, F. (1931a). *Ann. trop. Med. Parasit.*, **25**, 313.

YORKE, W., MURGATROYD, F. and HAWKING, F. (1931b). *Ann. trop. Med. Parasit.*, **25**, 351.

YORKE, W., MURGATROYD, F. and HAWKING, F. (1931c). *Ann. trop. Med. Parasit.*, **25**, 521.

YOUNG, M. D. (1957). *Amer. J. trop. Med. Hyg.*, **6**, 621.

YOUNG, M. D. (1961). *Amer. J. trop. Med. Hyg.*, **10**, 689.

YOUNG, M. D. and BURGESS, R. W. (1959). *Bull Wld Hlth Org.*, **20**, 27.

YOUNG, M. D. and MOORE, D. V. (1961). *Amer. J. trop. Med. Hyg.*, **10**, 317.

DISCUSSION

E. F. Whiteside (Veterinary Research Laboratory, Kenya): Dr. Bishop referred to the fact that resistance in *malaria* parasites to drugs developed sporadically here and there, and in some places it was common and in other places it was uncommon. I have observed exactly the same thing in resistance of *trypanosomes* to drugs. It is most puzzling that in some areas one continually gets trouble with drug resistance and in other areas one does not. I have often wondered why that is so.

Alving: We have produced resistance to primaquine experimentally against the Chesson strain of *vivax* malaria in man. It has not yet appeared in the field.

Primaquine and chloroquine are about to be used in association on a vast scale in weekly treatment. I am afraid that primaquine-resistance may appear in the future but this is speculation. Primaquine-resistance I do not believe is as hard to develop as it seemed to be in our first experiments. We can now produce it rather readily in experimental trials. Just before I left the United States we had obtained blood from a patient, a marine from Thailand, who had received very large doses of chloroquine, and in this marine chloroquine was only partially effective. He was infected with *P. falciparum*. These parasites are now in volunteers at Stateville Penitentiary; we do not know the results.

I might mention one other thing in regard to resistance of the Colombian strain of *falciparum* malaria which was first isolated by Moore, and studied by Dr. Martin Young and ourselves. If large enough doses of quinine are given there is no relapse or recrudescence, but we occasionally end up with patients who are deaf for quite a while when you give the drug. Quinine is hardly the ideal treatment.

Goodwin: I should like to ask if the primaquine-resistant strain is transmissible by mosquitos.

Alving: We failed to transmit it on two occasions although oocysts developed and there were sporozoites in the salivary glands of the mosquitos. Then we lost the strain.

P. C. Elmes (Queens University, Belfast): I should like to ask a question of each of the speakers. First, phenacetin in human beings produces methaemoglobinaemia and occasionally haemolytic anaemias. Has Dr. Alving investigated it with regard to his glucose-6-phosphate dehydrogenase phenomenon? Second, I should like to ask Dr. Bishop whether she has investigated the phenomenon which you find in bacterial resistance, that is, if you give two drugs at the same time you can prevent resistance appearing, provided the two drugs are really acting separately in the metabolism of the parasite.

Bishop: I myself have not tried the effect of two drugs but I think that chloroquine and pyrimethamine have been tried together in Africa.

Goodwin: Yes, this is true. Chloroquine and pyrimethamine together seem to prevent the development of resistant strains, but there is a certain amount of evidence that pyrimethamine-resistance does come through occasionally if treatment is not adequate.

Elmes: Has anyone tried proguanil and pyrimethamine together because they appeared to be acting pretty closely to each other on the folic acid system?

Bishop: I do not know whether that has been tried. They do not potentiate each other's actions; they merely summate.

Alving: Phenacetin causes fairly severe haemolysis in primaquine-sensitive individuals. We have tried the antimalarial activity of diaminodiphenylsulphone, because that is also a haemolytic drug. It has just recently been recognized that one has to cover these drugs with the blood schizonticides such as chloroquine or quinine, in order to detect the effect on the tissue stages, and we have just tested a few drugs.

F. L. Rose (Imperial Chemical Industries): p-Chloraniline produces methaemoglobinuria, and it has no antimalarial activity.

Alving: Have you tried it together with chloroquine in order to test the tissue stages of *vivax* malaria? There is a very important difference.

Rose: No, we have not.

Goodwin: Dr. Alving is on very strong ground because he is one of the few people in the world who can do it!

P. L. Bradley (Wellcome Laboratories of Tropical Medicine): I cannot quite agree with Dr. Alving's insistence on the necessity for the demethylation of primaquine in order to produce high activity. This does appear to be so for pentaquine but I have recently done some *in vitro* experiments in which I have incubated infected chick blood containing *P. gallinaceum* with primaquine and its 6-hydroxy analogue at 0·02 and 0·05 millimolar concentrations, and the two compounds are equally active.

I think there is probably quite good reason for the 6-methoxy-8-aminoquinolines themselves being active. At the moment I am trying to do an experiment to see whether you can get hydrogen acceptance in the 5-position, to make the methoxy-compound into a quinonoid structure. I think that perhaps pentaquine is a special case. I know that primaquine itself is really quite active on the malarial parasite.

Alving: I am very glad to know that. I have been trying to get our American chemists to make the 6-hydroxyprimaquine, and they say that it is too unstable. Are you dealing with 6-hydroxyprimaquine given by mouth, or *in vitro* ?

Bradley: This is *in vitro*, and it *is* a very evanescent substance; I think it goes to the 5,6-quinone.

Alving: I was dealing with *in vivo* tests in man, and I think the 6-methoxy-group protects the 5-position so that the drug is not degraded too fast in man. I do not think we are in disagreement if you are dealing with the *in vitro* activity of these drugs. If you are dealing with the drugs as you feed them by mouth to man, that is a different matter. I am very glad to hear of your experiments because theoretically the hydroxy compound should be more active.

E. Bueding (Johns Hopkins University): I should like to ask Dr. Alving whether the quinol derivative of primaquine has any effect on enzymes of the pentose phosphate cycle or on glutathione reductase.

Alving: The derivatives, like acetylphenylhydrazine, cause methaemoglobin formation in the glutathione stability test. Ultraviolet irradiation of primaquine yields degradation products which cause an increase in oxygen utilization in the *in vitro* system—the same as methylene blue does.

B. Lacey (Westminster Hospital Medical School): With regard to the irregular geographic distribution of resistance in trypanosomes, would it not be reasonable to assume that mutation towards resistance is a rare occurrence ? Once having occurred and become established in the local vector or human carriers or in other animals, it is bound thereafter to crop up sporadically within an area. Is there any need to postulate any other explanation ?

Bishop: Once resistant malaria has appeared in an area the mosquitos carry the resistant strain. The curious thing, however, is that it does not spread very far in the district even where there are the mosquitos for transmitting it. I think it remains relatively localized, but there is not much information on this point.

H. J. Barber (May and Baker): Some twenty years ago we made what I suppose is a chemical curiosity, a tetrahydro-derivative of pamaquine;

it was active against *P. gallinaceum*. One wonders, since the chemical nature of the whole molecule is different; whether there would be cross-resistance between pamaquine-resistant strains and tetrahydropamaquine-resistant strains.

Bishop: We have not tested it at all.

Goodwin: Perhaps Dr. Barber will send you some!

INTERACTIONS BETWEEN DRUGS, TRYPANOSOMES AND CATTLE IN THE FIELD

E. F. WHITESIDE

Veterinary Research Laboratory, Kabete, Kenya

THE particular complex of drug, parasite and host described here consists of trypanocidal drugs, trypanosomes and cattle, and the "field" is the African bush. The two species of trypanosomes that commonly infect cattle in Africa are *Trypanosoma vivax* and *T. congolense*. They are blood-parasites. Most cattle get trypanosomiasis from the bite of a cyclically infected tsetse fly, though other blood-sucking flies occasionally transmit the disease by direct inoculation ("mechanical transmission"). All the present drugs are injected parenterally.

Almost from the beginning, the large-scale use of chemotherapy against cattle trypanosomiasis in Africa encountered obstacles, some of them rather surprising. It was clear that a complicated system of interactions between drug, parasite and host was involved. One of the first surprises came from something that seemed to interfere with the action of prophylactic drugs.

Natural incidence and prophylaxis

In 1954 there was only one good prophylactic drug, quinapyramine (I), better known as antrycide pro-salt. It is interesting to recall that at that time, after four years' experience, we could still ask what protection it really did give, because the results had been so variable. In different places it had produced anything from three or four months' protection to less than a month (Davey,

1950; Unsworth and Chandler, 1952; Fiennes, 1953a, b; Robson and Wilde, 1954). Reviewing these capricious results, which had been mostly obtained by veterinarians, it looked as though tsetse fly density was at the root of the matter. On the whole, quinapyramine semed to give a good protection in a low fly density and poor protection in a high fly density.

A direct test of this in Kenya during 1954 showed that it was so. Two groups of cattle were given the same regimen of quinapyramine every two months (prophylactic) in places not very far apart. Both places had the same species of tsetse fly (*Glossina pallidipes*) with the same infection rate (3 to 5% contained trypanosomes). The only difference was that fly density was ten times greater in one area than in the other. In the low density area cattle spent seven months with no signs of infection. In the high density area protection began to fail within two months; 5% of the cattle became infected before the second treatment, and at the end of six months 20% were infected; moreover, mostly with resistant strains that had not been there before. Since the frequency of infective bites must have been proportional to the fly density in this experiment, it was concluded that a given regimen could withstand a low incidence of infections but not a high incidence (Kenya, 1955). Later experiments on the same lines showed that even a high incidence could be withstood by more frequent treatments (Kenya, 1956), and conversely, that fewer treatments afforded good protection when the fly density was low (Kenya, 1956, 1957; Davey, 1957; Whiteside, 1958, 1962).

It was, of course, realized that the essential factor must be the density of *infected* flies, or transmission rate. Attempts to measure the transmission rate by an index based on infected fly density (Whiteside, in Smith and Rennison, 1958) did not give very good results. There was obviously some quantitative relationship between the index and the length of prophylaxis but there were also discrepancies. These could have arisen from flaws in technique (Smith and Rennison, 1961; Leggate and Pilson, 1961), or more likely because certain modifying factors concerning the host and the trypanosome were not taken into account (Fiennes, 1953a, b; Whiteside, 1958). Both objections could be largely overcome by using the hosts themselves as indicators. Since 1959 I have measured the *natural incidence* of trypanosomiasis in many places (Whiteside, 1962) merely by keeping herds of cattle permanently in each area and treating every infection with the diamidine drug berenil (II). Berenil has virtually no prophylactic effect (Bauer, 1958), so cattle treated with it are almost at once open to fresh infection. The incidence thus recorded is not quite the same as the natural incidence owing to the host's immune response, mentioned later, but is near enough for practical purposes.

Figure 1 shows how this procedure has revealed a close quantitative relationship between natural incidence and the length of protection afforded by a single dose of drug. The drug used was prothidium (III); the data come from 22 field trials carried out in various parts of Kenya. A single-curve regression line has been fitted, but the true relationship must be represented by a sinusoidal curve. The correlation coefficient is about $+0.9$; both it and the regression coefficient are quite significant $(P < 0.001)$. Similar results have been obtained with other drugs.

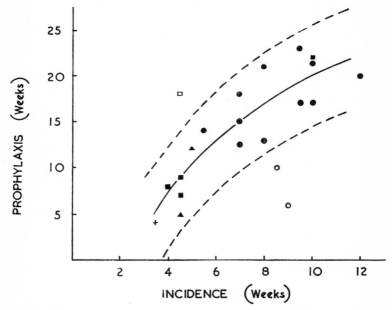

FIG. I. Relationship between incidence of trypanosomiasis and length of chemo-prophylaxis. Each symbol represents a field experiment in which the duration of prophylaxis was measured in one group of cattle and the natural incidence of trypanosomiasis in another group. Incidence is expressed as the mean time in weeks between treatments with berenil. The prophylactic drug was prothidium administered at 2 mg./kg.

● Lambwe (W. Kenya); ■ Meru (N. Kenya); + Burgoni (E. Kenya)
○ Drug-resistance confirmed; □ Cattle believed to be partially immune.
The dotted lines show the 95% confidence limits for the regression line.

Thus the effect of the incidence of trypanosmiasis on the length of prophylaxis is well established—the higher the incidence the shorter the prophylaxis—and I have set forth the evidence in some detail because it is rather a curious phenomenon and was once regarded by some workers as incredible. Long ago I asked persons engaged in malaria chemotherapy whether they had noticed anything like it; that is, whether they found drugs less effective, or even useless, in areas of high endemicity. They said they had not. However, it certainly occurs with cattle trypanosomiasis, and the mechanism by which it comes about is obscure. How can the number of trypanosomes entering the host—for that is what it amounts to—affect the length of prophylaxis in such a regular way? Davey (1957) quotes me as suggesting that the drug may be appreciably absorbed by the invading trypanosomes, and adds evidence in support; but this is by no means the only possible explanation. We might assume that the prophylactic period consists of two parts, one due to the drug and independent of trypanosome challenge, the other added to it and due to an immune response in the host, which may be antigenically stimulated during part or all of the protective period. If then, the immune response is governed by the challenge we should see the proportional effects noted above. Many workers have in fact suspected that chemoprophylaxis provokes some degree of immunity in cattle exposed to tsetse flies, and indeed there is evidence on this point below.

Immune response in cattle

At the present time there is no quick and accurate way of measuring the antibody titre against cattle trypanosomes, though Desowitz (1959) has made progress with a respiratory test. But there is no doubt about the existence of an immune response if we agree that it is indicated by failure to show infection under challenge. The response varies, especially with breeds of cattle. At one end of the scale are the N'dama and Muturu cattle of West Africa, with an almost perfect defence mechanism. They become virtually immune to the trypanosomes of the area they live in and can survive without the aid of drugs (Chandler, 1952). At the other end of the scale are the "grade" cattle of East Africa. These are crosses between indigenous and exotic breeds, and are difficult to maintain in fly-belts even with the aid of drugs. Experiments in Kenya (for example, Lyttle, 1960) have revealed that "grades" always get shorter protection from prophylactic drugs than do indigenous cattle. (I have recently investigated the immune response of "grade" cattle, amongst other ways by injecting mouse blood containing trypanosomes: they rapidly produce antibodies to mouse blood but not to trypanosomes.) In between these two extremes are the different kinds of indigenous cattle—Zebus and so on—which exhibit varying degrees of immune response; that is, under identical conditions some get trypanosomiasis more frequently than others, and different proportions survive the disease. Even amongst the shorthorned Zebus of Kenya such contrasts can be seen, often depending on the place of origin. Cattle from the Northern Province, which as a race have hardly any contact with tsetse flies, survive less well than cattle from between the fly-belts of the rest of Kenya.

It has been shown that the immunity of N'dama and Muturu cattle is developed in response to infection, and is not present in calves reared away from fly-belts (Desowitz, 1959). There is little doubt that this is true of African cattle generally. The following unpublished experiments reveal something of the nature of the immune response in ordinary Zebu cattle.

Immune response and drugs

At a place near Lake Victoria the incidence of trypanosomiasis amongst cattle freshly brought from fly-free country was observed for a year. This meant introducing new groups almost every month in order to cover fluctuations due to seasonal changes of fly density (Fig. 2). Over a whole year, the average time to visible parasitaemia (the normal incubation period is 8 to 14 days) was almost exactly 4 weeks, varying from 2 weeks at the peak fly period to 6 weeks at the nadir. Since one infection every 4 weeks is 13 a year, cattle *staying* in the area and always cured with a non-protective drug should get trypanosomiasis 13 times a year, provided they develop no immunity.

A herd of Zebu cattle stayed in the area and every infection was treated with berenil, which does not protect for more than two days (Fairclough, unpublished experiments). The results are shown in Table I; but it is easier to explain what happened if we assume that the expected interval was a uniform 4 weeks instead of fluctuating about that figure. When the cattle first went in they took 4

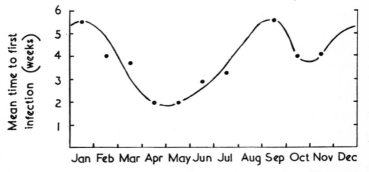

Fig. 2. Natural incidence of cattle trypanosomiasis at Lambwe, Kenya. Each point represents a group of cattle freshly introduced into the area during the appropriate month.

weeks to become infected. Then the interval between infections started to lengthen. They were removed for a month and put back again. Once more the first infection took 4 weeks and again the interval began to extend. After about the fourth infection the average interval reached 8 weeks and did not lengthen further. Meanwhile, two more groups of cattle were added at different times and went through the same process, starting at 4 weeks and gradually changing to 8; or in other words, starting as though they were going to get trypanosomiasis 13 times a year and ending by getting it only 6½ times.

What has to be explained is the extra 4 weeks between infections that appear after the cattle have been cured a few times; berenil could at most account for only a third of a week. The obvious explanation is that it is an immune response. If so, it is clearly

Table I

IMMUNE RESPONSE IN CATTLE TREATED WITH BERENIL

Mean time in weeks between

	Entry and 1st infection	1st and 2nd infection	2nd and 3rd infection	3rd and 4th infection	Subsequent infections
Cattle remaining in fly-bush	3·4	6·0	5·8	7·3	7·9
Expected interval*	3·4	3·3	3·4	4·3	4·0
Difference = interval due (?) to immune response	0	2·7	2·4	3·0	3·9

★ Time to first infection of fresh cattle introduced appropriately.

somewhat short-lived under these particular conditions, lasting on the average less than a month (though individual cattle vary). Nevertheless it is quite important in practice; and when drugs other than berenil are used the effects are more striking. Table II shows

Table II

IMMUNE RESPONSE IN CATTLE TREATED WITH DIFFERENT DRUGS

Mean time in weeks on treatment with

	Berenil	Quinapyramine sulphate	Homidium bromide
Observed interval between infections	8·6	14·0	17·6
Accounted for by prophylaxis	0·3	5·0	7·0
Accounted for by natural incidence	4·0	4·0	4·0
Unaccounted for = (?) immune response	4·3	5·0	6·6

the results of keeping three groups of cattle in the same place and treating every infection with either berenil, quinapyramine sulphate, or homidium (IV). Quinapyramine sulphate and homidium have a short protective action, lasting about 5 weeks (Whiteside, unpublished observations) and 7 weeks (Leach, Karib, Ford and

Wilmshurst, 1955) respectively. But the observed intervals between infections are not fully accounted for by these protective periods, nor by the natural incidence, nor by both added together (Table II). In every case there is a gap. Moreover, the gap seems to be greater when the protective effect of the drug is longer. Perhaps with a strongly prophylactic drug the gap is greater still—as was indeed suggested earlier when discussing chemoprophylaxis, though then it was called an immune response. Clearly it is very desirable to prove by serological tests that immunity is responsible

Table III

MEAN TIME TO FIRST INFECTION OF CALVES BORN IN FLY–BUSH

Prophylaxis in dams	Drug regimen	Weeks from birth to first infection	
		Observed	Expected*
Very heavy	Quinapyramine and berenil (2-monthly)	4	4
Heavy	Quinapyramine (2-monthly)	13	$4\frac{1}{2}$
Just sufficient	Prothidium (5-monthly)	67	16

* Time taken by freshly introduced adults to acquire first infection.

for these field results. Henceforth, to avoid further mention of gaps and intervals, I shall assume that it is.

There is one further connection between drugs and immune response that I want to mention before leaving the subject. It was noticed because the development of immunity in cows is often reflected amongst the calves they bear. There is a fly-belt on the Kenya coast where Zebu cows were kept for several years under a regimen intended to provoke immunity. Their earliest calves became infected in the normal time (5 weeks from birth); those born eight months later took an average time of 14 weeks, and those born after a year took an average time of 30 weeks. Meanwhile the cows had changed from the normal five infections a year to just over one. Thus the development of immunity in the cows was reflected by delayed infection of the calves. With this in mind, Table III shows that, judging from their offspring, cows *heavily* protected by drugs develop less immunity than those lightly protected.

Immunity and natural incidence

Natural incidence, already shown to affect chemoprophylaxis, must now be mentioned again because of observations suggesting that it influences the immune response as well. When the incidence of trypanosomiasis becomes exceptionally high the brief immunity of cattle treated with berenil almost disappears (Table IV). The

Table IV

IMMUNE RESPONSE IN CATTLE EXPOSED TO
DIFFERENT LEVELS OF NATURAL CHALLENGE

	Fly Challenge		
	Moderate	Heavy	Very heavy
Mean time to first infection of fresh cattle (weeks)	6	4	2
Mean interval between infections treated with berenil	$10\frac{1}{2}$	8	$3\frac{1}{2}$
Difference = (?) immune response	$4\frac{1}{2}$	4	$1\frac{1}{2}$

following experiments perhaps show the *gradual* swamping of immunity by a very high challenge.

Two groups of cattle were kept for some years in a moderate fly density under drug-regimens that just protected them. At the end of that time the second group was thought to be partly immune because the cattle scarcely ever showed infections (the mean interval was 91 weeks as compared with about 13 weeks for controls); and the first group was believed to be in rather a similar state, though they were not tested directly. Both were moved a few miles into a very dense fly area. Group 1 was given a prophylactic drug whose length of protection was known to be about 8 weeks in this area. But the first treatment produced 18 weeks protection, the next produced 13 weeks, the next 8 weeks, the next 9 and the next 7. Perhaps this means that immunity built up during the earlier period was slowly overcome by the very high challenge, so that after about six months the cattle exhibited a normal length of protection instead of an exceptionally long one. The second group of cattle did not get a prophylactic drug. They were treated with berenil when infected; and controls showed that the normal interval between such treatments varied only from 4 to $4\frac{1}{2}$ weeks throughout the year. But, in successive 3-monthly periods, group 2 cattle produced intervals of 12, 9, 8, 6 and 5 weeks. Again these results could be interpreted as showing an initial immunity slowly overcome by exposure to a very high challenge.

Immunity and virulence

Some strains of cattle trypanosomes are so virulent that the host is killed in a few days, before an immune response can come into play. It is difficult to see how these strains can be transmitted. They appear sporadically in East Africa, perhaps by a relatively common mutation. Other strains are so avirulent that the host can withstand them and in time throws off the infection, or possibly becomes premune. These again are somewhat rare in the field. The average strain of *T. vivax* or *T. congolense* eventually causes death in a large proportion of ordinary African cattle, after a period of fluctuating parasitaemia lasting weeks or even months. This is interpreted as a losing battle between antibody and antigen which may involve antigenic variation.

Antigenic variation

As far as pathogenic trypanosomes in general are concerned, it is well established that many species include antigentically different strains, that animals immune to one strain may be infected by another, and that antigenic changes take place during the course of an infection (Calver, 1945; Inoki, Kitauna, Nakabayasi and Kurogochi, 1952; Soltys, 1957). How far these findings apply to cattle trypanosomes is not yet entirely clear: the subject has recently been discussed by Weitz (1958) and by Desowitz (1960). Many workers, however, believe that the immunity developed by cattle is largely strain-specific and this probably accounts for the fact that even N'dama and Muturu cattle may suffer a brief outbreak of trypanosomiasis when moved to a new area (Stewart, 1951), and that cattle requiring little chemotherapy in one place need much more when moved elsewhere - other things being equal (da Silva, personal communication from Portuguese East Africa).

It is a pity we have so little knowledge of this subject as applied to cattle trypanosomes, for it seems to me that antigenic variation might have an influence on the *effective* incidence of trypanosomiasis. If so, it would explain a number of puzzling observations in the field.

Imagine two areas where the fly density and the fly infection rate are the same; that is, as where the rate at which cattle receive infective bites is identical. Suppose one area has only two antigenic variants of *T. vivax* and the other has, say, twenty (not an impossible figure on present knowledge). Then, granted that *some* immunity follows each infection, cattle in the area with only two strains would exhibit a lower incidence, for there would be times in which they are immune to the only strains about. But cattle in the second area would exhibit a higher incidence, for nearly every infective bite would introduce a different strain and therefore produce an infection. Such effects will only occur, however, where the incidence is high relative to the duration of the immune response.

This argument can be developed, with suitable modifications, to explain several things observed in the field. Three of them are:—
Prophylactic drugs give longer protection in some areas than in others, though the fly density and infection rate are the same; cattle develop apparent immunity more readily in some places than in others; drug-resistance develops quickly and repeatedly in

some areas and hardly at all in others. The argument in the last case depends on a connection between incidence and drug-resistance to be mentioned later.

Drug-resistance

So far I have mainly been discussing interactions between parasite and host, showing how they are sometimes modified by drugs. I now turn to direct interactions between parasite and drugs. The commonest of these, and in practice the most important, concerns drug-resistance.

Drug-resistance has been a recurrent problem in the chemotherapy of cattle trypanosomiasis, noted by workers too numerous to mention. The basic facts as regards trypanosomes in general were recently reviewed by Bishop (1959); she was not able to include certain aspects of cross-resistance in cattle trypanosomes now to be mentioned because they had not been published. The application of the facts to field practice has been described by Whiteside (1960), from whom the following account is largely taken.

(a) Cattle trypanosomes readily become resistant to all existing drugs except berenil.

(b) Resistance develops in the treated host. With one doubtful exception (Smith and Scott, 1961), strains naturally resistant to normal dosages have not yet been observed.

(c) Resistant strains can be transmitted by tsetse flies, though this usually happens some time after they have arisen in cattle.

(d) Resistant strains carried by tsetse flies disappear after six to twelve months provided the sources of infection (the cattle) are removed.

(e) Most resistant infections in cattle can be eliminated by "sanative" treatment. I use this convenient word (Whiteside, 1958) to mean any drug that cures infections resistant to any other drug.

(f) There is no way of directly eliminating resistant strains that are being transmitted throughout an area by tsetse flies.

All these facts emerge as a practical problem that is easy to describe. Wherever chemotherapy is used, drug-resistance is likely to arise sooner or later. When it does there are two possible situations to cope with: one in which the resistant strains are confined to cattle and are still accessible, the other in which they are not accessible because they have got into tsetse flies.

Control of drug-resistance in the field

For *curative drugs* a system has been devised that deals with either situation. It depends on the fortunate fact that there are two drugs neither of which produces strains cross-resistant to the other. The two drugs are homidium and berenil. In practice homidium is used over a wide area until signs of resistance appear somewhere. Then it is completely withdrawn and berenil is used instead for one year. This cures the cattle whether or not homidium-resistance was present; it also cures them even if they are being re-infected with homidium-resistant strains. At the end of a year such strains will (it is considered) have died out or been killed off. Homidium is thereupon resumed and the cycle begins again. During the year when berenil is used resistance to that drug could in theory develop. In practice it never seems to do so, and in any case the return to homidium would deal with it. The timing of this regimen depends on factors peculiar to the field. Berenil is never used for less than a year in order to ensure that every animal receives it; for cattle on curatives are treated only when infected, and some might miss berenil altogether if the period were too short. Too long a period, on the other hand, would raise the cost unnecessarily, because homidium is cheaper owing to the much longer intervals between treatments already referred to. The present compromise is a year (Whiteside, 1962).

With *prophylactic* drugs the position is nothing like so simple.

There are at present only two and they have a chemical group in common. They produce reciprocal cross-resistance and cannot therefore be alternated. At present the only available sanative drug is berenil. So the general practice is to interpolate a heavy dose of berenil into the prophylactic regimen at the first failure to get the normal length of protection, which is an almost infallible sign of drug-resistance (Fig. 1 open-circles). Even this does not always work when prophylactic quinapyramine is used, for, as mentioned later, some quinapyramine-resistant infections are cross-resistant to berenil. A difficult problem then arises; and the position is even more difficult if fly-transmission has been allowed to start. In both cases quinapyramine-resistant infections persist, either because of relapse through berenil or because of reintroduction from flies, and continued prophylaxis is impossible. The problem can in fact be solved by using isometamidium (VI; Berg, 1960; see below) which at prophylactic dosages eliminates infections resistant to quinapyramine (Whiteside, 1960); but this compound is not at present generally available.

Perhaps it is worth mentioning that the foregoing ways of controlling drug-resistance in the field all derive from laboratory studies, and are now undergoing the acid test of field practice. I want now to describe a few results of these studies which are of somewhat wider interest.

The development of drug-resistance by trypanosomes

Speaking first of laboratory conditions, it is a curious fact that drug-fast strains of *T. congolense* are difficult to produce in mice but are relatively easy to produce in cattle. I have used only one method in cattle—sub-curative dosages followed by relapse. Excepting only treatment with berenil, resistance never fails to develop with astonishing rapidity. It usually takes between three and six successive treatments to make strains resistant to 40 to 80 times the median curative dose (CD_{50}), that being usually as much as the cattle can tolerate. It does not seem to matter whether the relapse infections are subinoculated or not, and the whole process can take place in a single animal. Such strains retain their direct resistance and cross-resistance for more than a year when syringe passaged in cattle. If they are transferred to mice they usually retain the direct resistance indefinitely, but some cross-resistance may be lost at once.

At the Veterinary Research Laboratory in Kenya several non-resistant strains of *T. congolense* have been maintained in cattle by syringe passage for quite long periods. Their continued sensitivity to normal dosages of different drugs is tested as a routine, and normal dosages have never failed to cure. Yet at any passage chosen quite arbitrarily it has always been possible to produce a stable variant resistant to the normal dosage. The essential requirement is two or three exposures to sub-curative levels of drug, without which, it seems, resistant populations do not appear. These facts are difficult to reconcile with theories involving selection alone. We do not know whether resistant individuals exist permanently as a very small proportion of normal populations, or whether they arise at intervals by spontaneous mutation. But in either case, since the populations are large (the average bovine at the height of parasitaemia contains at least five thousand million *T. congolense*), one would expect that strains resistant to normal dosages should sooner or later be selected out by normal dosages. This, however, does not seem to happen, and one is left with the impression that drug-resistance is more in the nature of an adaptation, induced with unfailing regularity by exposure to sub-lethal dosages, and moreover inherited. Such a possibility has occurred to several workers; it is discussed briefly by Bishop (1959) and more extensively by Schnitzer and Grunberg (1957).

The conditions under which drug-resistance develops in the field are all essentially derived from underdosing; but underdosing can arise in several ways. Cattle left too long in fly-bush after prophylactic treatment nearly always sustain infections resistant to the drug that was used, even as much as nine months later (Kenya,

1960). Here natural incidence comes in, for "too long" means different things in different places. Exposing cattle to a very high incidence of trypanosomiasis has the same practical effect as underdosing since, as already mentioned, the high challenge somehow overcomes the protective effect of the drug. It is significant that the infections appearing are nearly always resistant, just as if there were not enough drug in the body. Sometimes a prophylactic regimen gives perfectly good protection for most of the year but breaks down during a brief period of high challenge at the seasonal fly peak. Afterwards the normal protection is not resumed because resistant infections have developed.

There must be a critical period after injection of any drug when the blood stream contains enough to produce resistance but not enough to prevent infection. The period must be longer with prophylactics, which are characteristically stored, and shorter with curatives, which are not stored so long. That is doubtless why under field conditions resistance to prophylactics turns up more frequently than resistance to curatives, and resistance to curatives turns up more frequently in high challenge than in low. It also explains why resistance to berenil never turns up at all; this drug is very quickly excreted (Bauer, 1958; Fussgänger and Bauer, 1960). Thus there is an interaction between drug-resistance and the metabolic fate of the drug in the body. Perhaps with diamidines the matter is not so simple. Fussgänger and Bauer (1960) failed to make *T. congolense* resistant to berenil in mice, but produced a strain which was cross-resistant to 5 times the usual curative dose by employing a different diamidine. Exposing this strain to further treatment with berenil did not raise resistance further; on the contrary, resistance disappeared after 13 passages. My own experience with *T. congolense* in cattle is somewhat similar. After, with difficulty, making a strain resistant to about 7 times the minimum curative dosage of berenil, I found that resistance had largely disappeared by about the tenth syringe passage. This has never happened with strains resistant to quinapyramine or phenanthridinium derivatives.

Cross-resistance amongst cattle trypanosomes

The early quinapyramine-resistant strains obtained from the field were sometimes cross-resistant to phenanthridinium compounds and sometimes not. Similarly, phenanthridinium-resistant strains were sometimes cross-resistant to quinapyramine and sometimes not (Wilson, 1949; Fiennes, 1953a, b; Karib, Ford and Wilmshurst, 1954; Whiteside, 1960). When the diamidine berenil first appeared it seemed to cure all types of resistant infections. Then a strain of *T. congolense* cross-resistant to berenil was made in the laboratory using quinapyramine (Whiteside, unpublished). Infections of *T. congolense* or *T. vivax* cross-resistant to berenil have since been observed in the field (Lyttle, 1960; Whiteside, 1960; Smith and Scott, 1961), but not very often.

In the course of laboratory studies the main reason for these conflicting results was discovered. The spectrum of cross-resistance depends on the degree of direct resistance that has been developed.

A strain of *T. congolense* was made just resistant to the normal dosage of quinapyramine, that is, to about 4 times the minimum curative dosage. It was then susceptible to normal dosages of homidium and berenil. After two further exposures to the normal dosage of quinapyramine it became cross-resistant to homidium but not to berenil. After still another two exposures to quinapyramine it became cross-resistant to normal dosages of berenil. An important point to note is that it was not possible to measure the rising resistance to quinapyramine during this sequence, for at quite an early stage it passed the maximum tolerated dosage in cattle.

When this principle had been grasped it became possible to study the full range of cross-resistance exhibited by trypanosomes resistant to each of the common drugs. The results are shown in Table V. The study was really carried out to find ways of controlling resistant infections in the field, and it was fortunate that few drugs were involved because the method was laborious. It consisted of making strains very highly resistant to each of the available drugs and then

Table V

SUMMARY OF PRINCIPAL CROSS-RESISTANCE TESTS WITH *Trypanosoma vivax*
AND *T. congolense* IN LABORATORY CATTLE (UNPUBLISHED DATA)

(*The figures are relapses/total cattle treated*)

No. of strains examined	Resistant to	Test drug and dosage in mg./kg.								
		Homidium		*Metamidium*		*Prothidium*		*Tozocide*	*Quinapyramine*	*Berenil*
		1	2	0·5	2	1	2	4·5	4·5	3·5–5
4	Homidium	R	R	4/6		10/20	0/21	2/8	30/43	0/57
3	Metamidium	6/6	2/4	R	R	2/2	0/6		20/38	0/42
2	Prothidium	+	+	+	0/3	R	R		4/12	0/32
1	Tozocide	+	+			+	1/3	R	3/7	0/21
10	Quinapyramine	4/9	10/34		0/14	+	1/23	1/3	R	14/61
4	Homidium and quinapyramine	R	R	5/5	2/12	5/14	3/19	3/4	R	14/76
4	Prothidium and quinapyramine	+	13/21	+	0/2	R	R	+	R	13/52
1	Berenil	0/15	–	0/12	0/3	–	–		0/15	R

R = direct resistance.

+ = cross-resistance can be assumed from other results.

– = absence of cross-resistance can be assumed.

determining the minimum curative doses of all the others. This gave repeatable results but was time-consuming, and an early search was made for general principles that would shorten it, by looking at chemical structure.

Cross-resistance and chemical structure

Drugs now in use against cattle trypanosomiasis arise from only three broad types of ring system. These are derivatives of quinaldine, represented by quinapyramine and tozocide (V; Austin, Collier, Potter, Smith and Taylor, 1957), derivatives of phenanthridine, represented by homidium, prothidium and isometamidium and a bisamidinophenyl, berenil (II, p.117).

As might be expected it was soon found that cross-resistance in the first two groups was complete, and that variations in substituents made differences only in degree of cross-resistance. In only one instance was the difference great enough for practical use. Large but tolerated dosages of metamidium were found to cure infections resistant to all other drugs, including even quinapyramine. With this solitary exception it was found that cross-resistance between quinaldine and phenanthridine derivatives was reciprocal and, for practical purposes, complete; it could reach a level exceeding the maximum tolerated dose. The work is not yet finished and there may yet be exceptions to this rule with *T. vivax*.

It is impossible to say much about the properties of strains directly resistant to berenil, since I know of only one—the *T. congolense* strain mentioned earlier as having been made resistant at Kabete. It was maintained for 22 syringe passages but resistance had to be continually boosted by treatment with berenil. During that time it remained susceptible to normal doses of all the other drugs. It did, however, show cross-resistance to the curative dosage of a complex diamidine [M & B 2242; 2-amino-4,6-di(*p*-amidinophenyl)-1,3,5-triazine, VII], used for experimental purposes. *T. congolense* made directly resistant to this compound became cross-resistant to berenil, which is also a *para*-diamidine. This is interesting

because we found recently that the same trypanosome made
resistance to another diamidine [M & B 4596; 2,7-di(*m*-amidino-

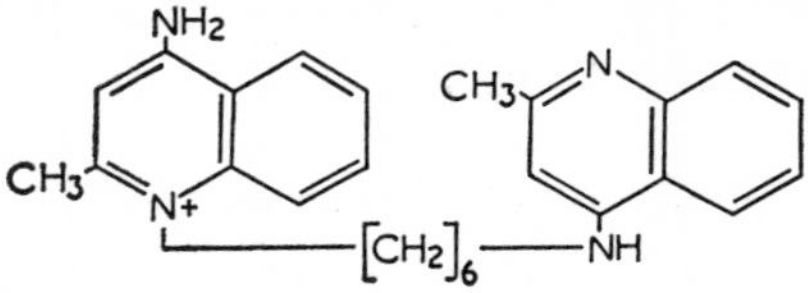

V

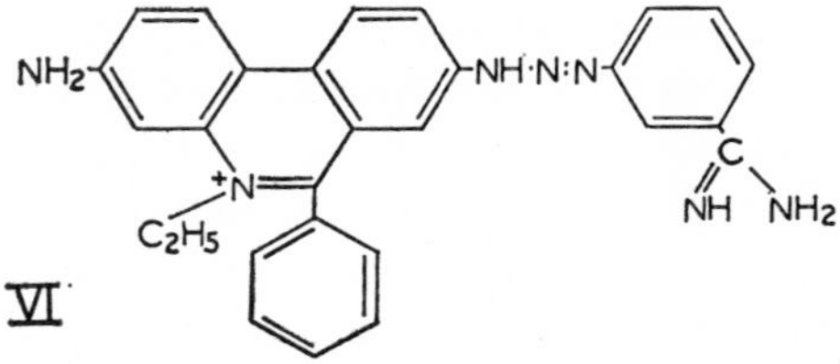

VI

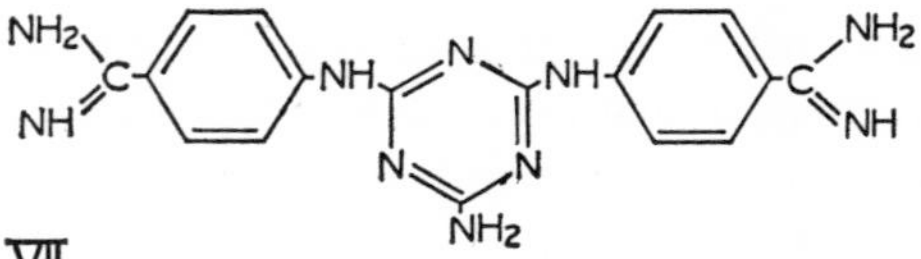

VII

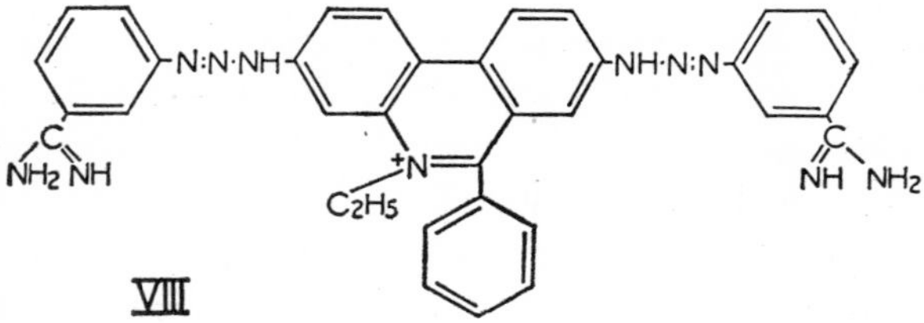

VIII

phenyldiazoamino)-9-phenyl-10-ethylphenanthridinium, VIII]
showed no cross-resistance to berenil.

There was at first some confusion about which drugs induced
cross-resistance to berenil, owing (it is now thought) to a wrong

interpretation of a resistant strain obtained from the field. Statements that prothidium induces it (Lyttle, 1960; Whiteside, 1960;
Smith and Scott, 1961) should be regarded as doubtful, and indeed
I believe they are mistaken. At an early stage of these investigations
it looked as though the pyrimidine moiety of quinapyramine and
prothidium might be responsible for inducing cross-resistance to
berenil, since drugs without a pyrimidine residue had never done
so. Moreover the chemists to whom this hypothesis was mentioned
were able to suggest how it might come about by a certain type
of splitting of the pyrimidine ring. The hypothesis was tested by
taking a single strain of *T. congolense* and making from it four
separate variants resistant to tozocide, quinapyramine, homidium,
and prothidium. The first pair are quinaldine derivatives, one with
and the other without a pyrimidine; the second pair are phenanthridine derivatives similarly with and without a pyrimidine. Each
variant passed through five or six stages of increasing resistance to
its particular drug, and cross-resistance towards berenil was tested
at each stage, using cattle throughout. The results are shown in
Table VI.

Table VI

TESTS OF CROSS-RESISTANCE TO BERENIL IN *T. congolense* MADE SUCCESSIVELY
MORE RESISTANT TO FOUR DIFFERENT DRUGS

Relapses/total cattle treated with 3·5 mg./kg. of berenil

Stage of resistance*	Tozocide-resistant variant	Quinapyramine-resistant variant	Homidium-resistant variant	Prothidium-resistant variant
a	0/6	—	0/3	0/5
b	0/2	0/7	0/4	—
a b	—	0/3	0/6	0/2
a a b	0/5	2/6	0/5	0/6
a a b b	0/8	4/7	0/6	0/6
a a b b b	0/4	—	—	0/5

* Represented by the number of dosages with each drug through which the strain had
relapsed, where:

a = Tozocide 2·25 mg./kg. or   b = Tozocide 4·5 mg./kg. or
    Quinapyramine 2·25 mg./kg. or   Quinapyramine 4·5 mg./kg. or
    Homidium 1 mg./kg. or   Homidium 2 mg./kg. or
    Prothidium 1 mg./kg.   Prothidium 2 mg./kg.

Whether tozocide would produce cross-resistance to berenil or not had never previously been determined, and the hypothesis was satisfied when it did not. Quinapyramine produced cross-resistance from the third stage onwards, as was expected from previous work. Homidium produced no cross-resistance at any stage, also confirming earlier work. Thus far the hypothesis was borne out by results. But prothidium also failed to produce cross-resistance to berenil, which was so unexpected that I at once made a new prothidium-resistant variant from the same parent strain. The result was again negative and was confirmed in a prothidium-resistant variant made from an entirely different strain of *T. congolense*.

Thus it seems—though further work is needed—that cross-resistance to berenil is not an inevitable consequence of including the pyrimidine ring in a trypanocidal drug. We are left to conclude that quinapyramine is unique in producing cross-resistance to diamidines. Why this should be so is at present a mystery.

Drug-resistance and other factors

The subject of drug-resistance has led us rather far away from the field, and I conclude by returning to it, though only to mention some interactions that have been observed, so to speak, dimly. There seems to be a curious connection between drug-resistance and immune response, for it is very noticeable that cattle cured of resistant infections often remain for remarkably long periods in natural challenge without showing parasitaemia. I have induced this effect several times in the field and have collected serum from the cattle in the hope of being able to detect antibodies. But so far the results have been negative, possibly because of unsatisfactory techniques, possibly because something other than an immune response is involved. It is, however, a very good way of keeping cattle in rather dense fly, for a partial immunity often follows; one herd on the Kenya coast has been in this state for nearly five years. The effect is to reduce by about three fifths the number of infections that need treatment.

Soltys (1957) has observed that trypanosomes passaged through certain laboratory animals which display chronic or relapsing infections seem to develop a protective mechanism against antibodies; they become antibody-resistant. If this is true of relapsing infections generally, then it is possible that drug-resistant cattle trypanosomes are also antibody-resistant. One would in that case expect them to be more than usually virulent, but rather the opposite actually occurs in the field. Resistant infections are sometimes relatively apathogenic to the cattle in which they develop (which is why drug-resistance may at first pass unnoticed) and transmission by syringe or by tsetse flies has not been accompanied by any observable increase of virulence. Indeed, at one place in Kenya where resistant strains persisted in cattle and tsetse flies for at least two years, a sort of balance was achieved and the cattle became very fit. Though they were continually infected, they did not need any drugs to maintain this balance.

Figure 3 shows diagrammatically some of the interactions between drug, parasite and host that have been observed in the field, and illustrates the surprising nexus of events that is set going when we try to kill a trypanosome with a drug. The toxic action of the drug (arrow 1) is countered by the ability of the trypanosome to become drug-resistant (2), which means that the chemotherapeutic attack has to be varied (3). The virulence of the trypanosome to the host (4) provokes an immune response (5) influenced by the breed of host and the drug used for treatment, which in turn is countered by antigenic variation on the part of the trypanosome (6), and perhaps by antibody-resistance (7). At the same time interactions develop between the *drug* and the host, for the drug is usually toxic to some extent (8) and the host responds by metabolizing it, storing it, and so on. These processes may work against the drug (9), reducing its effect on the trypanosome, or with the drug (10)—for instance storage enhances the prophylactic effect. Meanwhile the tsetse fly adds two complications because it is responsible for natural incidence, and a rising natural incidence works against the drug by shortening prophylaxis (11) and also very probably against the host by swamping the immune response (12). Finally, some of these processes themselves interact, and there is evidence that the metabolic fate of the drug influences the development of drug-resistance (13), while the development of drug-resistance in

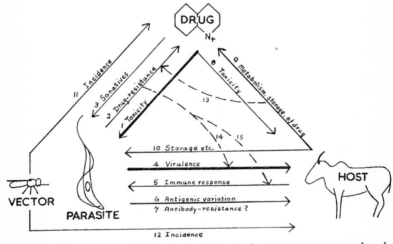

FIG. 3. Diagram representing interactions between drugs, trypanosomes and cattle observed in the field. The arrows point towards what is inimically affected, e.g. immune response works against virulence.

turn has peculiar effects on both virulence (14) and immune response (15).

[Discussion of this paper was postponed until after the following paper by B.A. Newton; see p. 161.]

REFERENCES

AUSTIN, W. C., COLLIER, H. O. J., POTTER, M. D., SMITH, G. K. A. and TAYLOR, E. P. (1957). *Nature, Lond.*, **179**, 143.
BAUER, F. (1958). *Zbl. f. Bakt. Abt. orig.*, **172**, 605.

BERG, S. S. (1960). *Nature, Lond.*, **188,** 1106.

BISHOP, A. (1959). *Biol. Rev.*, **34,** 445.

CALVER, K. M. (1945). Chemotherapeutic studies on experimental *T. congolense* infections; Ph.D. Thesis, University of Glasgow.

CHANDLER, R. L. (1952). *Ann. trop. Med. Parasit.*, **46,** 127.

DAVEY, D. G. (1950). *Trans. R. Soc. trop. Med. Hyg.*, **43,** 583.

DAVEY, D. G. (1957). *Vet. Rev. Annotations.* **3,** 15.

DESOWITZ, R. S. (1959). *Ann. trop. Med. Parasit.*, **53,** 3.

DESOWITZ, R. S. (1960). *Proc. VIII Int. Sci. Comm. Tryp. Res., Jos.*, 155.

FIENNES, R. N. T.-W. (1953a). *Brit. vet. J.* **109,** 280.

FIENNES, R. N. T.-W. (1953b). *Ibid.*, **109,** 330.

FUSSGÄNGER, R. and BAUER, F. (1960). *Vet. Rec.*, **72,** 1118.

INOKI, S., KITUANA, T., NAKABAYASI, T. and KUROGOCHI, H. (1952). *Med. J. Osaka*, **3,** 357.

KARIB, A. A., FORD, E. J. H. and WILMSHURST, E. C. (1954). *J. comp. Path.*, **64,** 187.

KENYA (1955). Department of Veterinary Services Annual Report 1954, 38, Nairobi: Govt. Printer.

KENYA (1956). *Ibid.* 1955, 45.

KENYA (1957). *Ibid.* 1956, 33.

KENYA (1960). *Ibid.* 1959, 46.

LEACH, T. M., KARIB, A. A., FORD, E. J. H. and WILMSHURST, E. C. (1955). *J. comp. Path.*, **65,** 130.

LEGGATE, B. M. and PILSON, R. D. (1961). *Bull. ent. Res.*, **51,** 697.

LYTTLE, C. N. (1960). *J. comp. Path.*, **70,** 18.

ROBSON, J. and WILDE, J. K. H. (1954). *Brit. vet. J.*, **110,** 459.

SCHNITZER, R. J. and GRUNBERG, E. (1957). Drug resistance of micro-organisms, pp. 193 *et seq.*, New York: Academic Press.

SMITH, I. M. and RENNISON, B. D. (1958). *Proc. VII Int. Sci. Comm. Tryp. Res., Brussels*, 63.

SMITH, I. M. and RENNISON, B. D. (1961). *Bull. ent. Res.*, **52,** 165.

SMITH, I. M. and SCOTT, W. N. (1961). *J. comp. path.*, **71,** 325.

SOLTYS, M. A. (1957). *Parasitology*, **47,** 375.

STEWART, J. L. (1951). *Vet. Rec.*, **63,** 454.

UNSWORTH, K. and CHANDLER, R. L. (1952). *Ann. trop. Med. Parasit.*, **46,** 240.

WEITZ, B. (1958). *Proc. VII Int. Sci. Comm. Tryp. Res., Brussels*, 71.

WHITESIDE, E. F. (1958). *Proc. VII Int. Sci. Comm. Tryp. Res., Brussels*, 83.

WHITESIDE, E. F. (1960). *Proc. VIII Int. Sci. Comm. Tryp. Res., Jos.*, 141, 188.

WHITESIDE, E. F. (1962). *E. Afr. agric. For. J.*, in press.

WILSON, S. G. (1949). *Nature, Lond.*, **163,** 873.

THE EFFECT OF QUATERNARY AMMONIUM TRYPANOCIDES ON CELL DIVISION, NUCLEIC ACID AND PROTEIN SYNTHESIS

B. A. NEWTON

*Medical Research Council Unit for Chemical Microbiology,
Biochemical Laboratory, University of Cambridge*

THE major advances in chemotherapy during the first half of the present century can, without doubt, be attributed to an empirical approach to the subject. In particular, this approach has yielded a number of excellent prophylactic and curative drugs capable of controlling both the human and bovine forms of African trypanosomiasis. However, as recently pointed out by Goodwin (1958), this does not eliminate the necessity for the development of new compounds. The need to combat drug-resistant variants is ever present and there is a need for compounds capable of exerting prolonged prophylactic action and which can be more easily administered to large populations. The empirical approach to this subject has also provided a wealth of data relating the structure of compounds to their biological activity but it has yielded little or no information about the mechanism of their action. Such information is vital to a more rational approach to chemotherapy as a whole and to the problem of drug-resistance in particular. It is the aim of this contribution to survey work carried out during the last ten years

I   II

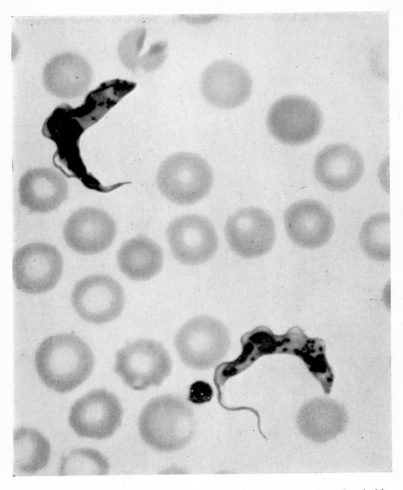

PLATE 2. *Trypanosoma equiperdum* in rat blood. Leishman stain. The darkly-stained inclusion bodies were produced by quinapyramine, 10 mg./kg. (Reproduced by permission of Dr. W. E. Ormerod and the editors from *Brit. J. Pharmacol.*, 1951, **6**, 325.)

To face p. 143

which may throw some light on the mode of action of two quaternary ammonium trypanocides. The compounds to be discussed are (I; R= C_2H_5) ethidium bromide (Watkins and Woolfe, 1952) and (II) quinapyramine (antrycide; Curd and Davey, 1950).

In vivo *studies*

The work of Lock (1950), Ormerod (1951*a*) and more recently that of Hawking and Sen (1960) has demonstrated marked differences between the *in vivo* action of some of the older trypanocidal agents, such as stilbamidine and trivalent arsenicals (group I compounds) and quaternary ammonium trypanocides (group II compounds). These differences may be summarized as follows:

(*a*) *Rate of action.* The quaternary ammonium compounds are characterized by slow action *in vivo*; there is frequently a latent period of 3 to 4 days before a significant fall in the number of bloodstream trypanosomes is observed. Administration of group I compounds results in a rapid fall in the trypanosome count.

(*b*) *Uptake of drug.* The avidity of trypanosomes for group I compounds is high; the intracellular concentration of tryparsamide has been estimated to be 5000 times the external concentration (Hawking, 1938). Group II compounds on the other hand appear to be bound to a much lesser degree (Newton, 1957; Taylor, 1960).

(*c*) *Morphological changes.* Ormerod (1951*b*) observed that growth of trypanosomes in the presence of dimidium (I; R= CH_3) or quinapyramine resulted in the appearance of basophilic cytoplasmic granules. By skilful application of cytochemical techniques and fluorescence microscopy he demonstrated that these granules (Plate 2) were composed of ribonucleoprotein and contained bound drug. He also observed that growth in the presence of these drugs resulted in an increase in the number of multinuclear forms and a decrease in the number of dividing forms of trypanosomes; the motility of the organisms was unaffected. On the basis of these results Ormerod postulated that these two drugs may act in a similar manner, preventing growth and cell division, but not nuclear division, by combining with cytoplasmic ribonucleoprotein. In support of this hypothesis he found that quinapyramine could not be detected in the nuclei of treated trypanosomes. It was clear from these results that a more detailed study of the action of these compounds on nucleic acid metabolism would be rewarding.

Development of an in vitro *test system—a rationale*

The major obstacle in studying the mechanism of action of trypanocidal drugs has been the lack of an *in vitro* test system suitable for biochemical studies. All attempts to cultivate the bloodstream forms of pathogenic trypanosomes have so far failed. In the work to be discussed this problem has been by-passed; an *in vitro* test system has been developed employing the trypanosomid flagellate *Strigomonas oncopelti*. This parasite occurs in the digestive tract of Hemiptera and was first isolated in bacteria-free culture by Noguchi and Tilden (1926); Lwoff (1937) reported that *S. oncopelti* can be cultivated in alkaline hydrolysates of silk supplemented with thiamine and pointed out that, in contrast to other members of the Trypanosomidae, it does not require haematin for growth. More recently (Newton, 1956) a simple chemically defined medium was developed for *S. oncopelti* and it was subsequently shown that the organism was sensitive to low concentrations of quaternary ammonium trypanocides. Thus, from the biochemist's point of view, it provided an ideal system for studying the mechanism of drug action. This approach to the problem may well be criticized by protozoologists since it is abundantly clear from the work of von Brand, Weinbach and Tobie (1955), Ryley (1956) and Fulton and Spooner (1959) that profound differences exist between the metabolism of bloodstream forms and insect forms of trypanosomes. In view of this it can be argued that the use of insect parasites in culture, as experimental tools for the study of drug action, may be misleading. Certainly the use of such organisms in screening tests for new drugs *is* misleading; many compounds are known which are active *in vitro* and yet are totally devoid of activity against bloodstream forms when tested *in vivo*. On the other hand, studies in bacterial chemotherapy lend some support to the view that if the growth of a number of different microorganisms is inhibited by a drug, then its mode of action may well prove to be the same in each case, despite any differences which may exist in the intermediary metabolism of the organisms. Clearly results obtained with an *in vitro* test system must, ultimately, be confirmed by studies employing bloodstream forms of pathogenic trypanosomes, but the initial use of an easily cultivated organism will certainly permit a more rapid elimination of many hypotheses of drug action and may yield information which will be of value in developing a more rational approach to chemotherapy.

Effects of ethidium and quinapyramine on cell division

Growth experiments have revealed major differences in the action of these two compounds (Newton, 1957, 1958). Multiplication of *S. oncopelti* in a peptone-glucose medium was not immediately inhibited by the addition of ethidium. At least a 70 to 80 % increase in cell numbers was always observed, and greater increases occurred before multiplication was finally inhibited by low concentrations of the drug (Fig. 1a). When multiplication had ceased in the presence of ethidium it did not start again after the removal of organisms to a drug-free medium.

In contrast to these results it was found that the multiplication of *S. oncopelti* was not inhibited by quinapyramine at concentrations within the range $0 \cdot 1 \mu$g. to 100μg. drug/ml. The pattern of growth however was changed by the drug from an exponential to a linear form (Fig. 1b). Removal of organisms to a drug-free medium at any time after the addition of quinapyramine resulted in a rapid return to exponential growth. At first sight these results appear to

conflict with the *in vivo* studies already described, but the work of
Sen, Dutta and Ray (1955) suggests that host defence mechanisms
play a vital role in the action of quinapyramine *in vivo*. These
workers have shown that splenectomy prevents quinapyramine
from clearing a trypanosome infection in experimental animals.
This suggests that the drug may also act *in vivo* by reducing the
growth rate of trypanosomes rather than by a direct trypanocidal

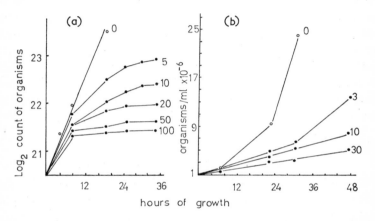

FIG. 1. Effect of quaternary ammonium trypanocides on the growth of *Strigomonas oncopelti*. Growth medium: 3% (w/v) peptone containing 0·5% (w/v) NaCl and 0·5% (w/v) glucose at 25°. Effect of ethidium (*a*), and of quinapyramine (*b*). Figures on graphs indicate concentration of drug in μg./ml.

action, and that elimination of parasites can be attributed to the
host's immune processes.

Changes in the nucleic acid content of drug-treated organisms

Examination of the ribonucleic acid (RNA) and deoxyribonucleic acid (DNA) content of organisms grown in the presence
of either ethidium or quinapyramine revealed a second difference
between the actions of these two compounds. Results summarized

Table I

EFFECT OF QUATERNARY AMMONIUM TRYPANOCIDES ON
THE RNA AND DNA CONTENT OF *Strigomonas oncopelti*

Time of sampling (hr.)	RNA (μg./10^9 organisms)			DNA (μg./10^9 organisms)		
	C	E	A	C	E	A
1	1904	1920	1916	236	240	284
3	2186	2060	2017	234	200	222
6	1593	2010	1608	212	174	253
12	1398	1780	1572	205	151	240
24	1462	1733	1262	218	114	233

Growth medium; peptone-glucose, 25°. Samples were taken at intervals from a control culture (C) and ethidium (20 μg./ml.)-containing culture (E) and an antrycide (30 μg./ml.)-containing culture (A). The number of organisms, RNA and DNA content were determined.

in Table I show that the DNA content of organisms grown for a period of 24 hours in the presence of ethidium fell to half the normal value. No such change was observed in organisms growing in the presence of quinapyramine; under these conditions linear growth was accompanied by a linear synthesis of RNA, DNA and protein. One interpretation of these results is that ethidium permitted limited cell division and RNA synthesis but rapidly inhibited DNA synthesis. These findings led to an investigation of the effects of ethidium and quinapyramine on RNA and DNA synthesis under more precisely controlled conditions.

Nucleic acid and protein synthesis by washed cell suspensions of Strigomonas oncopelti

When washed cell suspensions of *S. oncopelti* were incubated at 25° for 5 hr. in a buffered medium containing salts, glucose and a mixture of purines, pyrimidines and 18 amino acids, it was found that the nucleic acid and protein content of the suspension increased by about 70 % (Newton, 1957). Fig. 2 shows the dependence of RNA and DNA synthesis on the various components of the incubation medium. Work with numerous microorganisms has demonstrated a strong positive correlation between growth rate and RNA content of cells; furthermore, it has frequently been found that conditions which prevent protein synthesis also prevent nucleic acid synthesis (Casperson and Brand, 1941; Jeener and Brachet, 1944; Gale and Folkes, 1953). These findings hold true for *S. oncopelti*: omission of glucose or amino acids from the incubation mixture prevented RNA and DNA synthesis. It is

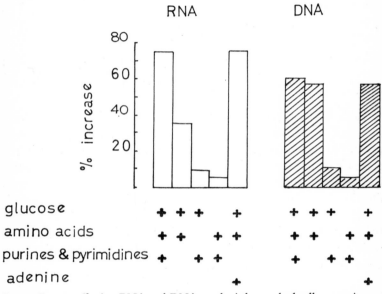

FIG. 2. Factors affecting RNA and DNA synthesis by washed cell suspensions of *Strigomonas oncopelti*. Washed organisms suspended in buffered salts solution (pH 7·2) with additions as indicated. Incubations at 25° for 5 hr.

interesting, and relevant to results to be discussed later, that adenine was found to replace the mixture of purines and pyrimidines and that complete omission of these bases had a more pronounced effect on RNA than on DNA synthesis.

Inhibition of nucleic acid and protein synthesis

Addition of ethidium to a washed cell suspension of *S. oncopelti*, incubated under conditions which permit nucleic acid synthesis, resulted in a rapid inhibition of DNA synthesis but allowed RNA synthesis to continue for 2 to 3 hr. (Fig. 3b). These findings are in accord with results obtained with cultures growing in peptone–glucose medium. In contrast quinapyramine had no detectable effect on the rate of DNA synthesis by washed cell suspensions over a period of eight hours, but caused a progressive inhibition of RNA synthesis (Fig. 3c). This finding is at variance with results obtained with organisms growing in peptone–glucose. Under these conditions, it will be recalled, addition of quinapyramine resulted in

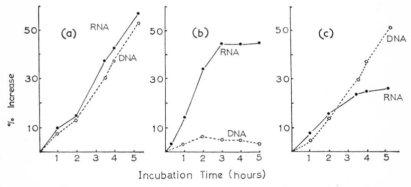

FIG. 3. Effect of quaternary ammonium trypanocides on RNA and DNA synthesis by washed cell suspensions of *Strigomonas oncopelti*. Washed organisms suspended in buffered salts solution containing glucose, 18 amino acids, purines and pyrimidines (a) and with addition of 20 μg./ml. ethidium (b) or of 30 μg./ml. quinapyramine (c).

linear growth and linear synthesis of both RNA and DNA. With either drug it was found that protein synthesis followed the course of RNA synthesis. These observations led to an examination of the effects of growth factors on nucleic acid synthesis by washed cell suspensions. The addition of *p*-aminobenzoic acid (*p*-AB) to the incubation mixture was found to annul the inhibition of RNA synthesis by quinapyramine. One interpretation of this result is that quinapyramine completely inhibits the synthesis of RNA only when organisms are dependent upon exogenous purines. To test this hypothesis the effect of quinapyramine on the incorporation of ^{14}C-adenine and ^{14}C-glycine has been studied.

Effect of drugs on the incorporation of radioactive nucleic acid precursors

When the incorporation of ^{32}P was used as a measure of nucleic acid synthesis by washed cell suspensions it was found that both quinapyramine and ethidium progressively inhibited this incorporation: the time course of this inhibition was, for both drugs, similar to that obtained by direct measurement of RNA (Figs. 3b and c). However when similar experiments were performed with ^{14}C-adenine as tracer it was found that only in the case of ethidium did the time course of inhibition compare with the net synthesis experiments. Quinapyramine rapidly inhibited adenine (or guanine) incorporation from the time that the drug was added. A study of ^{14}C-glycine incorporation into nucleic acid purines (Newton, 1960), revealed this to be little affected by concentrations of drug which markedly inhibited purine incorporation (Fig. 4).

Inhibition of ^{14}C-adenine incorporation by quinapyramine

The selective inhibition of adenine incorporation by quinapyramine raises two important questions: (a) Is the effect specific to quinapyramine? Eighteen compounds structurally related to either quinapyramine or to the pyrimidine or quinoline portions of the molecule have been tested for their effect on adenine and glycine incorporation. Of these only the monoquaternary derivatives of quinapyramine exhibited a selective activity comparable with that of the parent compound. Thus it seems that the effect illustrated in Fig. 4 is only produced by the intact "quinoline-pyrimidine conjugate" and that this must contain at least one quaternary nitrogen. (b) At which point in the synthesis of nucleic acid from exogenous adenine does quinapyramine act? This question has been investigated by considering three levels at which the drug may act: these are (i) the entry of exogenous adenine into cells, (ii) the conversion of intracellular adenine into adenine nucleotides and (iii) the synthesis of nucleic acid from nucleotides. It was found that quinapyramine does not affect the rate of entry of ^{14}C-adenine into the intracellular "pool" of acid soluble materials. Analysis of these "pool" materials, extracted from control or drug-treated organisms by chromatography on columns of the cation exchange resin Dowex 1 (chloride form), has revealed that

FIG. 4. Effect of quinapyramine concentration on the incorporation of ^{14}C-adenine or ^{14}C-glycine into nucleic acid of *Strigomonas oncopelti*. Washed organisms in buffered salts solution containing glucose, 18 amino acids, purines and pyrimidines. Incubations at 25° for 2 hr.

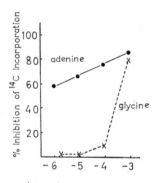

Log. molar conc. quinapyramine

in both cases the relative proportions of adenine compounds is the same, and that the distribution of ^{14}C-adenine in adenosine and the free adenine nucleotides was unaffected by drug treatment. These results suggest that quinapyramine inhibits the incorporation of ^{14}C-adenine into nucleic acid at some point between acid-soluble nucleotides and the formation of acid-precipitable nucleic acids. This being the case two further questions may be posed: first, can the incorporation of ^{14}C-adenine be assumed to measure normal nucleic acid synthesis? The incorporation might represent the addition of terminal residues to pre-existing nucleic acid chains or the synthesis of an abnormal macromolecule such as polyadenylic acid. Second, if adenine incorporation does represent normal nucleic acid synthesis, does quinapyramine affect this incorporation into all nucleic acid fractions of the cells to an equal extent?

Alkaline hydrolysis of nucleic acids labelled with ^{14}C-adenine has shown that less than 3 % of the total radioactivity is associated with the terminal residues of nucleic acid molecules. Base analysis of nucleic acid synthesized by S. oncopelti in the presence or absence of an exogenous source of adenine, has failed to show any significant change in the purine: pyrimidine ratios. Thus there is reason to believe that ^{14}C-adenine incorporation may represent normal nucleic acid synthesis.

In an attempt to answer the second question, the effect of quinapyramine on the incorporation of adenine into various cell fractions of S. oncopelti has been studied. Table II summarizes results of an

Table II

EFFECT OF QUINAPYRAMINE (30 μg./ml.) ON ^{14}C-ADENINE INCORPORATION INTO NUCLEIC ACID FRACTIONS OF Strigomonas oncopleti

Fraction	Nucleic acid (% of total)	Counts/min. Control	Counts/min. Antrycide	Inhibition (%)
Total nucleic acid	—	16016	7568	53
P$_1$(700 **g**, 10 min.)	11	14160	14044	0
P$_2$(9,000 **g**, 60 min.)	14	3948	1604	59
P$_3$(100,000 **g**, 120 min.)	69	31920	4804	85
S(supernatant)	6	3612	3348	8

Washed organisms incubated for 3 hr. at 25° in buffered salts solution containing glucose, 18 amino acids, and ^{14}C-adenine in the presence or absence of antrycide (quinapyramine). After disintegration of organisms in a bacterial press cell fractions were isolated by differential centrifugation as indicated, and the distribution of radioactivity determined.

experiment in which adenine incorporation into total cellular nucleic acid was inhibited by about 50%. Organisms were disrupted in a bacterial press (Hughes, 1951) and cell material fractionated by centrifuging. It is clear from the data shown in Table II that quinapyramine inhibited the incorporation of adenine into material which sedimented at 9,000 **g** and 100,000 **g** (P$_3$) to a much greater extent than into other cell fractions.

Effect of quinapyramine on ribosomes

Analysis of fraction P₃ in the Spinco Analytical ultracentrifuge showed that it was composed almost entirely of particles having a sedimentation constant of 78 S. Chemical analysis of purified particles has shown that they contain, on a weight basis, 45 % RNA and 55 % protein: they thus resemble ribosomes isolated from other sources. Examination of this fraction isolated from organisms grown in the presence of quinapyramine revealed that the amount of 78 S component decreased progressively; after 20 hours of growth in the drug organisms contained only 10 % of their normal

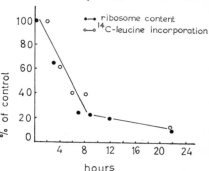

FIG. 5. Relationship between ribosome content of quinapyramine-grown *Strigomonas oncopelti* and the ability of these organisms to incorporate ¹⁴C-leucine. Organisms grown in peptone-glucose medium containing 30 μg. quinapyramine/ml.; samples removed at intervals for determination of ribosome content and ability to incorporate ¹⁴C-leucine in a washed cell system.

ribosome content (Fig. 5). Analysis of other cell fractions has shown that this loss was not due to a breakdown of ribosomal material, but to an aggregation of the particles with the result that nucleic acid normally found in fraction P₃ appeared in fractions P₁ and P₂ (Table II).

There is now considerable evidence to support the idea that ribosomes provide a site for protein synthesis (reviewed by Berg, 1961) and that the rate at which cells incorporate amino acids is directly related to their ribosome content (McCarthy, 1960). In view of this it was of interest to determine whether the aggregated ribosomes in quinapyramine-grown organisms were still able to incorporate amino acids. Ability of *S. oncopelti* to incorporate ¹⁴C-leucine into protein decreased at the same rate (Fig. 5) as ribosomes were lost from fraction P_3, during growth in the presence of quinapyramine. This suggests that the aggregation of ribosomes also results in a loss of their biological activity.

Microscopic examination of organisms grown with quinapyramine has shown that the time course for the formation of cytoplasmic basophilic granules of the type originally described by Ormerod (1951b) coincides with the rate of aggregation of ribosomal particles. Since the basophilic "chemotherapy granules" have been shown to contain ribonucleoprotein and bound quinapyramine it is tempting to suggest that they represent aggregates of ribosomes.

Recovery of organisms from quinapyramine treatment

As already mentioned organisms transferred from a drug-containing growth medium to a drug-free medium resumed exponential growth after a short lag period. Can this recovery of exponential growth be correlated with a disaggregation of quina-pyramine-bound ribosomes, or is it associated with the synthesis of new ribosomes? To investigate this question organisms were grown for 2 to 3 generations in a medium containing ^{14}C-uracil, prior to growth in a medium containing quinapyramine, but no labelled components. The first period of growth resulted in the nucleic acid of the cells becoming uniformly labelled with ^{14}C. During the second stage of the experiment growth changed from an exponential form to a linear form and ribosomes were aggregated, as judged by the loss of radioactivity from fraction P_3 and the increase in radioactivity of fractions sedimented by low speed centrifuging (Fig. 6). After 24 hours of growth in the presence of quinapyramine organisms were transferred to a drug-free, non-radioactive medium: under these conditions exponential growth was resumed after 10 hours. At this point in the experiment organisms were disintegrated and fractionated as already described. Examination of fraction P_3 in the ultracentrifuge showed that it contained a normal amount of particulate material which sedimented at 78 S. However, determination of the radioactivity in cell fractions showed that there had been no significant transfer of ^{14}C from the low speed fractions (aggregated ribosomes) to fraction

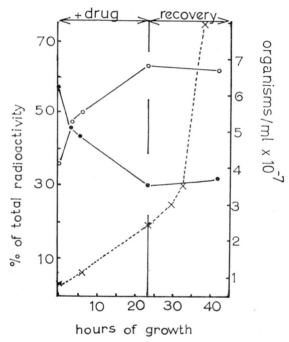

FIG. 6. Recovery of *Strigomonas oncopelti* from quinapyramine treatment. Conditions as described in the text. The figure shows changes in growth ($\times$ ---- $\times$), radioactivity in cell fractions sedimented by centrifugating at 9,000 **g** for 60 min. ($\circ$——$\circ$) and radioactivity in the ribosome fraction of cells ($\bullet$——$\bullet$).

P_3 during the recovery period. These results indicate that during recovery from treatment with quinapyramine new ribosomes are synthesized and that there is little disaggregation of quinapyramine-bound ribosomes.

The mechanism of action of ethidium and quinapyramine

In vivo experiments and histochemical studies led to the suggestion that ethidium and quinapyramine may act in a similar manner (Hawking, 1953). The *in vitro* studies described show that these two compounds differ fundamentally in their actions against *S. oncopelti*. While both compounds appear to combine with cytoplasmic RNA to form basophilic granules, only ethidium causes a rapid inhibition of DNA synthesis. The explanation of this difference is not yet clear: it seems unlikely that it is due to a difference in the affinity of the two drugs for DNA or for the enzymes involved in DNA synthesis, since both compounds interact with purified DNA and both have recently been found to inhibit DNA synthesis in a cell-free system obtained from bacteria (Dr. W. H. Elliott, personal communication).

A second point arising from these studies which remains unexplained is the selective inhibition of purine incorporation by quinapyramine. If the synthesis of purines from glycine by *S. oncopelti* follows the pathways established for other microorganisms (reviewed by Buchanan, 1960) the drug would be expected to inhibit the incorporation of adenine and glycine to an equal extent. (The incorporation of both precursors is thought to follow a common path from nucleotide to nucleic acid, and quinapyramine appears to act at some intermediate point on this path). It may be that this selective action of quinapyramine and the insensitivity of DNA synthesis by intact cells to this compound is due to failure of the drug to penetrate into all parts of the cell. With this idea in mind it is interesting to recall that DNA synthesis by washed cell suspensions of *S. oncopelti*, in contrast to RNA synthesis, was little affected by the absence of an exogenous supply of purine (Fig. 3). This could be due to purine deoxyribonucleotides being formed primarily by *de novo* synthesis, rather than from exogenous purine. In support of this, preliminary experiments have shown that when *S. oncopelti* was grown in the presence of adequate supplies of amino acids, adenine and growth factors, a much higher proportion of DNA purine than RNA purine appeared to be synthesized from glycine. If this synthesis is mainly localized in the nucleus, and if quinapyramine is unable to penetrate the nucleus of *S. oncopelti*, the insensitivity of DNA synthesis and of glycine incorporation to inhibition by this drug might be explained.

The role of the host

It is clear from the results of Sen *et al.* (1955), which have already been outlined, that host defence mechanisms play a vital role in the prophylactic action of quinapyramine. The differences observed between quinapyramine and ethidium, acting *in vitro*, suggest that this may not be the case for ethidium. The chemotherapeutic action of this drug may well be aided and accelerated by an immune reaction *in vivo* but, if the results of *in vitro* experiments hold true for pathogenic trypanosomes *in vivo*, it is likely that splenectomy will not prevent the curative action of ethidium.

Selective action

Any theory of drug action must provide an adequate explanation of selective activity. At first sight it would seem that a drug which inhibited such fundamental and universal processes as nucleic acid and protein synthesis would be of little value as a chemotherapeutic agent. However, research during the last decade has shown that a number of valuable antibacterial agents do act in such a manner (reviewed by Gale, 1958). Results described here suggest that ethidium and quinapyramine may act in this way. As yet not enough is known about the detailed reactions involved in nucleic acid and protein metabolism to say whether one synthetic mechanism is common to all tissues. Minor differences may exist which are sufficient to account for the selective activity of a drug. Other possibilities must be considered. The drug may be inactivated by host tissues. Differences in permeability may exist in host and parasite cells, or alternatively, both may be readily permeable to the drug but, as proposed by Ehrlich (1913), only the parasite may contain the requisite intracellular binding sites. With regard to this last possibility, it is important to realize that this may not be an "all or none" phenomenon; host cells may contain the same binding sites as the parasite but, due to differences in intracellular organization, they may be inaccessible to the drug. Yet another possibility is that the host cell may be capable of a rapid resynthesis of cellular components damaged by combination with the drug.

The results described suggest that quinapyramine may reduce the growth rate of *S. oncopelti* by aggregating ribosomes in the cytoplasm of cells, so reducing the number of sites available for protein synthesis. Ribosomes have been found to occur in a wide range of microorganisms, mammalian and plant tissues and chemical analysis suggests that ribosomes from different sources are basically similar in composition. Thus it might seem unlikely that ribosomes prepared from different organisms would display different affinities for quinapyramine; however, the results of preliminary experiments suggest that such differences exist. Fig. 7 compares the relationship between quinapyramine concentration and the mass of ribosomal material aggregated by the addition of drug to the cell sap of disrupted *S. oncopelti*, *Bacillus megaterium* (strain KM) and *Escherichia coli* B. It is clear that, under the conditions of these experiments, much higher concentrations of drug were required to aggregate ribosomal material in the *E. coli* preparation than in the other two preparations. With this in mind it is interesting that *E. coli* will grow in the presence of quinapyramine at a concentration of 300 μg./ml. whereas the growth of *B. megaterium* is inhibited by 25 μg./ml. Obviously, these results do not establish a relationship between the affinity of quinapyramine for the ribosomes of an organism and the sensitivity of that organism to the drug. However, such a relationship may exist and it is hoped that further investigation of this aspect of the problem will provide some insight into the question of selective toxicity.

Ethidium and a number of other phenanthridines are toxic to a wide variety of organisms: they have been reported to inhibit the growth of animal viruses, bacteriophage (Dickinson and Codd, 1952), bacteria (Seaman and Woodbine, 1954) protozoa (Watkins

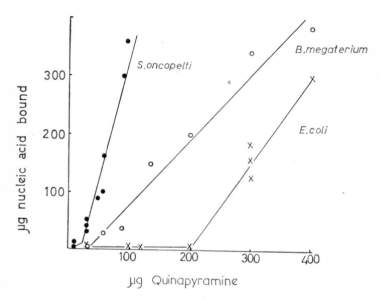

FIG. 7. Affinity of ribosomes for quinapyramine. Organisms were disrupted in a bacterial press (Hughes, 1951) and the cell debris removed by centrifuging at 9,000 **g** for 60 min. The supernatant fraction, which contains ribosomes, soluble protein and small molecular weight RNA was titrated with quinapyramine, and ribosomal material aggregated by the drug was removed by centrifugation at 9,000 **g** for 60 min. The amount of nucleic acid remaining in the supernatant fraction was measured.

and Woolfe, 1952) and mammalian cells maintained in tissue culture (S. R. Pelc and J. Micou, personal communication). If subsequent work shows that these drugs cause a rapid inhibition of DNA synthesis in all cases, then their success as trypanocidal agents may ultimately be explained in terms of an inability to reach the site of this synthesis in a significant number of host cells. This possibility emphasizes the importance of studying the "host-parasite unit" in addition to the isolated parasite if we are to understand the true nature of selective toxicity; it also stresses the urgent need for knowledge of factors affecting the permeability of cellular and intracellular membranes to drugs.

REFERENCES

BERG, P. (1961). *Ann. Rev. Biochem.*, **30**, 293.

BUCHANAN, J. N. (1960). *In* The Nucleic Acids, III, 304. Ed. Chargaff, E. and Davidson, J. N., New York: Acad. Press Inc.

CASPERSON, T. and BRAND, K. (1941). *Protoplasma*, **35**, 507.

CURD, F. H. S. and DAVEY, D. G. (1950). *Brit. J. Pharmacol.*, **5**, 25.

DICKINSON, L. and CODD, S. (1952). *J. gen. Microbiol.*, **6**, 1.

EHRLICH, P. (1913). *Lancet*, **ii**, 445.

FULTON, J. D. and SPOONER, D. F. (1959). *Exp. Parasitol.*, **8**, 137.

GALE, E. F. (1958). *In* The Strategy of Chemotherapy, Symp. Soc. gen. Microbiol biol., **8**, 212

GALE, E. F. and FOLKES, J. P. (1953). *Biochem. J.*, **53**, 483.

GOODWIN, L. G. (1958). *In* The Strategy of Chemotherapy, Symp. Soc. gen. Microbiol., **8**, 336.

HAWKING, F. (1938). *Ann. trop. Med. Parasit.*, **32**, 313.

HAWKING, F. (1953). Symp., Growth inhibition & Chemotherapy, p. 88. *VII* Int. Congr. Microbiol., Rome.

HAWKING, F. and SEN, B. S. (1960). *Brit. J. Pharmacol.*, **15**, 567.

HUGHES, D. E. (1951). *Brit. J. exp. Path.*, **32**, 97.

JEENER, R. and BRACHET, J. (1944). *Enzymologia*, **11**, 222.

LOCK, J. A. (1950). *Brit. J. Pharmacol.*, **5**, 398.

LWOFF, M. (1937). *C.R. Soc. Biol.*, Paris, **126**, 771.

McCARTHY, B. J. (1960). *Biochim. biophys. Acta*, **39**, 563.

NEWTON, B. A. (1956). *Nature, Lond.*, **177**, 279.

NEWTON, B. A. (1957). *J. gen. Microbiol.*, **17**, 718.

NEWTON, B. A. (1958). *J. gen. Microbiol.*, **19**, ii.

NEWTON, B. A. (1960). *Biochem. J.*, **77**, 12P.

NOGUCHI, H. and TILDEN, E. B. (1926). *J. exp. Med.*, **44**, 307.

ORMEROD, W. E. (1951a). *Brit. J. Pharmacol.*, **6**, 325.

ORMEROD, W. E. (1951b). *Brit. J. Pharmacol.*, **6**, 334.

RYLEY, J. F. (1956). *Biochem. J.*, **62**, 215.

SEAMAN, A. and WOODBINE, M. (1954). *Brit. J. Pharmacol.*, **9**, 265.

SEN, H. G., DUTTA, B. N. and RAY, H. N. (1955). *Nature, Lond.*, **175**, 778.

TAYLOR, A. E. R. (1960). *Brit. J. Pharmacol.*, **15**, 230.

Von Brand, T., Weinbach, E. C. and Tobie, E. J. (1955). *J. cell. comp. Physiol.*, **45**, 421.

Watkins, T. I. and Woolfe, G. (1952). *Nature, Lond.*, **169**, 506.

DISCUSSION

Whiteside: I understood Dr. Newton to suggest that the chemical action of ethidium is different from that of antrycide. In cattle, trypanosomes resistant to antrycide can be made invariably cross-resistant to ethidium and *vice versa*. Therefore, if their chemical action is different one also has to explain why, in fact, cross-resistance occurs.

Newton: I have no answer. We are trying to get some information on this point by studying the cross-resistance in our *in vitro* system. Unfortunately, all attempts to obtain an ethidium-resistant organism *in vitro* have failed. We have an antrycide-resistant strain now, and we are studying the biochemistry of this strain and its uptake of radioactive drugs. I hope that some time in the near future we will be able to give some information about this point.

R. H. Nimmo-Smith (Wellcome Laboratories of Tropical Medicine): Dr. Newton has shown us some extraordinarily interesting effects of ethidium and antrycide on DNA synthesis. It would be interesting to know the relationship between the concentrations of drug he used *in vitro* and those obtaining in the cow.

Newton: I should like to know this as well. I have asked many people who have worked with animals, and there do not seem to be any reliable estimates of the actual concentrations. You can get amounts in terms of mg. or g./kg. of animal, but as regards concentration in the blood stream, I would welcome any information which can be obtained from anyone.

Whiteside: I gather the concentrations in the blood of cattle are so low that nobody has yet been able to measure them.

Goodwin: I thought some people in East Africa were trying to measure them by a biological rather than by a chemical method.

Whiteside: A microorganism has been found that is sensitive to the concentrations which exist in the blood, and so by exposing them to the blood of animals it is hoped to get some sort of estimate.

W. E. Ormerod (London School of Hygiene and Tropical Medicine): Dr. Newton has suggested that ethidium because of its innate trypanocidal action may not have its activity inhibited by splenectomy and suchlike maltreatment of the host. We have not done the experiments so we do not know the answer. My prediction is the other way: that it *will* be inhibited. My reason for saying this is that some recent work by a Rumanian group (Muntiu *et al.*, 1961) has shown that after destruction of the reticuloendothelial system in rats by irradiation the animals survive only for about a fortnight. Under these conditions the activity of arsenicals, which are quite definitely trypanocidal in their own right, is inhibited.

A. Shulman (*Department of Physiology, Melbourne University*): Can I ask Dr. Newton if he has tried the effect of his two substances on yeast or staphylococcus? My reason for asking this is that cationic substances and metal complexes have been shown to induce "petit" formation (respiration–deficient variants) and this has been attributed by Ephrussi (1950) to a cytoplasmic factor which may be nucleic acid–dependent. This suggestion has been put very recently by Nagai and collaborators in Japan (Nagai *et al.*, 1961). Compounds of this sort, the type you have been discussing and which contain amidine residues, and substances like streptomycin with guanidine residues are strong cations. We have done some work in Melbourne (Butler, Harris, Laycock, Shulman, R. D. Wright and R. E. Wright, unpublished) which shows that cationic compounds produce "petits" providing they can penetrate the cell. One might predict that your compounds in staphyloccocus and certainly in yeast might produce variants which are respiratory-deficient.

Newton: We have not done any work at all with yeast. The strain of staphylococcus used in our laboratory is completely resistant to antrycide. We have not done any growth tests with ethidium. Professor Gale found that ethidium inhibits glycine incorporation in the staphylococcus at about 10^{-4} M (Gale and Folkes, 1957).   •

C. G. L. Beveridge (*May and Baker*): I do not think Mr. Whiteside was quite accurate in saying that berenil is the only amidine which shows activity against the cattle trypanosomes. I am sure he will agree that metamidium is in every sense an amidine.

Whiteside: It is a complex amidine containing a phenathridinium group. The amidine groups are in the *meta* position and not the *para* position as in berenil. It is curious that *T. congolense* shows no cross-resistance between these two drugs. If you make a berenil-resistant strain it is not cross-resistant to the *meta* amidine, and *vice versa*.

P. J. Walker (National Institute for Medical Research): I should like to ask Mr. Whiteside why he objects to mutation producing resistance in the presence of drug. After all, about 10^9 divisions occur before one would have a "+ +" infection in the blood. Surely there are enough divisions to allow mutation to occur at the accepted rate?

Whiteside: If mutations occur why do they never occur in the presence of a normal dose? Because they do not. If you use the normal dose on this strain, over and over again, it always cures. The idea that an acquired variation is inherited, in fact, is quite commonly held but that term is not used. In the books you will find it called an "induced mutation", and many people explain the ease with which drug resistance is produced in certain organisms by saying that it must be an induced mutation.

B. Lacey (Westminster Hospital Medical School): Nobody really believes in the directional induction of mutations do they? Would it not really be more reasonable to assume that it is a multi-step mutation and if there is enough drug you will never select the mutant? Have you tried infecting an animal carrying a resistant strain with a non-resistant to see whether the resistant strain is swamped entirely under these conditions?

Whiteside: No; I have wanted to do it for many years.

To answer the first question is more difficult. It depends what sort of impression you get from doing these things. Discussion of induced mutation is difficult because, if I might take up your time, a most odd accident happened. Induced mutations are referred to by Schnitzer and Grunberg (1957) in their book, and I was about to look up the references in this book. I was reading it at lunch-time outside the laboratory and fell asleep. This is a perfectly true story. The book fell from my hand, and the necessary ten pages were eaten by one of the experimental sheep!

R. J. Fitzpatrick (Department of Pharmacology, Bristol University): Mr. Whiteside mentioned an avirulent strain of trypanosomiasis which he found occurring naturally. Could he tell us if infection with the avirulent strain had any effect upon subsequent challenge with a virulent strain?

Whiteside: We have done a few tests in the laboratory and on the whole it does not seem to make any difference. The animal with an avirulent strain can be infected with a virulent strain after it has been cured. What happens if you try to superinfect an animal carrying an avirulent strain with a virulent strain I do not know.

Ormerod: I think that experiment has been done (von Brand and Tobie, 1960) and the strain with the faster rate of growth, in fact, outgrew the other at the speed which would have been predicted by its rate of growth.

REFERENCES

BRAND, T. VON and TOBIE, E. J. (1960). *J. Parasit.*, **46**, 129.

EPHRUSSI, B. (1950–51). *Harvey Lectures*, **46**, 45.

GALE, E. F. and FOLKES, J. P. (1957). *Biochem. J.*, **67**, 507.

MUNTIU, N., CHELEMAN, N., ARDRIAN, T., CORNECI, I., BĂDITOIU, I. and IUGA, C. (1961). *Arch. roum. Path. exp. Microbiol.*, **20**, 77.

NAGAI, S., YANAGISHIMA, N. and NAGAI, H. (1961). *Bact. Rev.*, **25**, 404.

SCHNITZER, R. J. and GRUNBERG, E. (1957). Drug Resistance of Microorganisms, New York: Academic Press.

STRUCTURE AND ACTIVITY OF
ANTIPROTOZOAL DRUGS ·

H. J. Barber and S. S. Berg

Research Laboratories, May & Baker, Ltd., Dagenham

As members of an industrial team engaged in the search for chemotherapeutic agents, we have inevitably thought first of the practical end—a useful drug—and speculations or experimental work on possible modes of action have been incidental means to that end. We do not wish to imply that fundamental studies ought to take second place but it has to be recognized, albeit with humility, that analogical chemistry has yielded results in the form of useful drugs which are far in advance of the state of our knowledge of how they achieve those results.

Let us for a moment reflect on what we mean by the terms "structure" and "activity". Structure means to most of us a two dimensional representation of an organic molecule. Few have really trained their minds to think regularly in three dimensions when designing molecules for chemotherapeutic studies. Some do, but most make the model afterwards and try to rationalize the observed properties with the shape or size of the collection of coloured balls which we hope is one step in advance of the unreality of the planar formula. How much do we think in advance about the distribution of the charged centres of electrical forces in the molecule? It is only when a drug has proved of outstanding interest that really detailed studies of the structure of the molecule in the fullest and most fundamental sense are undertaken. Rarely has an homologous series been studied from all aspects. There are, of course, many excellent studies in which one or two properties— perhaps quite significant ones—such as dissociation constants,

(Bell, Bone, and Roblin, 1944; Hogben, Tocco, Brodie and Schanker, 1959) partition coefficients (Hammick and Mason, 1950; Albert, Goldacre and Heymann, 1943) and the like have been shown to correlate in a limited and closely related series with a particular biological property.

But let us now look at the "activity" side of the title. It seems to us that we can view the term "activity" from two quite different aspects and that it may well have entirely different meanings in respect of particular drugs and particular diseases according to the point of view. The physician using the drug will equate activity with its ability to cure or alleviate the disease; the possibility that it may be a metabolite of the administered drug which in fact is the active agent in killing or removing the organism is not primarily the physician's concern and he might well be amused at the laboratory scientist's endeavours to explain that the drug was really inactive *per se*. It is inevitable that the biologist who wishes to probe the more fundamental aspects of activity of chemical substances on a particular living system will seek to carry out his comparisons with as simple a system as possible—normally an *in vitro* culture or an isolated organ in which the conditions can be standardized to a considerable extent. But the more artificial is the experimentally created situation, the further it is from the realities of the vastly more complex host in which many growth phases of protozoa may be present at the same time. What should one's concept of "activity" be in discussing structure and activity? The relatively simple *in vitro* results which might be nice and tidy, or the *in vivo* ones which are full of complexities? We have always tended to view the *in vivo* results as the only ones that really matter in our search for useful drugs, and the nearer the experimental host is to the natural one, the better. We have therefore in the more general part of this paper construed the word "activity" to mean reasonably well established activity *in vivo*. We know that this may exclude substances which have some intrinsic activity, but which have failed to reveal this in an *in vivo* test for one or more of a variety of reasons, such as inadequate absorption, too rapid excretion, metabolism and inactivation, inaccessibility to the parasite, and so forth. Fig. 1 is a general map of the chemical areas in which significant antiprotozoal action has been observed—a map of the

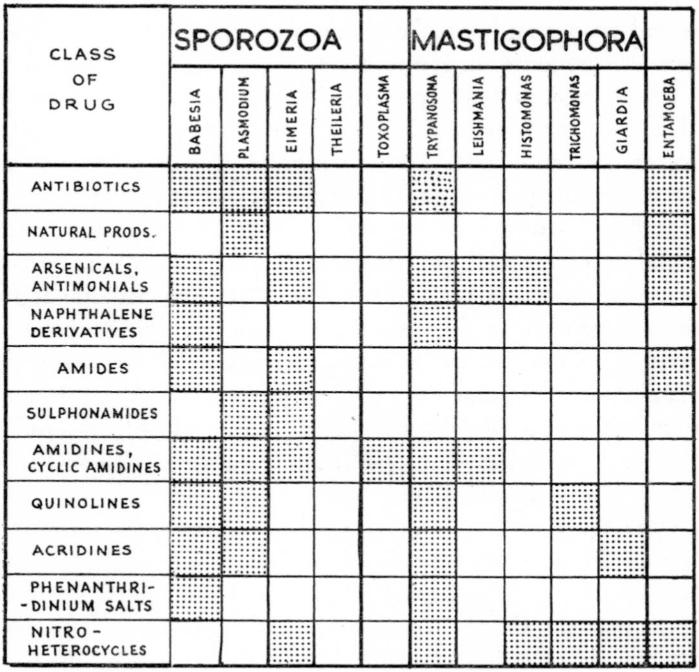

CLASS OF DRUG	SPOROZOA				TOXOPLASMA	MASTIGOPHORA					ENTAMOEBA
	BABESIA	PLASMODIUM	EIMERIA	THEILERIA	TOXOPLASMA	TRYPANOSOMA	LEISHMANIA	HISTOMONAS	TRICHOMONAS	GIARDIA	ENTAMOEBA
ANTIBIOTICS	▓	▓	▓			▓					▓
NATURAL PRODS.		▓									
ARSENICALS, ANTIMONIALS	▓		▓			▓	▓				▓
NAPHTHALENE DERIVATIVES	▓					▓					
AMIDES	▓		▓								▓
SULPHONAMIDES		▓	▓								
AMIDINES, CYCLIC AMIDINES	▓	▓				▓	▓				
QUINOLINES	▓	▓							▓		
ACRIDINES	▓	▓								▓	
PHENANTHRI-DINIUM SALTS	▓										
NITRO-HETEROCYCLES			▓			▓			▓	▓	▓

FIG. 1. Pattern of antiprotozoal activity.

chemotherapeutic world of antiprotozoal agents. The chemical types in which activity resides are very diverse.

The size and shape of models of trypanocidal drug molecules

At this point we should like to discuss some thoughts we had about ten years ago when we switched the emphasis of our diamidines programme from human to animal trypanosomiasis.

It became obvious that the admittedly crude structure-activity generalizations that we had derived for the one (Ashley, Barber, Ewins, Newbery and Self, 1942) did not apply to the other.

No one working in chemotherapy can fail to be influenced by Ehrlich's classic concepts of the interaction between trivalent arsenical groups and postulated chemoreceptors in trypanosomes. However, the amidine group is not characterized by such a well defined reaction as that between thiol and arsenic and it seemed to us that the very powerful basicity of the group must be a major factor in its binding or complexing (to use loose terms) with receptor sites having anionic character. It did not seem to us very profitable to study basic strengths at this stage but it seemed reasonable to have a look at the spacing of the two amidine groups, bearing in mind that we had not found any worthwhile activity with monoamidines. We then had data for the trypanocidal activity of over 200 diamidines and we made models of active drug molecules, in particular dimethyl stilbamidine ("M & B 991"; Barber, Slack and Woolman, 1943), 2-amino-4,6-di-(p-amidino-anilino)-1,3,5-triazine ("M & B 2242"; Ashley, Berg and Lucas, 1960) and, later, berenil ("Hoechst 12,753"; Jensch, 1955).

It appeared that diamidine molecules fulfilling certain requirements might be expected to have activity:—the amidine groups should be 12 to 15 Å apart, the linkage between the two aromatic amidine moieties should confer a measure of rigidity on the molecule by double bonds and through steric hindrance, and the whole system linking the amidine groups should be conjugated. In retrospect it seems naif and simple, and these concepts did not take us very far in developing trypanocidal diamidines more active than M & B 991 (which was too expensive)and M & B 2242 (which was not over promising in the field; Fairclough, personal communication). Table I shows how easily such simplified concepts can be demolished. This series of homologues and analogues of M & B 2242 all comply with our special requirements for trypanocidal activity; most of them have no effect against *Trypanosoma congolense*.

Table I

SOME DIAMIDINES LINKED THROUGH THE 1,3,5-TRIAZINE SYSTEM

M & B No.	R	R'	Distance between polar groups $A°$	Trypanocidal activity	
				T. congolense in mice	T. rhodesiense in mice
2242	H	$\overset{+}{Am}$—⟨⟩—NH	12–15	+ +	+ +
2522	Me	..	12–15	+	+ +
2523	Et	..	12–15	o	+ +
2450	H	⟨⟩—NH, $\overset{+}{Am}$	11–15	o	o
2368	H	$\overset{+}{Am}$—⟨⟩—O	12–15	o	o
2276 (Hoechst 10455)	H	$\overset{+}{G}$—⟨⟩—NH	14–19	+	o
2511	H	$Me_3\overset{+}{N}$—⟨⟩—NH	12–15	o	o

Am = amidino; G = guanidino; o = inactive; + = some activity; + + = active.

We also formed at that time some impressions of the size and shape of the molecular models of antrycide (Curd and Davey, 1950), of dimidium (Morgan and Walls, 1938), of the bis-cinnoline compound L.528 (Morley and Simpson, 1952) and of surfen (Jensch, 1937). A considerable element of flatness seems common to all of these, and the cationic centres, mainly quaternary nitrogens, are about 9 or 10 Å apart. In the specific field of phenanthridines we can distinguish two types—the straightforward dimidium types to the development of which Dr. L. P. Walls has contributed so much, and what we might call the more coruscated type of which prothidium (Short and Watkins, 1957; Watkins and Woolfe, 1956) and metamidium (Wragg, Washbourn, Brown and Hill, 1958) are prototypes. Compounds of the former (dimidium) group have no significantly prophylactic activity, but the latter undoubtedly have. The structural requirements for curative activity in the dimidium series have been discussed by Walls (1945) and we need do no more than summarize his conclusions: (1) All amino phenanthridinium salts show distinct activity except those in which amino-substituents are restricted to the 9-phenyl group, (2) the 2,7-diamino compounds which possess a "benzidine" type of

structure are the most active and (3) acetylation of the amino groups greatly reduces activity. From (3) it might be inferred that other forms of substitution on the amino group would also reduce activity.

The metamidium series

We now turn to the metamidium series of which some members exert a prophylactic action and some do not. It is here that we have to be very cautious in seeking to establish any direct relationship between structure and activity. But with a reminder that the term "prophylactic activity" represents the resultant of a complex of many distinct activities, the picture is presented as we see it. When homidium is coupled with diazonium salts, red diazo-amino- and purple aminoazo-isomers are formed (Berg, 1960). The red diazoamino members of the series are up to 10 times as active, both curatively and prophylactically, as the purple aminoazo

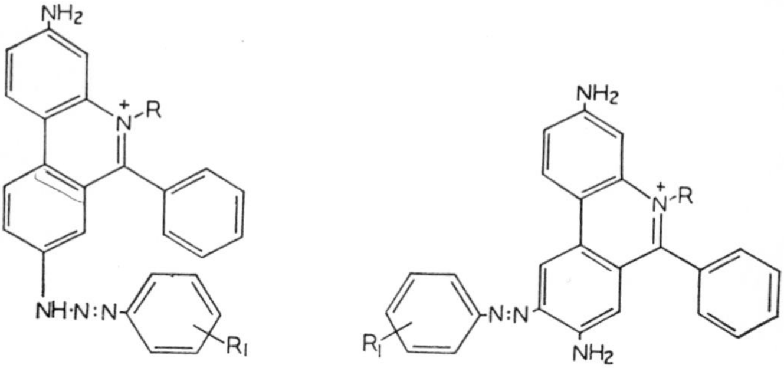

Red Isomer

Purple Isomer

series and isometamidium (M & B 4180; red isomer, R = Et, $R_1 = m$-amidino-) is the most active member of the metamidium series. The ethyl quaternary series are possibly slightly more active than the methyl series (Brown, Hill and Holland, 1961). But the most intriguing feature from our point of view was the favourable influence of the *meta* position for the amidine group as contrasted with the *para* position, isometamidium being considerably more active than its *para* isomer (M & B 4261). Traditionally, from early experience we had always favoured *para-para* substitution for diamidines. In the *para* series, optimum activity was obtained in compounds where the substituent was amidino, sulphamyl and carbamyl (Brown *et al.*, 1961) but these were generally somewhat less active than the parent homidium; the molecule might be regarded as being diluted with therapeutically irrelevant components. The guanidine substituent was somewhat less favourable than the amidine group (Brown *et al.*, 1961) and this was in line with our earlier experience.

When we gilded the lily by adding a second *m*-amidinophenyl-diazoamino moiety to the isometamidium molecule, we obtained a product less active therapeutically but giving somewhat longer prophylaxis in mice (Brown *et al.*, 1961; Berg, Brown, Hill and Wragg, 1961). It might be mentioned here that the activity, both curative and prophylactic, of isometamidium against various strains of *T. congolense* and *T. vivax* has been confirmed in field trials in Africa by various workers (Fairclough, 1958; Smith and Brown, 1960; Stephen, 1960; MacOwan, 1959; Scott, 1958; Willett, 1959; Whiteside, 1960). Doses of 0·5–2·0 mg./kg. will protect cattle for 2 to 6 months depending on the challenge, strain of parasite, cattle, and other factors. But it would be inappropriate in this paper to discuss the complexities of evaluation of veterinary trypanocides in the field.

Diamidines in babesiasis

The broad requirements of chemical structure for babesicidal activity appear to be similar to those for trypanocidal activity and since Nuttall and Hadwen (1909) first showed that trypan blue was curative in canine babesiasis, searches for trypanocidal and babesi-cidal drugs have proceeded side by side. Until 1925, only trypan blue had found general use as a babesicide but it was soon to be superseded by acriflavine. In the early 1930's Kikuth and his co-workers (Kikuth, 1935) examined a large number of bis-quinolinium ureas and amides formally related to suramin for activity against *Babesia canis*. The most active compound was acapron, a bis-quinolinium urea, which was also active against other babesial infections of domestic animals, but had no significant trypanocidal activity. Schönhöfer and Henecka (1946) concluded that the structural features essential for babesicidal activity in this series were:

(1) The urea link must be attached to the 6- or 7-position of the

quinoline ring; (2) both ring nitrogens must be quaternized; (3) the urea link may be replaced by azo, azoxy or pseudo-imino bridges without loss of activity.

The activity of aromatic diamidines against B. *canis* was first reported by Lourie and Yorke (1939) but of the early amidines examined only phenamidine has been successfully used in *Babesia* infections (Carmichael, 1942 *a, b, c*; Pierse, 1943; Randall and Laws, 1947). The recent introduction of berenil (Enigk and Reusse, 1955) and amicarbalide, (Ashley, Berg and Macdonald, 1960; Berg, 1961*a*) has however renewed the interest in diamidines for the chemotherapy of *Babesia*.

Since the discovery of *Babesia rodhaini*, which was transmissible to laboratory mice (Van den Berghe, Vincke, Chardôme and Van den Bulcke, 1950), this parasite has been used for the laboratory testing of compounds for antibabesial activity (Rodhain, 1951; Beveridge, 1953, 1956; Ryley, 1957; Lucas, 1960). The high activity of amicarbalide (M & B 5062A) was discovered as a result of screening a large number of compounds against B. *rodhaini* in mice, and then testing selected compounds against B. *divergens* in calves (Lucas, 1960). Amicarbalide is being used successfully for the treatment of B. *divergens* (Beveridge, Thwaite and Shepherd, 1960) and has activity against B. *bigemina* (Shone, Wells and Waller, 1961) and B. *berbera* (Kemron, Pipano, Hadani and Neumann, 1960). Its activity against B. *canis* appears to be variable and unpredictable (Van der Walt, 1960).

Berenil which contains the diazoamino linkage is the only diamidine so far examined which has significant activity against both *T. congolense* and B. *rodhaini* and this dual activity has also been found in the amidinophenyldiazoamino and aminoazocompounds of the metamidium series. Isometamidium and its purple isomer (M & B 4250) were the most active compounds of this group, and unlike the ten-fold difference in activity previously reported against *T. congolense*, there was little difference in their activities against B. *rodhaini*.

Although there is no evidence that positional isomerism in the berenil series has any significant effect on activity, we have shown that in the metamidium and the related amidinophenyldiazoaminoquinolinium and quinazolinium series (Berg, 1961*b*, *c*; 1962) the *meta*-amidino compounds are significantly more active against *B. rodhaini* than their *para* isomers. This has been further demonstrated with the *meta* diamidine amicarbalide (M & B 5062A) and its *meta–para* isomer, M & B 7642, which are highly active against *B. rodhaini*, whereas the *para–para* isomer, M & B 875 has no activity (Table II).

A clear structural pattern has not yet been obtained which could distinguish between trypanocidal and babesicidal compounds, but a closer study of the mode of action of the new babesicidal drugs might reveal some important structural requirements.

The fate of trypanocides in host and organism

The most striking feature which emerges from all studies of the fate of trypanocides in host and parasite is the extremely rapid disappearance of the drugs from the circulating blood. This is true of stilbamidine (Reid and Weaver, 1951; Fulton and Mathew, 1959), of pentamidine (Launoy, Guillot and Jonchère, 1960), of berenil (Fussgänger and Bauer, 1958, 1960), of prothidium (Taylor, 1960) and of carbidium (Goodwin, Goss, Lock and Walls, 1950). Stilbamidine and pentamidine are initially concentrated in the kidney and liver and are released moderately rapidly at first, but more slowly as the concentration falls. In excretion studies, Reid and Weaver (1951) accounted for 80% of a dose of stilbamidine after 5 days and 97% after 30 days; Launoy *et al.* (1960), using a less elaborate procedure, accounted for 80% of administered pentamidine in 200 days. On the other hand, Fussgänger and Bauer (1958, 1960) could not detect any excretion of berenil after 48 hours and imply that there is none left in the body. At any rate, berenil has no significant prophylactic activity. We can agree

Table II

COMPARISON OF TRYPANOCIDAL AND BABESICIDAL ACTIVITY

M & B No.	Compound	Activity	
		T. congolense	B. rodhaini
875	Am⟨benzene⟩NH·CO·NH⟨benzene⟩Am	o	o
7642	Am⟨benzene⟩NH·CO·NH⟨benzene⟩Am	o	+
5061	⟨benzene⟩NH·CO·NH⟨benzene⟩ Am ... Am	o	+ +
Hoechst 12753 (p) 12754 (m)	⟨benzene⟩N:N·NH⟨benzene⟩ Am ... Am	+ +	+ +
744	Am⟨benzene⟩CH:CH⟨benzene⟩Am	o	+
991	Am⟨benzene⟩C=C⟨benzene⟩Am (Me Me)	+	+
—	Antrycide	+ +	+
4180	Isometamidium	+ +	+ +

Am = amidino.

readily with these authors when they say that one diamidine is not like another. Pentamidine is bound and held in the animal body and exerts a prolonged protective action against susceptible species of trypanosomes but this activity is lost before the last traces of the amidine have disappeared from the tissues. Prothidium on the other hand has a definite and a reasonably long protective action, but according to Taylor (1960) is eliminated rapidly. It is detectable for 7 days in the liver and kidneys and Taylor observes that one might have predicted that it would protect for 10 days or so. But, in fact, it protects for 7 weeks. Isometamidium disappears rapidly from the circulating blood and is detectable by its fluorescence in kidney and liver (Benazet, 1961; J. Hill and J. A. McFadzean, personal communication) for one week. In considering the duration of the protective action of isometamidium we must note the importance of the depôt effect, usually at the site of injection, which has been well recognized by many workers. Here it is emphasized by the fact that 0·6 mg./kg. intravenously gives protection against *T. congolense* in the mouse for 1 week only, whereas the same dose subcutaneously protects for 5–6 weeks and fluorescence can be detected at the injection site for longer still. In the rat that same dose subcutaneously has given protection for 16 weeks.

A pattern of the uptake of trypanocides by trypanosomes is gradually emerging. The data are difficult to correlate because they often relate to different species of trypanosome, different concentrations of drug, different periods of exposure and perhaps to unknown factors. Taylor (1960) in her study on the uptake of prothidium by *T. rhodesiense* summarizes the "partition coefficients" at equilibrium as between drug solution and trypanosomes in suspension at 10 to 45 μg./ml. drug concentration. She quotes partition coefficients for prothidium, stilbamidine, reduced tryparsamide and for acriflavine of 400, 1,100, 5,000 and 8,000 respectively. Our colleagues Mr. J. Hill and Dr. J. A. McFadzean, have found that isometamidium is rapidly taken up by *T. rhodesiense*,

Hawking (1960) has made a tentative classification of trypanocides into two groups according to the characteristics of their type of action. The first group comprises arsenicals, acriflavine and diamidines which exert a rapid action *in vivo*, and the second, suramin, quinapyramine and the phenanthridines (metamidium was not then examined). According to Hawking's criteria compounds of the first group are rapidly and immediately absorbed by trypanosomes *in vitro* and those of the second are not. But perhaps more important is the observation that trypanosomes exposed to the second group are rapidly rendered non-infective although they remain active and motile for 24 hours, whereas arsenicals, acriflavine and diamidines do not reduce infectivity until the organisms are killed. A possible bearing of such factors on development of drug-resistance is underlined by the observations of Bauer (1962) who correlates the rapidity of action of berenil with the difficulty of producing berenil-resistant strains; this is substantiated by experience in the field. Studies on development of resistance and on the pattern of cross-resistance to drugs is gradually leading to a classification which may ultimately be related to sites if action if not to detailed modes of action.

What conclusions can we draw from this complex pattern of chemical structures and biological properties? There is only one, and it is that far too little attention has been paid to *inactive* compounds which are seemingly close chemical relatives of the active ones. Are some of these rapidly taken up by organisms *in vitro?* Do they inhibit the synthesis of nucleic acids?

If they do then it would show that we are not yet probing at the sites or mechanisms of their action.

[Discussion of this paper was postponed until after the following paper by B. Weitz; see p. 191.]

REFERENCES

ALBERT, A., GOLDACRE, R. and HEYMANN, E., (1943). *J. chem. Soc.*, 651.

ASHLEY, J. N., BARBER, H. J., EWINS, A. J., NEWBERY, G. and SELF, A. D. H. (1942). *J. chem. Soc.*, 103.

ASHLEY, J. N., BERG, S. S. and MACDONALD, R. D. (1960). *J. chem. Soc.*, 4525.

ASHLEY, J. N., BERG, S. S. and LUCAS, J. M. S. (1960). *Nature, Lond.*, **185**, 461.

BARBER, H. J., SLACK, R. and WOOLMAN, A. M. (1943). *J. chem. Soc.*, 99.

BAUER, F. (1962). *Vet. Rec.*, **74**, 265.

BELL, P. H., BONE, F. J. and ROBLIN, R. O. (1944). *J. Amer. chem. Soc.*, **66**, 847.

BENAZET, F. (1961). *Biochem. Pharmacol.*, **8**, 45.

BERG, S. S. (1960). *Nature, Lond.*, **188**, 1106.

BERG, S. S. (1961a). *J. chem. Soc.*, 5097.

BERG, S. S. (1961b). *J. chem. Soc.*, 4041.

BERG, S. S. (1961c). *Nature, Lond.*, **189**, 4758.

BERG, S. S. (1962). *J. chem. Soc.* 677.

BERG, S. S., BROWN, K. N., HILL, J. and WRAGG, W. R. (1961). *Nature, Lond.*, **192**, 367.

BEVERIDGE, C. G. L., THWAITE, J. W. and SHEPHERD, G. (1960). *Vet. Rec.*, **72**, 383.

BEVERIDGE, E. (1953). *Ann. trop. Med. Parasit.*, **47**, 134.

BEVERIDGE, E. (1956). *Ann. trop. Med. Parasit.*, **50**, 85.

BROWN, K. N., HILL, J. and HOLLAND, A. E. (1961). *Brit. J. Pharmacol.*, **17**, 396.

CARMICHAEL, J. (1942a). *J. comp. Path.*, **54**, 183.

CARMICHAEL, J. (1942b). *E. Afr. med. J.*, **19**, 96.

CARMICHAEL, J. (1942c). *Vet. Rec.*, **54**, 158.

CURD, F. H. S. and DAVEY, D. G. (1950). *Brit. J. Pharmacol.*, **5**, 25.

ENIGK, K., and REUSSE, U. (1955). *Z. Tropenmed. u. Parasit.*, **6**, 141.

FAIRCLOUGH, R. (1958). *Proc. VII Int. Sci. Comm. Tryp. Res., Brussels*, 51.

FULTON, J. D. and MATHEW, K. K. (1959). *Brit. J. Pharmacol.*, **14**, 137.

FUSSGÄNGER, R. (1955). *Vet. Med. Nachr. H.*, **3**, 146.

FUSSGÄNGER, R. and BAUER, F. (1958). *Med. u. Chem.*, **6**, 504.

FUSSGÄNGER, R. and BAUER, F. (1960). *Vet. Rec.*, **72**, 1118.

GOODWIN, L. G., GOSS, M. D., LOCK, J. A. and WALLS, L. P. (1950). *Brit. J. Pharmacol.*, **5**, 287.

HAMMICK, D. L. and MASON, S. F. (1950). *J. chem. Soc.*, 345, 348.

HAWKING, F. (1960). *Brit. J. Pharmacol.*, **15**, 567.

HOGBEN, C. A. M., TOCCO, D. J., BRODIE, B. B. and SCHANKER, L. S. (1959). *J. Pharmacol.*, **125**, 275.

JENSCH, H. (1937). *Angew. Chem.*, **50**, 891.

JENSCH, H. (1955). *Arzneim. Forsch.*, **5**, 634.

JONES, H. R. and BENTLEY, R. B. (1961). *Proc. chem. Soc.*, 348.

LAUNOY, L., GUILLOT, M. and JONCHÈRE, H. (1960). *Ann. Pharm. franc.*, **18**, 273, 424.

LOURIE, E. M. and YORKE, W. (1939). *Ann. trop. Med. Parasit.*, **33**, 305.

LUCAS, J. M. S. (1960). *Res. vet. Sci.*, **1**, 218.

KEMRON, A., PIPANO, E., HADANI, A. and NEUMANN, M. (1960). *Refuah vet.*, **17**, 226.

KIKUTH, W. (1935). *Zbl. Bakt.*, **135**, 135.

MACOWAN, K. D. S. (1959). *Annual Report, Veterinary Department, Kenya*, 43.

MORGAN, G. and WALLS, L. P. (1938). *J. chem. Soc.*, 389.

MORLEY, J. S. and SIMPSON, J. C. E. (1952). *J. chem. Soc.*, 2617.

NUTTALL, G. H. F. and HADWEN, S. (1909). *Parasitology*, **156**, 229, 236.

PIERSE, R. R. (1943). *Vet. Rec.*, **55**, 387.

RANDALL, J. B. and LAWS, S. G. (1947). *Ann. trop. Med. Parasit.*, **41**, 39.

REID, J. C. and WEAVER, J. C. (1951). *Cancer Res.*, **11**, 188.

RODHAIN, J. (1951). *Rev. belge. Path.*, **21**, 129.

RYLEY, J. F. (1957). *Ann. trop. Med. Parasit.*, **51**, 38.

SCHÖNHÖFER, F. and HENECKA, H. (1939–1946). *Fiat Review of German Science "Chemotherapy"*, **43**, 57.

SCOTT, W. N. (1958). *Rep. E. Afr. Tryp. Res. Org.*, 82.

SHONE, D. K., WELLS, G. E. and WALLER, F. J. A. (1961). *Vet. Rec.*, **73**, 736.

SHORT, W. F. and WATKINS, T. I. (1957). *Brit. Patent. Spec.*, 767, 588.

SMITH, I. M. and BROWN, K. N. (1960). *J. comp. Path.*, **70**, 161.

STEPHEN, L. E. (1960). *Vet. Rec.*, **72**, 80.

TAYLOR, A. E. R. (1960). *Brit. J. Pharmacol.*, **15**, 230, 242.

VAN DEN BERGHE, L., VINCKE, I., CHARDOME, M. and VAN DEN BULCKE, M. A. (1950). *Ann. Soc. belge. Med. trop.*, **30**, 83.

VAN DER WALT, K. (1960). *J. Afr. vet. Med. Assoc.*, **31**, 261.

WALLS, L. P. (1945). *J. chem. Soc.*, 294.

WATKINS, T. I. and WOOLFE, G. (1956). *Nature, Lond.*, **178**, 368.

WHITESIDE, E. F. (1960). *Proc. VIII Int. Sci. Comm. Tryp. Res. Jos.*, 141.

WILLETT, K. C. (1959). *Rep. W. Afr. Inst. Tryp. Res.*, 33.

WRAGG, W. R., WASHBOURN, K., BROWN, K. N. and HILL, J. (1958). *Nature, Lond.*, **182**, 1005.

IMMUNITY IN TRYPANOSOMIASIS

B. WEITZ

The Lister Institute of Preventive Medicine, Elstree

DISCUSSION of the immune processes in trypanosomiasis may seem perhaps somewhat remote from the subject of this Symposium. It is not only because the use of chemotherapeutic methods in the field is so vital to the control of trypanosomiasis that experimental trypanosome infections provide a suitable system for studying the relationship between the host, the organism and drugs, but also because our knowledge about the behaviour of trypanosomes is, in some respects at least, more complete than that about other pathogenic protozoa.

It is only comparatively recently that immunological techniques have developed sufficiently to allow the accurate study of some of the problems concerned with trypanosomes. In the past, investigations were largely limited to observations in the field and in attempts to demonstrate antibody in man or animals infected with trypanosomes as means of diagnosis. Such tests were not always based on a clear understanding of the principles involved and the assumption was made that the immunological behaviour of protozoa was similar to the behaviour patterns of bacteria. Although this assumption may be justified in some respects, there are peculiarities in the immunological behaviour of trypanosomes which may have misled earlier workers in some of their conclusions. In the last decade much progress has been made towards a clearer understanding of the immunological patterns affecting the parasite as well as the host, although, of course, there remains a multitude of still unsolved problems.

The host

One of the chief problems related to trypanosome infection in the field concerns the relative susceptibility of animals to infection in nature. The natural resistance of some species of animals to these organisms is well established and indeed the distinction between the closely allied species of the *brucei* group of trypanosomes depends on the ability of these trypanosomes to infect man or animals. Some species appear to be naturally and completely resistant to infection with certain trypanosomes. The demonstration by Terry (1957) of specific antibodies to *Trypanosoma vivax* in the globulins of cotton rats which are naturally resistant to infection with the organisms, may be a step towards the understanding of this phenomenon. Ashcroft, Burtt and Fairbairn (1959) recently reviewed the susceptibility of a number of wild species of mammals to infection with some trypanosomes and demonstrated a gradation in the resistance of these hosts, which they related to the frequency with which such hosts are normally bitten by tsetse flies, suggesting that the resistance might be acquired by the species which are constantly bitten. There are, however, many inconsistencies in this correlation which perhaps make it more acceptable to regard such varying susceptibilities as grades of "natural resistance". Differences in the susceptibilities of even different breeds of the same species have been known for some time. The Muturu and N'dama cattle are naturally more resistant to trypanosomes than the native Zebu cattle. Desowitz (1959) tested the response of one of the so-called resistant breeds, the N'dama cattle, to trypanosomal challenge and compared the antibody response with that obtained in Zebu "susceptible" cattle. He found that N'dama cattle which were born and bred *outside* the tsetse fly belt were at first equally susceptible, although the secondary antibody response to the trypanosome infection was much more efficient than in Zebu cattle. This showed that, although these breeds of cattle may have a genetic ability to produce antibody more efficiently than Zebu cattle, they were equally susceptible to a primary infection when they had never experienced the trypanosomal antigen. It is necessary, therefore, to be cautious when speaking of natural resistance as this appears to be the result of a combination of factors, some possibly genetic and others environmental and acquired.

The parasite

It has perhaps been more usual to study the reaction of the host to the parasite than to study the reaction of the infecting organisms to the vertebrate host. Trypanosomes are particularly versatile organisms and are able to survive by their adaptibility to environmental changes in the host. It has long been recognized that relapses of infection occur and the behaviour of these so-called relapsed strains has been of particular interest to immunologists. A great deal of work was done during the 1930's to investigate these relapsed strains, but the limitation of the serological methods used at that time prevented the full development of this work. As more precise techniques became available, for example the standardized agglutination procedure evolved by Cunningham and Vickerman (1961), the methods for the deep freezing of strains established by Polge and Soltys (1957) and the use of gel diffusion, it was possible to obtain more accurate information about relapsed strains. Quite recently, Gray (1962) from the West African Institute for Trypanosomiasis Research, Nigeria, initiated some studies in our laboratories on the relationships of relapsed strains to the parent strain using the agglutination test. Although this work is still in progress, these are some facts which have emerged and which are of particular interest.

Rabbits were infected by a monomorphic strain of *T. brucei* and variants of the original infecting strain were isolated at regular intervals during the course of the infection. These variants were maintained by rapid passage in mice and then deep frozen. They were injected into a series of rabbits to study the antibody pattern produced by these variants in relation to the parent strain and to other variants. During the course of infection with the original strain, the serum of the rabbit showed a series of antibody peaks coinciding with the development of new variants. When the new variants were injected into new rabbits, a similar series of variant-specific antibodies occurred. There appears to be no end to the number of variants and the consequent antibodies which can be produced from a single strain of trypanosome. The rise in antibody coincided with the disappearance of the homologous variant, and the production of a new variant immediately followed the elimination of a given antigenic type. A predetermined antigenic type developed when the parent strain was injected into rabbits previously immunized passively with antibodies to the unwanted antigenic types. This leaves little doubt that the production of antigenically variable trypanosomes depends on the ability of an animal to produce antibody. It also appears that antibody is not formed in anticipation of a forthcoming variant because there is no evidence that a rabbit produces antibody to a variant which develops subsequently. Soltys (1957) has reported that after continuous slow passage through rabbits a strain becomes "resistant to antibody". In my view, apart from the fact that resistance was not really demonstrated, it would seem in the light of Gray's findings that the phenomenon described by Soltys was more likely to have been due to the absence of antibody to the antigens of the particular "resistant" variant. This would depend on the time at which the variant was isolated in relation to the formation of antibody. In the terminal stages of the disease there is a decrease in antibody production so that eventually the final variant is uninhibited by specific antibody. Such a variant is antigenically different from any of the previous variants and from the parent strain so that it would fail to react with any of the antisera concerned.

Gray was able to obtain as wide a range of antigenic variants from a clone, indicating that these variants do not result from a selection of antigenic types present in a heterogeneous strain but that trypanosomes have an enormous potentiality for antigenic mutation.

In the light of these studies the antigenic relationships between strains or species of trypanosomes must be reconsidered. Cunningham and Vickerman (1962) obtained a pattern of the antigens of various strains of *T. brucei* and *T. rhodesiense* and they were able to classify the strains studied into various antigenic groups by cross-agglutination tests using the serum of rabbits four weeks after infection. These authors do not claim to have exhausted the antigenic analysis of each strain. Certainly the apparent relationships of one strain or species to another alter, depending on the time at which antibody is collected from infected animals and on the antigenic pattern of the strain at the time of isolation. The extent to which such inter-strain or species relationships may alter in the course of infection was studied in our laboratories by extending these studies with these same strains. In our experiments rabbits infected with the various species and strains were bled at weekly intervals until they died of the disease, usually at 4 or 5 weeks after infection. The serological relationships between the selected species and strains of trypanosomes were established by testing all sera for their agglutinin content with each of the strains, which were kept frozen at $-70°$ to avoid any alteration in the strain during the experiment. Usually, but not always, antibody to the homologous strain appeared first. The levels of the first antibody provoked were at their peak within a week or two of infection, but had noticeably decreased by the fourth week (the time when Cunningham and Vickerman examined these antibodies). By the third and fourth weeks of infection new heterologous antibodies appeared, indicating the development of new antigenic forms of trypanosomes. At any time during infection the antibody pattern varied in relation to the parent strain and in relation to heterologous species or strains with the effect that, although the antigenic pattern was preserved in the strains under test (by keeping them at $-70°$), it appeared to vary from time to time. These differences were not consistent in all the rabbits infected with the same parent strain, thus revealing further differences in the apparent antigenic relationship.

The pattern of antibody produced in pairs of rabbits infected with known *T. rhodesiense* strains was compared with the pattern in rabbits infected with known *T. brucei* strains (Fig. 1); the rabbits infected with *T. rhodesiense* had high antibody levels to other *T. rhodesiense* strains as well as to the homologous strains, while the rabbits infected with *T. brucei* produced no antibody to these *T. rhodesiense* strains, or only small amounts which appeared late in the infection. However, an alleged *T. brucei* strain (strain 86 which was derived from cattle) elicited broadly the same pattern of antibody as was obtained in rabbits infected with known *T. rhodesiense* strains, thus matching the antigenic pattern characteristic of *T. rhodesiense*. The *T. brucei* strain concerned, although isolated from a cow, was obtained from an area of endemic human *T. rhodesiense* infection, but to my knowledge was never tested for infectivity in man. With such few strains of these two species of trypanosomes, it would be unwise to draw any conclusions except that perhaps there may be some reason to doubt the identity of this strain, and that it may be possible to observe certain patterns of antigenic development characterizing these two species of the *brucei* group. Similarly there are seldom, if ever, cross-reactions between the *brucei* group and the *vivax* or *congolense* groups, but again caution must be exercised in view of the few strains of each species tested.

It is of some importance to establish the nature of these antigenic changes. Although the agglutination test is probably the most sensitive means of demonstrating them it is largely a manifestation of a complex of antigen–antibody reactions. We have shown that exoantigens (soluble antigens liberated in the serum of the infected animal) are at least partly concerned with the specific agglutination of trypanosomes (Weitz, 1960), and it is therefore logical to expect some changes in the exoantigens in the course of antigenic variation of the organism. Both protective and precipitating antibodies

7

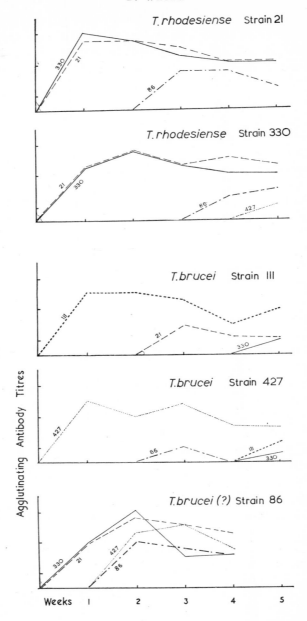

to exoantigens are largely species specific (Weitz, 1962). The *T. brucei* strain 86 referred to above promoted precipitins to the exoantigens of all the *T. rhodesiense* strains and not to *T. brucei* exoantigens (Table I). Apart from confirming the results of agglutination

Table 1

PRECIPITIN REACTIONS

Exoantigen of		Antibody from rabbits infected with				
		T. rhodesiense		*T. (?) brucei*	*T. brucei*	
	Strain	330	21	86	427	111
T. rhodesiense	330	+++	+++	+++	−	−
	21	+++	+++	+++	−	−
T. (?) brucei	86	+++	+++	+++	−	−
T. brucei	427	−	−	−	+++	−
	111	−	−	−	−	++

tests in this respect, these observations indicate that perhaps cross-protection may well be limited to strains having similar exoantigens, because so far as is known, cross-protection tests correlate with precipitin cross-reactions of exoantigens (Weitz, 1962).

FIG. 1. Agglutinins in the sera of rabbits infected with *T. rhodesiense* strains 21 and 23 and with *T. brucei* strains, 111, 427 and 86. The agglutinins were titrated weekly against all the antigens. The pattern of development of antibodies infected with the alleged *T. brucei* strain 86 resembled the pattern in rabbits infected with the *T. rhodesiense* strains.

When animals are actively immunized by exoantigen of, for example, *T. vivax* and *T. brucei* they are protected against the homologous species only. The protection afforded by the exoantigens of the suspect *T. brucei* 86 is being investigated in relation to other strains and species.

Morphological changes (involving the appearance and numbers of 'volutin granules') during the course of infection with *T. lewisi* were described by Ormerod (1958) and related by him to production of antibody in the host. They provide another example of the influence of antibodies on the characters of trypanosomes. It would be most interesting to know whether similar morphological changes occurred during the course of infection with *T. rhodesiense* and *T. brucei* as exemplified in our experiments. Indeed, Ormerod (1960) has reported differences in the granular pattern of *T. rhodesiense* strains and related them to the type of disease which they produced in man.

The drug

It is perhaps too early to relate drug-resistance and antigenic behaviour. Brown (1962) recently studied the antigenic relationships between a parent strain and its daughter strains which had been made resistant to chemotherapeutic treatment, and noted an absence of antigenic relationship between the drug-resistant daughter strains and the drug-susceptible parent strain. In the light of what has been said, this is not entirely surprising and should not necessarily be attributed to the drug-resistant properties of the daughter strains. It is, perhaps, more likely that any given variant produced during the course of infection as a result of antibody formation or other environmental stimulus, may have inherent drug-resistant characters. Such a variant would be the only one to survive in the presence of drugs.

The acquisition of drug-resistance by a strain could be merely the result of the selection of a suitable antigenic variant rather than an acquired change directly attributable to drug treatment. In this event it would be unlikely that such strains would acquire antigenic patterns characteristic of drug-resistance. This possibility is being investigated by testing a number of random variants for their ability to become drug-resistant. Soltys (1959) noted that the so-called "antibody-fast strain" (which was merely a strain which had undergone a number of variations) became more easily drug-resistant than the parent strain. Although he associated this with the alleged "antibody-fastness" of the strain, it is clearly possible that other variants might possess similar properties and that this is merely *a survival* of a drug-resistant variant. The development of drug-resistant forms in animals under treatment assumes the presence of living organisms hidden somewhere in the body, outside the influence of drug or of antibody. Overt blood stream infection may only occur when a mutant develops which is resistant to the concentration of drug in the blood, and which has an antigenic specificity not covered by the humoral antibodies of the animal. The chances of such variants occurring are, of course, considerably increased if constant natural reinfection supplies a greater variety of possible mutants and this might explain the rapid appearance of drug-resistant trypanosomes in areas of high challenge reported by Mr. Whiteside.

Artificial immunity

The production of artificial immunity to trypanosomal infection in animals is a very attractive prospect, although an extremely remote one at present. Examples in the field have been quoted by Mr. Whiteside showing the specificity and the very transient nature of the immunity developed in cattle after recovery from infections. Although it is possible to protect laboratory animals by active immunization with trypanosomal antigens, for example with exoantigens (Weitz, 1960), the duration of the immunity has yet to be established. The specificity of the protection (Weitz, 1962) indicates little hope for an overall field protection, particularly against the large number of antigenic variants which would be encountered. Perhaps our wildest hopes in this direction would be to provide sufficient protection to young animals actively immunized against infection, while constant reinfection from natural sources would reinforce this initial artificial immunity. Much remains to be done before contemplating even such remote hopes and perhaps it may be somewhat presumptuous to expect to succeed where nature has so consistently failed.

Acknowledgement

I am grateful to Mr. A. R. Gray for allowing me to refer to the results of some of his recent unpublished experiments.

REFERENCES

ASHCROFT, M. T., BURTT, E. and FAIRBAIRN, H. (1959). *Ann. trop. Med. Parasit.*, **53,** 147.

BROWN, K. N. (1962). *In* Garnham, P. C. C., Pierce, A. E. and Roitt, I. M., *Eds.* Immunity to Protozoa: Symp. Brit. Soc. Immunol., Oxford: Blackwell Scientific Publications, in press.

CUNNINGHAM, M. P. and VICKERMAN, K. (1962). *Trans. R. Soc. trop. Med. Hyg.*, **56,** 12.

CUNNINGHAM, M. P. and VICKERMAN, K. (1962). *Trans. R. Soc. trop. Med. Hyg.*, **56,** 48.

DESOWITZ, R. S. (1959). *Ann. trop. Med. Parasit.*, **53,** 293.

GRAY, A. R. (1962). *Ann. trop. Med. Parasit.*, **56,** 4.

ORMEROD, W. E. (1958). *J. gen. Microbiol.*, **19,** 271.

ORMEROD, W. E. (1960). *Trans. R. Soc. trop. Med. Hyg.*, **55,** 313.

POLGE, C. and SOLTYS, M. A. (1957). *Trans. R. Soc. trop. Med. Hyg.*, **51,** 519.

SOLTYS, M. A. (1957). *Parasitology*, **47,** 375.

SOLTYS, M. A. (1959). *Parasitology*, **49,** 144.

TERRY, R. J. (1957). *Exp. Parasit.*, **6,** 404.

WEITZ, B. (1960). *J. gen. Microbiol.*, **23,** 589.

WEITZ, B. (1962). *In* Garnham, P. C. C., Pierce, A. E. and Roitt, I. M., *Eds.* Immunity to Protozoa: Symp. Brit. Soc. Immunol., Oxford: Blackwell Scientific Publications, in press.

DISCUSSION

E. F. Whiteside (*Veterinary Research Laboratory, Kenya*): Dr. Weitz said that immunity is a remote possibility. In Kenya we have fairly consistently managed to provoke resistance to infection in cattle lasting about six months by doing certain things, so there is some possibility of obtaining a useful degree of immunity.

I should like to ask a question concerning the antigenic variants which occur during the course of an infection. Suppose you take out the third variant, is anything known as to whether when it passes through tsetse flies it emerges from them as the same antigenic variant or does it go back to the original?

Weitz: It is quite possible that each time the trypanosomes divide, whether they divide in the fly or in the animal, different mutants may appear. The survival of a strain obviously depends on certain characters. Certain antigens seem to survive better than others, for example the exoantigens seem to survive better than the bound antigens. This seems to indicate that some antigens are responsible for species characteristics or even strain characteristics, whereas others are possibly more responsible for the variants which appear during the course of infection in chronic disease.

I do not quite agree with your first statement. I think that protection after infection is quite a different thing from artificial immunity induced by trypanosomal antigens in the forms of a vaccine, which is what I had in mind.

W. G. M. Jones (*Imperial Chemical Industries*): I should like to ask a question about prothidium and metamidium. One of the things which interests chemists about these two compounds is that they present rare examples of compounds which have been formed by chopping in two already-existent trypanocidal drugs, quinapyramine and berenil, and joining them on to the phenanthridine type of trypanocide. Can Dr. Barber tell us anything about the mode of action of these compounds? Has this effect been one just of increasing molecular weight, or do you in these compounds get two modes of action of trypanocides of different structure brought together in the one molecule? Is there any evidence from cross-resistance experiments which will tell us anything about this?

Barber: I think that the short answer is that I do not know. It is a matter of very considerable surprise that if you graft a component of one active molecule on to another you rarely get anything worth while. A thing which also puzzles us is that all our previous work with other trypanosomes showed that *meta*-substitution in the amidine series was dystherapeutic and that is why we first made the *para*-derivatives. It was, I suppose, just a matter of being tidy and trying to complete the series which made us go on and make the *meta*-compounds just to make sure. We found that in one particular class of antibabesial drugs, the *p-p'*-diamidine was inactive and the *m-m'*- and *m-p'*- were active. I am sure that the amidine group must have something to do with the prolonged action of isometamidium, though why we do not know, any more than why pentamidine gives protection against *T. gambiense* in man for such a long time.

B. Lacey: (*Westminster Hospital Medical School*): Are the *para* and *meta* diamidines metabolized in the same way? Can you detect them several months after injection in the same sites?

Barber: There is a depot effect. You can detect by fluorescence the presence of isometamidium for some considerable time. We are not in a position to say for certain that the fluorescence is that of the unmetabolized drug; it is possible that there might be fluorescent metabolites. With regard to metabolism, I would have thought that the diazoamino group might be split but we do not know. It is a little puzzling to me that berenil has no prophylactic action.

Lacey: If the diazoamino group were split you would lose the fluorescence, would you not?

Barber: No. The parent phenanthridines fluoresce at certain wavelengths. We are studying this but we have not got very far.

E. J. L. Soulsby (*School of Veterinary Medicine, Cambridge*): Is there any definite sequence of events in the mutation of trypanosomes? For example, do they go to type A and then to type B and then to type C in any given strain that Dr. Weitz chooses? Would he care to speculate on the mechanism of this? Is it a random or an induced mutation?

This brings to mind the story of *Paramecium*, concerning an induced cytoplasmic mutation into different serotypes under the influence of antibodies. Is there any possibility that the same mechanism operates in trypanosomes?

Weitz: The variants occur according to no special sequence at all. One strain seems to give, in different rabbits, different variants. Depending on when you isolate these variants they will again be different.

When you ask me to speculate, I would be quite happy to do so providing you regard it as speculation. I think what happens is that the trypanosome population of a given antigenic type is depressed as soon as the antibody rises, and then some other trypanosome variant comes up which again gets depressed, and so on, and this goes on all the time. It is extremely difficult to do the appropriate experiments because there are such small numbers of parasites circulating in the blood of the rabbit. I am sure, from the character of the variants isolated at different intervals, that they are related to antibody. In other words, as soon as the antibody rises, you find the previous variant is depressed. More than that I cannot say.

W. E. Ormerod (London School of Hygiene and Tropical Medicine): Almost all the drugs we have heard about this afternoon have been of veterinary interest. Could I make a plea for research on human trypanocides? This country has not produced one for at least fifteen years, possibly more. It is perfectly true that not a great number of cases of sleeping sickness occur, but drugs are of particular importance in the control of the disease, and I think that control ought not to be overlooked

B. A. Newton (Medical Research Council Unit for Chemical Microbiology, Cambridge): May I take up a point made by Dr. Barber? I think he expressed a desire that people studying the mode of action of drugs should study *inactive* compounds. One of the characteristics of antrycide which we have established is the differential effect on the incorporation of adenine and glycine into nucleic acid. We have now tested some eighteen derivatives of antrycide and none of them shows the effect of the parent compound. When the pyrimidine portion of antrycide is attached to the phenanthridine nucleus to make a compound such as prothidium, in transferring this portion you transfer selective activity against adenine incorporation, and the prothidium molecule now has selective activity which is not shown by ethidium.

Lacey: Dr. Weitz made two statements which seemed to me to conflict. He said that the trypanosomes can go on indefinitely producing different antigenic types and also that he could predict which type would emerge following injection of the rabbit with trypanosome.

Weitz: If you immunize an animal passively with a set of given types of antibodies, and then you inject the parent strain which has various possible lines of antigenic variation, the line of antigenic variation which will develop is the one for the missing antibody. If you take, for the sake of simplicity, four different variant antibodies, numbers one, two, three and four, and you inject the rabbit passively with numbers two, three and four, it will be number one variant which will appear. Of course, at the same time, apart from numbers two, three and four there might be five to seventy-six appearing at the same time, but you would not know that because you would not be looking for them.

K. N. Brown (National Institute for Medical Research): I should like to ask Dr. Weitz how he defines his strains. When he is talking about a cross-reaction between two *T. rhodesiense* strains with his precipitin test, could he not be testing two samples of the same thing?

Weitz: I am rather trusting the people who isolated them. Indeed, you may well be quite correct in assuming that. But these strains are isolated from different patients with *T. rhodesiense* infections and from different cattle in the case of the *brucei* strains and have been maintained either frozen or by quick passage and then sent to me. What happens in the post might well be what you suggest but I do not think so because they have got other characteristics.

P. C. Williams (Imperial Cancer Research Fund): I am still puzzled by the same thing which is puzzling Professor Lacey. I gather that if you put in a parent strain the variants come up in temporal succession. Then surely if you are going to say that seventy-six are produced, you are presuming that they are produced at the same time, but why does *one* come up at *that* time?

Weitz: Simply because it is defined as such. To be able to show a variant of a different antigenic character you must be able to extract the antigen and to test the serum. You take a serum, you extract the antigen from the rabbit at that moment. That is your predetermined variant. Then afterwards when the rabbit has continued to produce antibody you can examine the antibody in the blood of the rabbit to that particular variant. That means if you were to examine another variant the next day you would find another curve going up, and unless you examined it you would not find it. You have to have the particular variant isolated at the particular time to define it and to spot it.

Brown: On the question of the order in which the variants appear, in my experiments—and in a number of others of previous workers (Lourie and O'Connor, 1937)—there is a tendency for one type of variant to appear more commonly than another. In all of five rabbits I have examined, one particular variant has appeared at the first relapse, and after that there tends to be a much more random appearance of different types.

I should also like to correct one point which Dr. Weitz made about my work. At no time have I tried to correlate this relapse variation question with drug-resistance although that does not, in fact, alter his argument.

REFERENCE

LOURIE, E. M. and O'CONNOR, R. J. (1937). *Ann. trop. Med. Parasit.*, **31**, 319.

Session 3: Bacterial Infections

CHAIRMAN: J. S. K. Boyd

THE UTILISATION OF BIOCHEMICAL DIFFER-ENCES BETWEEN HOST AND PARASITE AS A BASIS FOR CHEMOTHERAPY

G. H. HITCHINGS

The Wellcome Research Laboratories, Tuckahoe, New York

THE basis of chemotherapy is the selective toxicity of the chemotherapeutic agent; in the trial of host, parasite and drug, the drug must produce in some way a differential effect which is of benefit to the host.* Traditionally the search for chemotherapeutic agents has had a major component of empiricism, and many programmes continue to rely almost entirely on trial and error as the basis for selection of new drugs. An alternative approach has been described (Hitchings *et al.*, 1950*a*, 1950*b*; Hitchings, 1955*a*, 1955*b*, 1960, 1961) in which the primary emphasis has been placed on the synthesis of antimetabolites which cause specific biochemical lesions. Ideally, such agents are chemotherapeutically active because of qualitative differences in the biochemical pathways of host

---

* This rather elemental fact appears to have been overlooked in much recent work in cancer chemotherapy where a great deal of ingenious and meticulous experimentation has been expended in defining the "mechanism of action" of "antitumour agents" (better unnamed) which have essentially the same toxic effects on tumour and host. The term "mechanism of action" in the sense of a *locus* of action is a misnomer in the framework of chemotherapy. The mechanism of action of a chemotherapeutic agent is the means whereby the agent exerts an effect which is *selectively* damaging to the parasite.

and parasite, but differential effects also are attainable when sub-stantial quantitative differences exist in the binding of the drug to the enzyme or other cell receptor. Moreover, agents representing the latter sort of mechanism of action may be combined with those representing the former with resultant increases in effectiveness and selectivity. The present paper deals primarily with small molecule inhibitors of dihydrofolic acid reductase and explores the bases for the selectivity which they exert. This will take the form first of a review of the ways in which their inhibitory action acquires greater specificity both in the presence of metabolites which selec-tively protect the host and upon the addition of other antimetabo-lites which selectively damage the parasite. Finally, some new studies will be presented which explore in greater depth the relation-ship between the geometry and distribution of charge of the anti-metabolite to its binding to the enzyme surfaces. From this work it appears probable that details of fine structure in dihydrofolic reductase vary from species to species and that a given inhibitor may exhibit considerable selectivity as a result of looser or tighter binding to the corresponding enzyme of host or parasite, respec-tively.

One of the early findings of the present programme was the discovery that essentially all derivatives of the 2,4-diaminopyri-midine system possess activity as antagonists of folic acid (Hitchings et al., 1948, 1952b). The synthesis and testing of a variety of modi-fications of this molecule, including not only pyrimidines and condensed pyrimidine systems but also unsymmetrical and sym-metrical triazines (Hitchings et al., 1952c) have led to a large family of antifolic acids, a number of which already have found appli-cations in chemotherapy (Hitchings, 1960; Hitchings and Bushby, 1961).[*]

At this point a more precise definition of the term "antifolic acid" is in order. The vitamin, folic acid, appears to be present in

* For example diaveridine, 2,4-diamino-5-(3,4-dimethoxybenzyl)pyrimidine has a coccidiostatic action.

all living things in one form or another, although the chemical substance which goes by this name is possibly an artifact. Recent studies suggest strongly that the primary product of biosynthesis is, in fact, dihydrofolic acid (Brown, Weisman and Molnar, 1961). Since the coenzymic forms of the vitamins are all derivatives of tetrahydrofolic acid, further reduction of this primary product is necessary to its function. Furthermore, it is clear that at least one of the one-carbon transfer reactions in which the tetrahydrofolic acid derivatives participate results in oxidation of the pteridine nucleus from the tetrahydro to the dihydro state (Wahba and Friedkin, 1961). Enzymes capable of performing this reduction are widely distributed, as indeed are enzymes capable of catalysing the reduction of the fully aromatic structure (Huennekens and Osborn, 1959).* Under ordinary circumstances the reduced and aromatic forms are equally capable of satisfying a nutritional requirement for the vitamin.† However, in the presence of an antifolic acid, the reduced form of the vitamin may show a striking superiority. Thus in the growth of *Streptococcus faecalis*, folic acid and leucovorin (N-5-formyltetrahydrofolic acid) are essentially equivalent. However, in the presence of a small concentration of a folic acid antagonist, such as aminopterin or pyrimethamine, growth with folic acid is completely blocked while that with leucovorin is unaffected, and it is only when the concentration of the inhibitor has been greatly increased (perhaps by several hundred-fold) that inhibition is observed in the presence of leucovorin (Hitchings,

---

* Some difference of opinion prevails regarding the existence of separate dihydrofolic and folic acid reductases. The evidence suggests that several such enzymes can in fact reduce both the aromatic and dihydro forms of the nucleus (Zakrzewski and Nichol, 1960). However, the extracts which were found by Brown (1961) to synthesize dihydrofolic acid from aromatic pteridines were incapable of the reduction of folic acid, but were able to reduce dihydrofolic acid to tetrahydrofolic acid.

† *Pediococcus cerevisiae* is an apparent exception to this rule since it gives a growth response to derivatives of tetrahydrofolic acid at concentrations at least one thousandth that of the oxidized forms. However, this appears to be a transport problem rather than lack of ability to use the oxidized form internally (*cf.* Nichol, 1959).

1952, 1961; Hitchings *et al.*, 1952*a*; Hitchings, Elion and Singer, 1954). It was assumed from experiments of this type that the primary locus of action of an antifolic acid is the block in the reduction of the pteridine nucleus of the vitamin and much subsequent work at the enzymic level has served to document this conclusion (Werkheiser, 1961).

Aminopterin and methotrexate are well known for their effects in leukaemia, but they have little toxicity for bacteria or protozoa. A few of the small molecule antifolic acids can cause remissions of acute leukaemia (Murphy *et al.*, 1954) but they are much more notable for their effects on protozoa (Falco *et al.*, 1951*b*) and bacteria (Hitchings and Bushby, 1961). This rather striking difference is perhaps best analysed in the context of an analysis of the ways in which the small molecule antifolic acids exert their selective effects in the chemotherapy of infections with unicellular organisms.

The prime source of folic acid for a given organism may be synthesis *de novo* or the incorporation of preformed folic acid derivatives from exogenous sources (Fig. 1) and only exceptional organisms are able to utilize both means (Wood, Ferone and Hitchings, 1961).* Moreover, the incorporation of exogenous folic acid appears to be an active, energy-requiring process (Wood, Ferone and Hitchings, 1961). Assimilation of the close structural analogues of folic acid appears to require the same mechanism, and these antimetabolites thus are inhibitory only to those species which utilize preformed folic acid. † The small-molecule antifolic acids however, seem to penetrate cells by diffusion and their

* Synthesis *de novo* prevails throughout the plant kingdom and among protozoa. At some point in the scale of animal life, as yet unknown, the ability to utilize exogenous folic acid appears to have been acquired. Loss of the ability to synthesize the vitamin may have occurred simultaneously or later.

† A few exceptional micro-organisms appear to assimilate aminopterin by a mechanism which ordinarily deals with the uptake of thiamine (Wood, Ferone and Hitchings, 1961; Loebeck, 1960; Pine, 1960).

This interpretation is supported by direct measurements of uptake using radioactively-labelled materials, and by the inhibitory effects which the structural analogues exert on the folic acid reductases of cell-free extracts of species which are relatively indifferent to the analogues in systems involving intact cells.

entrance into a cell is unrelated to the ability of the cell to assimilate folic acid. They thus are able to inhibit the growth and mutliplication of a variety of unicellular organisms which are unrespon-
sive to the structural analogues.

The difference in toxicity which an inhibitor of dihydrofolic
acid reductase exhibits for different species depends in part on the

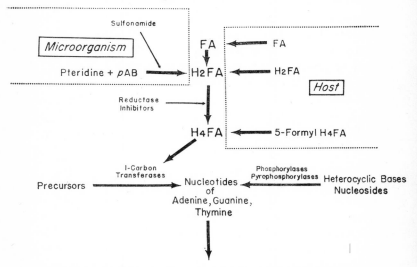

FIG. I. Diagrammatic representation of biochemical pathways leading to purine-
and pyrimidine-containing end-products. The portions which are enclosed in
dashed lines represent pathways peculiar to the type of organism indicated; the
remainder of the pathways are believed to exist, with minor variations, in most
organisms. The *loci* of action of the inhibitors are indicated by lines crossing the
appropriate reaction arrows.

abilities of the species in question to utilize metabolites beyond the
block anabolically. Thus, as has been mentioned above, the higher
species can use preformed folic acid and its various reduction products, whereas micro-organisms cannot. Derivatives of tetrahydrofolic acid are beyond the metabolic block imposed by the
reductase inhibitors, and thus act as antidotes through a by-pass

mechanism (Fig. 1). Since these substances can be assimilated by the host and not, in general, by the parasite, they may have a desiderative effect on the differences which the compound exhibits in its toxicities for the two species. This conclusion has been documented for infections with *Toxoplasma gondii* (Frenkel and Hitchings, 1957) and for malarial infections in man (Hurly, 1959). It could be shown that the administration of leucovorin together with a regimen of pyrimethamine and sulphadiazine did not suppress the therapeutic effectiveness of the drugs but did overcome toxic side effects (Frenkel and Hitchings, 1957).

Still another way in which the chemotherapeutic index of a folic acid reductase inhibitor may be enhanced is through the simultaneous use of an inhibitor which acts at another *locus* in the same biosynthetic sequence. Such combinations of sequential blocking agents frequently give rise to striking potentiating effects. Thus combinations of sulphonamides (which interfere with the biosynthesis of folic acid) with folic acid reductase inhibitors (which interfere with the further anabolism of folic acid to its coenzymically active forms) are uniformly potentiating when used chemotherapeutically against organisms which produce folic acid by biosynthesis *de novo* (Elion, Singer and Hitchings, 1960; Eyles and Coleman, 1953; Greenberg and Richeson, 1950; Hitchings, 1955*a*, 1955*b*; Kendall, 1956; Rollo, 1955) (Fig. 2).

End-product analogues may also produce potentiating effects in combination with 2,4-diaminopyrimidines (Elion, Singer and Hitchings, 1954). Furthermore, using combinations of diaminopyrimidines with sulphonamides as a base line, it was possible to show further potentiating effects through the addition of end-product analogues in experiments with *Proteus vulgaris in vitro* (Elion, Singer and Hitchings, 1960). However, these combinations of three biochemically-related antimetabolites have so far failed to exhibit potentiating effects *in vivo* (unpublished experiments with T. Herrmann), which suggests that the end-product analogues do not in themselves produce a differential effect.

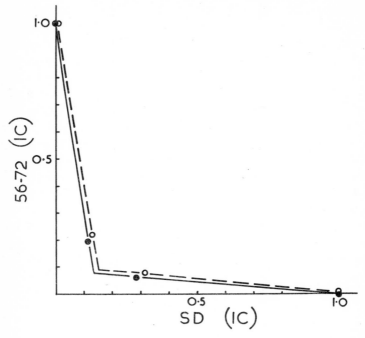

FIG. 2. Graphical representation of potentiation between trimethoprim (B.W. 56–72) and sulphadiazine (S.D.) in the treatment of infections with *Proteus vulgaris* in mice. Groups of 10 mice were inoculated intraperitoneally with a 5-hour culture of *P. vulgaris*, and observed for 160 hours. Each point on the graph represents the dose of drug or drugs required to give 50 per cent protection in terms of percent. survival (solid line) or survival time (dashed line). The individual inhibitory concentrations (I.C.) as determined from dose response curves were, 0·14 mg. of sulphadiazine and 4 mg. of trimethoprim/mouse, respectively. The other points are plotted as fractions of these unitary values. At the apices of the triangular figures the combinations represent 0·12 I.C. of sulphadiazine and 0·08 I.C. of trimethoprim (percent. survival) and 0·145 I.C. of sulphadiazine and 0·09 I.C. of trimethoprim (survival time).

It has been shown above that the two types of antifolic acid respond differently to specific assimilative processes. They differ also in the relative binding of folic acid reductases when the dissociation of the enzyme-inhibitor complex from one species is compared with that from another. The binding of mammalian folic acid reductase by aminopterin is essentially stoichiometric, and pseudo-irreversible (Werkheiser, 1961). Evidence is scanty concerning its binding to the similar enzymes of other types of organism but it may be inferred from studies with cell-free extracts (Wood, Ferone and Hitchings, 1961) that the enzyme-inhibitor complexes have very low dissociation constants for enzymes from diverse sources. The small-molecule antifolic acids, however, appear to exhibit considerable selectivity with respect to the binding of enzymes from different sources. The data which bear directly on this point are limited, but the conclusion is supported by a variety of indirect evidence.

It is perhaps not at once apparent that these substances should be folic acid antagonists at all, and, indeed, efforts have been made to assign them other roles in metabolism (Modest, Foley and Farber, 1960). The structural analogy between pyrimethamine, for example, and folic acid is somewhat remote. However, an analogy between pyrimethamine and the portion of the folic acid molecule which is involved in the 5-membered rings of the cofactors is quite credible. In Fig. 3, for example, the pertinent parts of the molecule of anhydroleucovorin have been indicated by lines of double thickness, for comparison with the structure of pyrimethamine. It is seen that a close structural relationship exists between pyrimethamine and this portion of the anhydroleucovorin molecule. The phenyl group of pyrimethamine occupies an area very similar to that of the imidazolium ring of the coenzyme, and the two molecules have the pyrimidine ring and its 2-amino group in common. The exact role of the 4-amino group of the inhibitor is uncertain, but this group is present in all the stronger folic acid reductase inhibitors and appears to be involved in binding to the enzyme surface.[*] The concept that for maximal activity the diaminopyrimidine must intrude physically into the area normally occupied by

[*] There is the possibility suggested by this and the other structural considerations to be discussed later, that the primary *locus* of action of the diaminopyrimidine is

the 5-membered ring has proved to be extremely useful in the design of new drugs. It was found very early that weighty substituents such as phenyl, phenoxy and benzyl in the 5-position of the 2,4-diaminopyrimidine system greatly enhanced its antimetabolic activity, whereas similar substituents in the 6-position

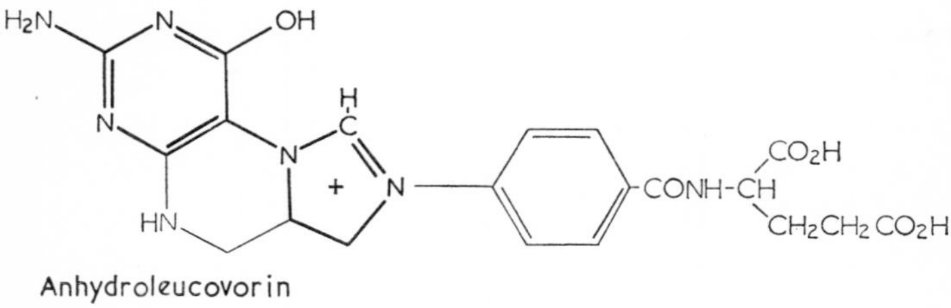

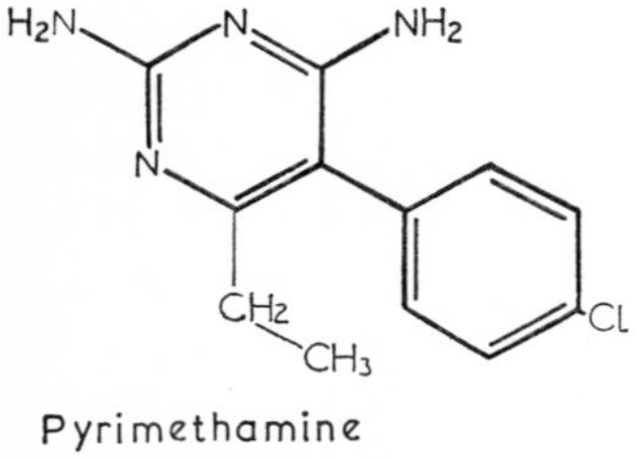

Anhydroleucovorin

Pyrimethamine

FIG. 3. Structural formulae of anhydroleucovorin and pyrimethamine. Parts of the formula of anhydroleucovorin have been darkened to emphasize the comparison.

were much less effective (Hitchings *et al.*, 1948) Further refinements became possible as the work progressed. Thus, for example, in the antibacterial quinazoline and pyrido (2,3-d)pyrimidine series it was predicted, and verified experimentally, that substances of types I and II in Fig. 4 would have significantly greater activity than those

interference with the function of the cyclic transferases, rather than with the reduction of the pteridine. However, the preponderance of the biological evidence favours action at the reductive step. Perhaps the best resolution of this dilemma at the moment is the suggestion that during reduction the dihydrofolic acid assumes the configuration which later is fixed by the introduction of the one-carbon fragment.

of types III and IV, i.e. substituents in the 5- and 6-positions of these systems greatly enhance the effectiveness, whereas substituents in the 7- and 8-positions add little or diminish the activities of the parent ring systems. This geometrical specificity may extend to very fine degrees of structural change and show itself in differences in the responses of closely related species. Thus among the pyridopyrimidines (II, Fig. 4) a substituent which enhances the

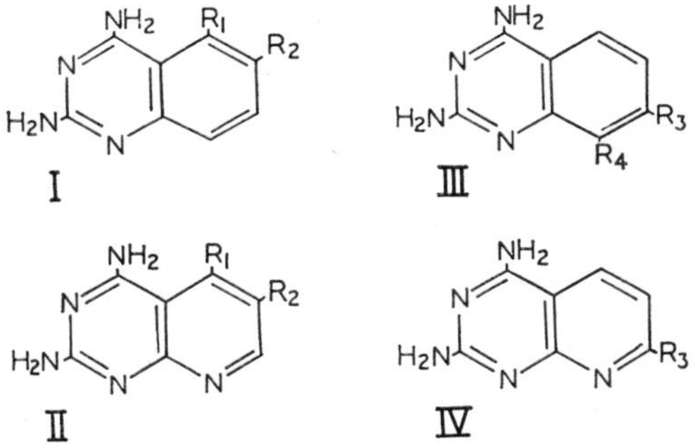

FIG. 4. Structural formulae of 2,4-diamino-quinazolines and pyrido(2,3-d)-pyrimidines.

activity against *P. vulgaris* may at the same time diminish that against *Staphyloccus aureus*. Compare, for example, the relative activities of the 5- and 6-substituted pyridopyrimidines of Table I. The introduction of a methyl group into the 5-position increases the activity of the 6-butyl derivative against *Proteus* by 2000-fold, but diminishes the activity against *Staphylococcus* 250-fold. These results suggest that there is either a geometrical or a charge requirement of considerable significance for both organisms in the region of the cell receptor surface occupied by the 5-substituent. That this region is restricted geometrically is suggested by experiments in progress with 5-alkyl groups of greater length. Such substituents appear to diminish the activity against both organisms. The difference between *Proteus* and *Staphylococcus* in their responses to a

Table I

EFFECTS OF STRUCTURAL MODIFICATIONS ON THE TOXICITIES OF
2,4-DIAMINOPYRIDO(2,3-d)PYRIMIDINES TOWARD TWO BACTERIAL SPECIES[*]

Substituent		Minimum Inhibitory Concentration $\mu g/ml.$	
R_1	R_2	P. vulgaris	S. aureus
H	C_6H_{13}	>1000	0·00025
H	C_4H_9	500	0·002
CH_3	C_4H_9	0·125	0·5

[*] Data supplied by Dr. S. R. M. Bushby.

5-methyl group might be attributable to a difference between the two in either a space or a charge requirement, and a decision between these alternatives awaits the synthesis of appropriate derivatives.

Up to this point the significance of charge in this region has been mentioned only in passing, but the nature and distribution of formal charges in the region of the 5-membered ring was recognized early as a factor of primary significance to activity. Thus, for example, among the 5-benzylpyrimidines it was found that an electron-attractive substituent in the p-position of the benzene ring and a pyrimidine-6-methyl group enhance antimalarial activity while the same substituents diminish antibacterial activity. Conversely, an electron-donating substituent in the benzene nucleus increases antibacterial activity and diminishes antimalarial activity (Falco, DuBrueil and Hitchings, 1951). This difference in response of plasmodia and bacteria to rather delicate changes in structure is exhibited by other species with respect to these and other compounds; in fact a spectrum of chemical structures can be arranged on the basis of the relative responses of various species to the agents.

Perhaps this is best illustrated by reference to the extremes (Table II) where pyrimethamine represents the ultimate in the "electron-attractive" type and trimethoprim the ultimate in the "electron-donor" type. It will be seen that *Lactobacillus casei* and *Eimeria tenella* respond to both types of compound. However, pyrimethamine is only feebly active against *Proteus*, and trimethoprim is essentially inactive against the plasmodia, while pyrimethamine is at least ten-fold more toxic than trimethoprim for the mouse.

The interpretation of these differences as a reflection primarily of details in the fine structures of the various dihydrofolic acid reductases will require ultimately determinations of the bindings of the compounds by the isolated enzymes. There are many technical

Table II

TOXICITIES OF 2,4-DIAMINOPYRIMIDINES FOR VARIOUS SPECIES

	Lactobacillus casei	Eimeria tenella	Plasmodium berghei	Proteus vulgaris	*Mouse*
Pyrimethamine*	+ + +	+ +	+ + +	−	+
Trimethoprim†	+ + +	+ +	−	+ + +	−

* 2,4-Diamino-5-*p*-chlorophenyl-6-ethylpyrimidine.
† 2,4-Diamino-5-(3,4,5-trimethoxybenzyl)pyrimidine.

difficulties. With bacteria in particular, a large part of the enzymic activity is lost on rupturing the cells and there is a consequent doubt whether the remaining activity is representative of the whole. This problem has been approached, as a first approximation, through a study of the conversion of folic acid to "citrovorum factor" by acetone-treated cells. Treatment with acetone increases the permeability of organisms such as *P. vulgaris* and *Escherichia coli* to folic acid to the point where this reaction can be studied at physiological concentrations (1 μg./ml.). Under these conditions it can be shown that the inhibitory effects of the various pyrimidines on this reaction are more or less parallel to their effects on growing cultures; for instance, trimethoprim is some five-fold more inhibitory than pyrimethamine on the conversion of folic acid to citrovorum factor by acetone powder preparations of *P. vulgaris* (unpublished experiments with S. Singer).

Some preliminary studies of the binding of various pyrimidines to mouse liver dihydrofolic acid reductase also are available (Table III). A comparison of these values with the toxicity data for the mouse shows a parallelism which is perhaps too close to be maintained when a larger series of agents has been tested, but it does suggest that the primary locus of toxic action may be inhibition of the reductase.

Table III

RELATIVE BINDING TO MOUSE LIVER DIHYDROFOLIC ACID
REDUCTASE AND TOXICITIES OF VARIOUS PYRIMIDINES

2,4-*Diaminopyrimidine*	*Dissociation of complex with reductase*	*L.D.$_{50}$ mouse* (*mg./kg.*)
5-(3,4,5-Trimethoxybenzyl)	8×10^{-6}	> 500
5-*p*-Chlorophenoxy-6-methyl	2×10^{-6}	> 500
5-*p*-Chlorophenyl-6-ethyl	4×10^{-9}	65
5-Methyl-6-*sec*-amylpyrido(2,3-d)	5×10^{-9}	57
Aminopterin	$< 3 \times 10^{-11}$[*]	4[†]

[*] Werkheiser (1961)   [†] Goldin *et al.* (1952)

The primary purposes of the programme with which the present paper has dealt is to take advantage of exploitable biochemical differences between host and parasite. It has been shown that these differences include biosynthetic pathways and assimilative mechanisms for both antimetabolites and metabolites. Through the use of by-pass mechanism to diminish host toxicity and through sequential biochemical blockade to potentiate the actions of the drugs, it has been possible to increase the advantage of the host in the host–drug–parasite triad. But the time-honoured process of synthesis and testing of structural modifications of active agents has not been discarded. Much can be accomplished through enlightened empiricism. There appear to be many subtle variations among species in the geometry and charge of the enzyme surfaces and cell receptors which lend themselves to exploitation by the chemotherapist.

Acknowledgement

I am grateful to Miss Gertrude Elion for her assistance in the preparation of this manuscript.

[Discussion of this paper was postponed until after the paper by H. Williams Smith; see p. 239.]

REFERENCES

BROWN, G. M., WEISMAN, R. A. and MOLNAR, D. A. (1961). *J. biol. chem.*, **236**, 2534.

ELION, G. B., SINGER, S. and HITCHINGS, G. H. (1954). *J. biol. Chem.*, **208**, 477.

ELION, G. B., SINGER, S., and HITCHINGS, G. H. (1960). *Antibiot. Chemother.*, **10**, 556.

EYLES, D. E. and COLEMAN, N. (1953). *Antiobiot. Chemother.*, **3**, 483.

FALCO, E. A., DuBREUIL, S. and HITCHINGS, G. H. (1951*a*). *J. Amer. chem. Soc.*, **73**, 3758.

FALCO, E. A. GOODWIN, L. G., HITCHINGS, G. H., ROLLO, I. M. and RUSSELL, P. B. (1951*b*). *Brit. J. Pharmacol.*, **6**, 185.

FRENKEL, J. K. and HITCHINGS, G. H. (1957). *Antibiot. Chemother.*, **7**, 630.

GOLDIN, A., GREENSPAN, E. M., VENDITTI, J. M. and SCHOENBACH, E. B. (1952). *J. natl. Cancer Inst.*, **12**, 987.

GREENBERG, J. and RICHESON, E. M. (1950). *J. Pharmacol. exp. Ther.*, **99**, 444.

HITCHINGS, G. H. (1952). *Trans. R. Soc. trop. Med. Hyg.*, **46**, 467.

HITCHINGS, G. H. (1955*a*). *In* Antimetabolites and Cancer, p. 231, *ed.* Rhoads, C. P., Washington: Amer. Ass. Adv. Sci.

HITCHINGS, G. H. (1955*b*). *Amer. J. clin. Nutrition*, **3**, 321.

HITCHINGS, G. H. (1960). *Clin. Pharmacol. Therap.*, **1**, 570.

HITCHINGS, G. H. (1961). *Trans. N.Y. Acad. Sci.*, **23**, 700.

HITCHINGS, G. H. and BUSHBY, S. R. M. (1961). *Proc. V Internat. Congr. Biochem.*, Moscow, p. 165.

HITCHINGS, G. H., ELION, G. B., FALCO, E. A., RUSSELL, P. B., SHERWOOD, M. B. and VANDERWERFF, H. (1950*a*). *J. biol. Chem.*, **183**, 1.

HITCHINGS, G. H., ELION, G. B., FALCO, E. A., RUSSELL, P. B. and VANDERWERFF, H. (1950*b*). *Ann. N.Y. Acad. Sci.*, **52**, 1318.

HITCHINGS, G. H., ELION, G. B. and SINGER, S. (1954). *Ciba Found. Symp. Chemistry and Biology of Pteridines*, p. 290. London: Churchill.

HITCHINGS, G. H., ELION, G. B., VANDERWERFF, H. and FALCO, E. A. (1948). *J. biol. Chem.*, **174**, 765.

HITCHINGS, G. H., FALCO, E. A., ELION, G. B., SINGER, S., WARING, G. B., HUTCHISON, D. J. and BURCHENAL, J. H. (1952a). *Arch. Biochem. Biophys.*, **40,** 479.

HITCHINGS, G. H., FALCO, E. A. VANDERWERFF, H., RUSSELL, P. B. and ELION, G. B. (1952b). *J. biol. Chem.*, **199,** 43.

HITCHINGS, G. H., MAGGIOLO, A., RUSSELL, P. B., VANDERWERFF, H. and ROLLO, I. M. (1952c). *J. Amer. chem. Soc.*, **74,** 3200.

HUENNEKENS, F. M. and OSBORN, M. J. (1959). *Adv. Enzymol.*, **21,** 369.

HURLY, M. G. D. (1959). *Trans. R. Soc. trop. Med. Hyg.*, **53,** 410.

KENDALL, S. B. (1956). *Proc. R. Soc. Med.* **49,** 874.

LOEBECK, M. E. (1960). *J. Bact.*, **79,** 384.

MODEST, E. J., FOLEY, G. E. and FARBER, S. (1960). *Acta unio internat. contra Cancrum*, **16,** 702.

MURPHY, M. L., ELLISON, R. R., KARNOFSKY, D. A. and BURCHENAL, J. H. (1954). *J. clin. Invest.*, **33,** 1388.

NICHOL, C. A. (1959). *Nature, Lond.*, **183,** 550.

PINE, M. J. (1960). *J. Bact.*, **79,** 835.

ROLLO, I. M. (1955). *Brit. J. Pharmacol.*, **10,** 208.

WAHBA, A. J. and FRIEDKIN, M. (1961). *J. biol. Chem.*, **236,** PC 11.

WERKHEISER, W. C. (1961). *J. biol. Chem.*, **236,** 888.

WOOD, R. C., FERONE, R. and HITCHINGS, G. H. (1961). *Biochem. Pharmacol.*, **6,** 113.

ZAKRZEWSKI, S. F. and NICHOL, C. A. (1960). *J. biol. Chem.*, **235,** 2984.

PENICILLINS, PENICILLINASE AND THE STAPHYLOCOCCUS

M. R. POLLOCK

National Institute for Medical Research,
Mill Hill, London

THE subject of penicillin and its action is large enough, even when confined within the limits of the above title, and it is hardly possible to do more here than discuss certain aspects which have recently come into the forefront. This article, therefore, is not really intended to be anything more than a brief essay. The subject has been covered fairly thoroughly at a recent Ciba symposium (1962), and the reader is referred to the published report of the papers given at that meeting and the ensuing discussions for most of the relevant facts.

When a new chemotherapeutic agent, of unquestioned potency and low toxicity, has been isolated, it is perhaps useful to consider what more is needed in order to exploit the discovery to its maximal extent, apart from routine knowledge and experience regarding the control of its administration to the patient. What, in other words, is the ideal antibiotic? And what can be done to bring the use and development of any particular class of antibiotic closer to the ideal? There would probably be little difference of opinion about the answer to the first question: the ideal antibiotic is cheap and easy to produce, effective in minute doses, of negligible toxicity to the patient, does not evoke sensitization reactions, is active against the widest range of pathogenic parasites and does not lead to the development of resistance amongst the population of organisms originally sensitive to its action. However, there would presumably be a fairly wide divergence of opinion as to how to attempt to approach this ideal. On the one hand it must be admitted that so far progress has been largely by empirical discoveries. On the other, there would be general agreement that a firm basis for a rational approach to chemotherapy must depend on fundamental knowledge of (a) the chemistry of the antibiotic and its derivatives; (b) the biochemical mechanism of its inhibitory effect; (c) the biochemical basis of naturally occurring resistance, and (d) the genetical and biochemical mechanism underlying the *development* of resistance.

Considering now the specific example of penicillin: for a long time little progress was made either in fundamental knowledge of the penicillins or in practical developments for their chemotherapeutic applications. Five years ago the situation was far from satisfactory. Although outstanding amongst antibacterial agents in general, penicillin was still restricted in its application, being for all intents and purposes completely ineffective against most Gram-negative organisms; and the naturally occurring penicillin-resistant, penicillinase-producing strains of staphylococci had come to dominate the wards of most of the large hospitals in this and other countries where penicillin was in widespread use. Fundamental knowledge of how to "beat staphylococcal penicillinase" and of why Gram-negative (and many other) species of bacteria were "intrinsically" resistant to penicillin was lacking. Now, however, the position has been changed, and present and future research greatly stimulated, by two discoveries of major importance.

The new penicillins

One of these discoveries is the isolation by Batchelor, Doyle, Nayler and Rolinson (1959) of the long sought-after penicillin "nucleus", 6-aminopenicillanic acid (Fig. 1). This has permitted the production of a wide range of synthetic penicillins, all differing only in their side-chain, yet often with interesting new and important properties. This advance has been paralleled by the isolation and characterization, by Abraham and Newton (1961) and Crompton *et al.* (1962), of the analogue, cephalosporin C, and its derivatives (Fig. 2), which may prove to be of equal practical importance and are certainly of equal interest. To the clinician, the microbiologist and the biochemist there is now available a very large number of penicillins and their analogues, differing considerably in relative and absolute antibiotic activities against different types and strains

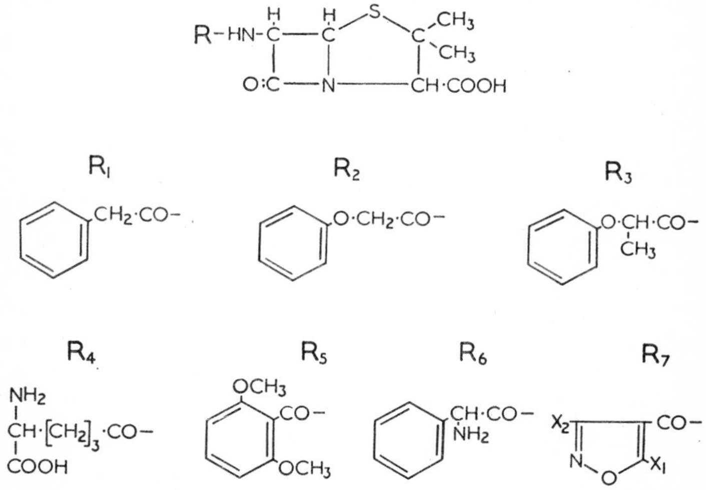

FIG. 1. Penicillins. The basic structure is shown at top; R = H, 6-aminopenicillanic acid; R_1, benzylpenicillin (penicillin G); R_2, phenoxymethylpenicillin (penicillin V); R_3, phenoxyethylpenicillin ("broxil"); R_4, D-(4-amino-4-carboxy-*n*-butyl)-penicillin ("cephalosporin N"); R_5, dimethoxyphenylpenicillin ("methicillin"); R_6, α-aminobenzylpenicillin ("penbritin"); R_7, isoxazolylpenicillins, where X_1 is phenyl and X_2 is methyl or *vice versa*.

of bacterium, and in their enzymological properties in relation to penicillinase (induced formation of which, in certain strains of staphylococci and several other types of bacterium, is exclusively responsible for penicillin-resistance). However, they all probably act by inhibiting the same metabolic function in the sensitive microorganisms concerned. Some of these compounds, for example, dimethoxyphenylpenicillin ("methicillin") have greatly reduced affinities for, and maximal rate of hydrolysis by, staphylococcal and other bacterial penicillinase (Rolinson, *et al.*, 1960); others (such as cephalosporin C and some of its derivatives) retain their high affinity for the enzyme but are almost, if not completely, insusceptible to hydrolysis by it. Several retain considerable antibiotic activity. They all induce synthesis of penicillinase, and thus owe their activity against benzylpenicillin-resistant staphylococci to their relative immunity to hydrolysis by the enzyme rather than to any failure in evoking its production.

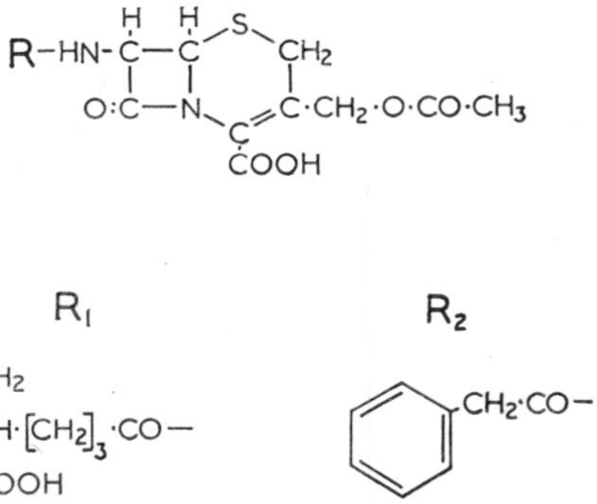

FIG. 2. Cephalosporins. The basic structure is shown at top; R_1, cephalosporin C; R_2, *N*-phenylacetyl-7-aminocephalosporanic acid ("benzyl ceph. C").

One interesting new derivative, α-aminobenzylpenicillin ("penbritin") has been synthesized and is considerably more effective against *Escherichia coli* and other Gram-negative bacteria than any penicillin hitherto available (Rolinson and Stevens, 1961). And it has been possible to combine the property of resistance to acid (permitting oral administration), previously restricted to the penicillinase-sensitive phenoxymethyl- and phenoxyethyl-penicillin, with resistance to hydrolysis by penicillinase in certain 4-isoxazolyl substituted variants (Doyle, Long, Nayler and Store, 1961; Fig. 1). Beyond all these practical achievements, basic biochemical research on penicillinases and their induction (until recently largely confined to *Bacillus cereus* and *B. subtilis*) as well as genetic studies on the control of their inheritance and evolution in microorganisms as a whole, has been greatly stimulated and facilitated. A study of the biological properties of the compounds available within the wide range of chemical variations on the penicillin "theme" thus disclosed should help to elucidate the nature of the substances with which they interact in the cell as a prelude to inhibiting growth and multiplication.

There are reasons for supposing that the properties of a penicillin which, in summation, will determine its overall antibiotic potency against a penicillinase-producing staphylococcus, depend upon its reactions with four, formally distinct, types of "receptor" molecule in the cell: the enzyme, penicillinase; the penicillin "fixation centre" (= PBC or penicillin-binding component; Cooper, 1956), which binds it irreversibly in the cell; the induction "centre", with which it reacts specifically in stimulating formation of penicillinase; and the antibiotic action "centre", interaction with which leads to inhibition of some function vital to the cell (Pollock, 1962). Of these only the first, as studied in soluble preparations, has any *precise* biochemical meaning. And it has been argued, with some justification, that the "fixation centre", the "induction centre" and the "antibiotic action centre" may be very closely related, since the ratios of the "affinities" of various penicillins (and derivatives) for these three receptor "centres" are found to be rather similar (Pollock, 1957; Crompton, *et al.*, 1962; Pollock, 1962) although, of course, their absolute antibiotic activities may differ enormously. However, although conceptually distinct, these "centres" cannot be operationally isolated from each other entirely satisfactorily, so that any conclusion regarding their possibly close relationship must be tentative.

At all events, with the very large number of penicillins now available, it is beginning to be possible to determine what specific features in the molecule contribute to the various biological properties it possesses. The ideal penicillin would be one having maximal "affinity" for the antibiotic action "centre" and the fixation "centre", and minimal degree of effective combination with the induction "centre" and with penicillinase itself. Such a penicillin would be expected to inhibit bacterial growth at concentrations insufficient to allow production of more than traces of penicillinase, which would, in any case, only be capable of hydrolysing it at a very low rate. It may be too much, perhaps, to hope that this can be achieved; but it should now be possible to design a compound which approaches the ideal. For instance, it is known that the penicillin side-chain is very important, both for antibiotic action and for resistance to penicillinase. So far, all potentially useful modifications to the phenylacetyl chain result in diminished antibiotic activity. If substituted by aminoadipic acid, as in cephalosporin N (Fig. 1), the activity is reduced 100-fold, although susceptibility to penicillinase is only slightly decreased. If the ring structure of the cephalosporin N "nucleus" is suitably modified, as in cephalosporin C, the antibiotic activity is still further reduced (about 10-fold), but almost total resistance to penicillinase is achieved. It might reasonably be supposed that a phenylacetyl side-chain combined with a cephalosporin C "nucleus" might yield a compound which combined the desirable properties of benzylpenicillin with those of cephalosporin C. This, indeed, proved to be very nearly true. "Benzyl-ceph. C" (N-phenylacetyl-7-aminocephalosporanic acid)—Fig. 2—is highly resistant to penicillinase (although it has an affinity for the enzyme many times greater than has benzylpenicillin) and has an activity against *Staph. aureus* as much as 12% of that of benzylpenicillin. Similar principles apply, of course, to the various modifications to the side-chain of penicillin itself, already referred to.

Inhibition of cell wall synthesis: the significance of muramic acid

The second great advance has resulted from the steady accumulation of evidence from a variety of sources during the last 10 years

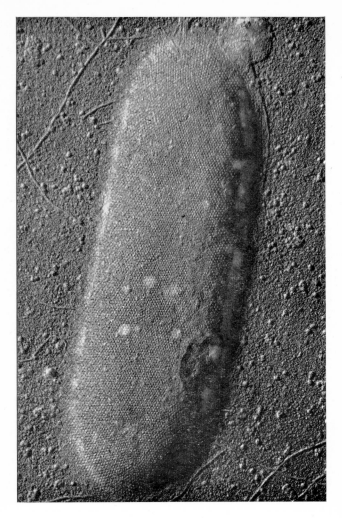

PLATE 3. Electron micrograph of *Halobacterium halobium*. The lattice of hexagonally packed molecules in the cell wall is clearly shown (× 52,500).
(By courtesy of A. L. Houwink, V. Mohr and B. J. Spit)

To face p. 216

regarding the mechanism of penicillin antibiotic action. This has culminated recently in the demonstration that the primary point of attack must almost certainly be inhibition of mucopeptide synthesis in the bacterial cell wall (Rogers, 1962). Without this rigid, protective cell wall, bacterial cells fall to pieces. The key building block here appears to be N-acetylmuramic acid (Fig. 3), the 3-dimensional structure of which, as has recently been demonstrated by Collins and Richmond (1962), bears a striking similarity (not apparent in 2-dimensional diagrams) in several different ways

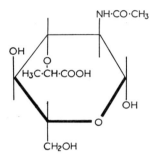

FIG. 3. N-Acetylmuramic acid.

to the basic structure of penicillin and cephalosporin. These workers suggest (private communication) that part of the molecule of bacitracin (Fig. 4), which also inhibits cell wall formation in bacteria, may also bear a significantly close resemblance to muramic acid. Similarity of mechanism is indicated by the accumulation in treated cells of that same "Park" uridine diphosphate muramic acid peptide (Fig. 5) as is found with penicillin (Abraham and Newton, 1958). However, the accumulation of the same "Park" peptide with penicillin and bacitracin does no more than indicate that the mechanisms of their action are closely related; they may in fact inhibit quite distinct reactions (sequential or parallel), both involving muramic acid. Abraham and Newton (1958) have pointed out that the effects of penicillin and bacitracin on accumulation of the "Park" compound vary independently of each other

8

(in contrast with penicillin and cephalosporin C), rather as would be expected were two separate reactions being affected.

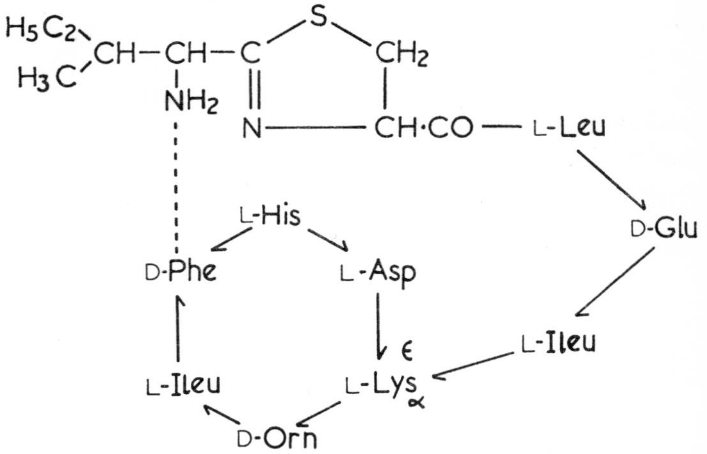

FIG. 4. Bacitracin.

Cycloserine, however, which also interferes with cell wall formation, has a very different structure, analogous to D-alanine (as pointed out by Strominger, Threnn and Scott, 1959)—see Fig. 6—

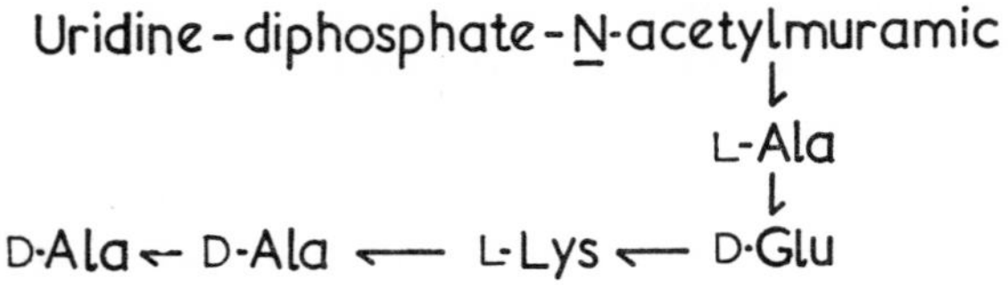

FIG. 5. The "Park" peptide.

rather than to the thiazolidine ring of penicillin (as suggested by Ciak and Hahn, 1959), and almost certainly acts in quite a different way—probably by preventing the formation of D-alanine, by inhibiting the action of alanine racemase (Strominger, Ito and Threnn, 1960). D-Alanine is an essential component of the cell wall mucopeptide and is known to antagonize the growth-inhibiting effect of cycloserine (Shockman, 1959). Indeed, the uridine-muramic peptide which accumulates after treatment of *Staph. aureus* with cycloserine has been shown to lack the two terminal D-alanine residues (Strominger, Threnn and Scott, 1959) present in the usual "Park" peptide found with penicillin and bacitracin, as might be expected on this hypothesis.

In this connection it is interesting to note that cycloserine is also very different from the penicillins in being highly toxic to the host (Walker and Murdoch, 1957) as well as to the parasite. This may be related to its property of combining with an essential coenzyme,

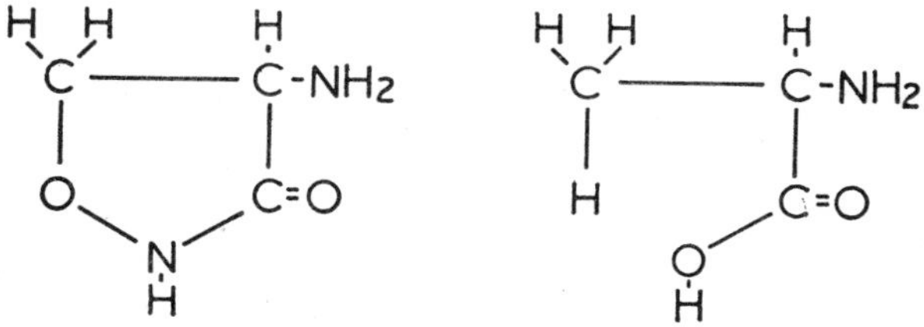

FIG. 6. Cycloserine (on left) and D-alanine.

pyridoxal phosphate, which appears to be the basis of its inhibitory action, not only on alanine racemase, but also on transaminase reactions (Vyshepan, Ivanova and Chernukh, 1959), which might be expected to be at least as important to the host as they are to the parasite. The action of vancomycin, which also inhibits the synthesis of mucopeptide in the cell wall (Reynolds, 1961; Jordan, 1961), however, is rather less certain. It appears to lead to the accumulation of the same "Park" uridine-muramic acid peptide that is found with penicillin and with bacitracin; yet it is claimed that no cross-resistance occurs with penicillin-resistant strains (Reynolds, 1961) as has been reported for bacitracin (Paine, 1951). It will be most interesting to learn more of its chemical structure, which at the moment is almost entirely unknown. Further light on the metabolic relationships between these various compounds which inhibit cell wall formation might be thrown from more work on the *development* of cross-resistance resulting from *single* mutations (rather than simple comparisons between quite distinct strains or species); and from studies on possible synergism between them (with respect both to growth inhibition and to accumulation of "Park" peptide) in one strain.

It is now known that even those organisms, such as *E. coli*, which are relatively resistant to penicillin, possess the same muramic acid mucopeptide in their cell walls, and its synthesis is specifically inhibited by penicillins in the same way as in staphylococci although, of course, higher concentrations are generally necessary (Rogers and Mandelstam, 1962).

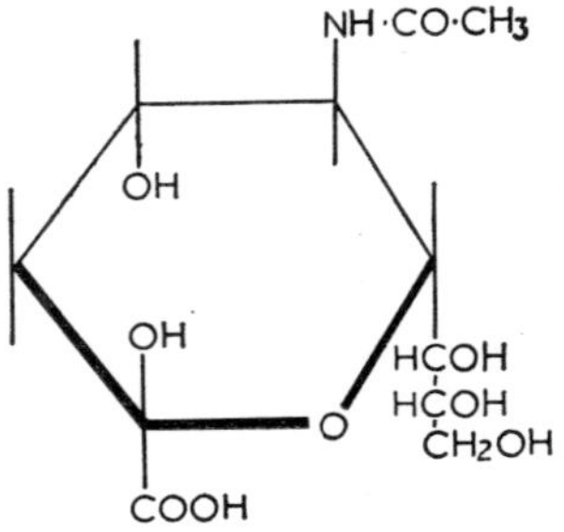

FIG. 7. Sialic acid.

The physiological basis of the highly selective toxicity of the penicillins can now be considered as established. Mammalian cells do not contain muramic mucopeptides in their wall or anywhere else. The closest counterpart to muramic acid produced in higher organisms is sialic acid (Fig. 7), which also contains a N-acetyl-hexosamine unit, and which might perhaps be considered to have a somewhat analogous role since it occurs in extracellular linings and secretions (Gottschalk, 1960); but its structure is only super-ficially similar to that of muramic acid, the hexose unit being mannose and not glucose, with a different type of ring closure. It is not surprising, therefore, that mammalian cells are quite unaffected by penicillin. On the other hand, all organisms containing muramic acid must be considered as potentially susceptible. It is not yet certain whether all bacterial genera possess this muramic acid mucopeptide, but it seems likely that it will eventually be shown to occur at least in all members of the *Eubacteriaceae*. Bacterial types which appear to lack a cell wall, such as the "pleuro-pneumonia-like organisms" (Klieneberger-Nobel, 1962) and the so-called "L" forms (Dienes and Weinberger, 1951) which have become adapted, temporarily or otherwise, to dispense with a cell wall are, as might be expected, resistant to penicillin. Muramic acid has now been found in rickettsia (Allison and Perkins, 1960; Jenkin, 1960) and even in some of the larger viruses belonging to the psittacosis group, but was not detectable in vaccinia or influenza viruses; this no doubt explains the relative sensitivity of the psitta-cosis-lymphogranuloma group to the inhibitory effect of peni-cillin, as compared with other viruses. There is now renewed hope that any parasite possessing this compound as an essential part of its structure might be rendered susceptible to a pencillin with a suitably modified architecture.

Genetics

Alongside these two major advances has been the rapid growth in knowledge of microbial genetics. The great problem for chemo-therapy, both now and in the future, is the development of drug resistance. From a purely theoretical standpoint it might be sup-posed that penicillin resistance might be achieved in the following ways.

(1) Production of penicillin-destroying enzyme. Apart from the penicillinase (penicillin β-lactamase) already discussed, organisms may produce penicillin amidase (Batchelor, *et al.*, 1961), and two cephalosporin-destroying enzymes are already known (Crompton *et al.*, 1962).

(2) Formation of an accessibility barrier to penetration of peni-cillin into the cell.

(3) Development of a penicillin-insensitive pathway for muco-peptide synthesis.

(4) Development of a muramic acid substitute in cell-wall synthesis or dispensing with the need for a cell-wall of any kind.

Little is known regarding the biochemical basis of any of these possible mechanisms, apart from (1), but the so-called "intrinsic" (non-penicillinase) type of penicillin-resistance may become increasingly important in relation to naturally acquired staphylococcal resistance to the penicillinase-resistant methicillin, since this appears at the present time not be due to an increased rate of methicillin destruction (Knox, 1961) and is therefore presumed to belong to types (2) or (3). In any case, it is reasonable to suppose that, from a genetical point of view, all these changes involve alterations in cell proteins (presumably enzymes) whose production is controlled by specific genes. The "original" penicillin-sensitive type of staphylococcus does not possess the complete gene permitting it to produce penicillinase. The relevant penicillinase gene from naturally-occurring penicillin-resistant strains of staphylococci can now, however, be artificially inserted into the chromosome of the sensitive strain, by transduction with bacteriophage (Ritz and Baldwin, 1961), thus rendering the transduced cells genetically resistant. It may not, perhaps, be too long before the mechanism of the evolution of a "new" enzyme in a bacterial population is fully understood *at a biochemical level*, and thereby brought more closely under control. It should be noted that such hypothetical understanding and control could and must include not only the various types of "intrinsic" resistance already referred to, but also the possible emergence of an altered penicillinase which might destroy the hitherto insusceptible penicillins as rapidly as the present penicillinase hydrolyses benzylpenicillin. A relatively slight change in the penicillinase molecule might result in a large increase in affinity for a substrate, and this could rapidly lead to the "therapeutic neutralization" of methicillin, benzyl-cephalosporin C, and other of the recently developed penicillins, some of which are proving useful in the treatment of benzylpenicillin-resistant staphylococcal infections. Microbial genetics must also, surely, be applied in the widest sense, not only to the understanding and control of the evolution of a new and dangerous gene, but also—more immediately and practically— to the control of its reproduction within the bacterial population concerned. Even if the mechanisms by which a mutant gene appears in the cell cannot yet be controlled, its reproduction may be. This is largely a matter of natural selection, and will be determined by proper control of drug administration and cross-infection.

Probably more is now known about the chemistry and biology of the penicillins than about any other class of antibiotic. But it is only relatively recently, 30 years after its discovery and nearly 20 years after its isolation, that a strictly rational approach to the problem can at last be said to be leading to practical advances on a wide front. The empirical approach will no doubt continue to give valuable results, but the future for penicillin will now be increasingly determined by basic research into the biochemistry and genetics of the parasite. Presumably the same is, or will soon be, true for other antibiotics; but host reactions and host metabolism might be expected to be more often important with drugs that do not act through a mechanism so classically selective as that of interference with the metabolism of the highly exclusive muramic acid.

[Discussion of this paper was postponed until after the following paper by H. Williams Smith; see p. 239.]

REFERENCES

ABRAHAM, E. P. and NEWTON, G. G. F. (1958). *Ciba Found. Symp., Amino Acids and Peptides with Antimetabolic Activity*, p. 205. London: Churchill.

ABRAHAM, E. P. and NEWTON, G. G. F. (1961). *Biochem. J.*, **79,** 377.

ALLISON, A. C. and PERKINS, H. R. (1960). *Nature, Lond.*, **188,** 796.

BATCHELOR, F. R., DOYLE, F. P., NAYLER, J. H. C. and ROLINSON, G. N. (1959). *Nature, Lond.*, **183,** 257.

BATCHELOR, F. R., CHAIN, E. B., RICHARDS, M. and ROLINSON, G. N. (1961). *Proc. Roy. Soc.* **B., 154,** 514.

CIAK, J. and HAHN, F. E. (1959). *Antibiot. Chemother.*, **9**, 47.

CIBA FOUNDATION STUDY GROUP REPORT (1962). *Resistance of Bacteria to the Penicillins*, London: Churchill.

COLLINS, J. F., and RICHMOND, M. H. (1962). *Nature, Lond.*, **195**, 142.

COOPER, P. D. (1956). *Bact. Rev.*, **20**, 28.

CROMPTON, B., JAGO, M., CRAWFORD, K., NEWTON, G. G. F. and ABRAHAM, E. P. (1962). *Biochem. J.*, **83**, 52.

DIENES, L. and WEINBERGER, H. J. (1951). *Bact. Rev.*, **15**, 245.

DOYLE, F. P., LONG, A. A. W., NAYLER, J. H. C. and STORE, E. R. (1961). *Nature, Lond.*, **192**, 1184.

GOTTSCHALK. A. (1960). The Chemistry and Biology of Sialic Acids and Related Substances. Cambridge Univ. Press.

JENKIN, H. M. (1960). *J. Bact.*, **80**, 639.

JORDAN, D. C. (1961). *Bioch. biophys. Res. Com.*, **6**, 167.

KLIENEBERGER-NOBEL, E. (1962). Pleuropneumonia-Like Organisms. (PPLO) Mycoplasmataceae. Ch. IX. London and New York: Academic Press.

KNOX, R. (1961). *Guy's Hosp. Rep.*, **110**, 134.

PAINE, T. F. (1951). *J. Bact.*, **61**, 259.

POLLOCK, M. R. (1957). *Biochem. J.*, **66**, 419.

POLLOCK, M. R. (1962). *Ciba Found. Study Group, Resistance of Bacteria to the Pencillins*, p. 56. London: Churchill.

REYNOLDS, P. E. (1961). *Biochim. biophys. Acta*, **52**, 403.

RITZ, H. L. and BALDWIN, J. N. (1961). *Proc. Soc. exp. Biol. Med., N.Y.*, **107**, 678.

ROGERS, H. J. (1962). *Ciba Found. Study Group, Resistance of Bacteria to the Penicillins*, p. 25. London: Churchill.

ROGERS, H. J. and MANDELSTAM, J. (1962). *Biochem. J.*, in press.

ROLINSON, G. N., STEVENS, S., BATCHELOR, F. R., WOOD, J. C. and CHAIN, E. B. (1960). *Lancet*, **ii**, 564.

ROLINSON, G. N. and STEVENS, S. (1961). *Brit. med. J.*, **ii**, 191.

SHOCKMAN, G. D. (1959). *Proc. Soc. exp. Biol. Med., N.Y.*, **101**, 693.

STROMINGER, J. L., THRENN, R. H. and SCOTT, S. S. (1959). *J. Amer. chem. Soc.*, **81**, 3803.

STROMINGER, J. L., ITO, E. and THRENN, R. H. (1960). *J. Amer. chem. Soc.*, **82**, 998.

VYSHEPAN, E. D., IVANOVA, K. I. and CHERNUKH, A. M. (1959). *Bull. exp. Biol. Med. (U.S.S.R.)*, **48**, 971.

WALKER, W. C. and MURDOCH, J. McC. (1957). *Tubercle*, **38**, 297.

ANTIBIOTICS AND THE BACTERIAL FLORA OF THE ALIMENTARY TRACT

H. Williams Smith

The Animal Health Trust, Stock, Essex

A CONSIDERATION of all the effects, direct and indirect, of anti-biotics on the bacterial flora of the alimentary tract represents a vast subject. Consequently, I shall make only brief mention of their effects on the host and then discuss in more detail a few aspects of their effects on the bacterial flora itself.

I think it is at times necessary to remind oneself that the usual and most obvious effect on the bacterial host of the rational use of anti-biotics is clinical improvement. Occasionally, however, this im-provement is accompanied by unpleasant side effects which in a small minority of cases may be more serious than the primary disease. The direct side effects may be of a toxic or of a hyper-sensitive nature. The indirect ones arise mainly from the influence of the antibiotics on the alimentary tract flora by depressing the multiplication of bacteria which produce metabolites of value to the host, or by permitting the proliferation of antibiotic-resistant bacterial pathogens previously present in too small numbers to produce disease.

Apart from their therapeutic use, some antibiotics have an addi-tional application in agriculture because their continuous administra-tion in low levels in the food of certain species of domestic animals usually increase their growth rate. The animals principally concerned are pigs and poultry and the antibiotics usually penicillin and the tetracyclines. A voluminous literature has rapidly accumu-lated on this aspect of growth promotion. Much of it is contra-dictory and much appears illogical but the salient fact remains that antibiotic feeding under certain conditions—conditions which cannot always be defined—may result in increased growth rate. For those unfamiliar with the subject I should mention that this increased growth rate, although not difficult to measure, is not of the order that can be appreciated merely by glancing over the farmyard gate.

A great deal of energy has also been spent in trying to discover why the increased growth rate is produced. Much of this energy has been concentrated in studying the effect of antibiotic feeding on the bacterial flora of the alimentary tract, working on the hypothesis that the antibiotics produce their effect either by depressing the multiplication of harmful bacteria or by stimulating the multiplication of beneficial ones. Luckey (1959), however, in summarizing the data obtained from these studies, comments: "It is apparent that conflicting data are absent only when there is not more than one report on the topic". This confusion arose from the multiplicity of methods used by the earlier investigators, coupled with a lack of basic information on the ecology of the alimentary tract from the bacteriological aspect. It was also not appreciated that many of the bacteria present in the alimentary tract during or after antibiotic feeding, although belonging to the same species or genera as those present before treatment, differed from them in the important respect that they were antibiotic-resistant. In recent years more positive information has emerged on the effect of antibiotic feeding on the bacterial flora of the alimentary tract and also, as a consequence, on the mode of action of antibiotics in stimulating growth (Lev, Briggs and Coates, 1957; Lev and Forbes 1959).

First, I would like to present some ecological data pertinent to these studies. Figure 1 illustrates the development of the faecal bacterial flora of the calf and the changes that occur with age. The bacterial groups which become established as the main components in the first few days of life can be classified into *Escherichia coli*, *Clostridium welchii*, streptococci, bacteroides and lactobacilli, five groups which also comprise the bulk of the faecal bacterial flora of most domestic mammals and man. The numbers of *Cl. welchii* present decrease rapidly with age but those of the other bacterial groups decrease much more slowly until eventually at 4 to 6 months of age the total viable bacterial count of the faeces of the calf may

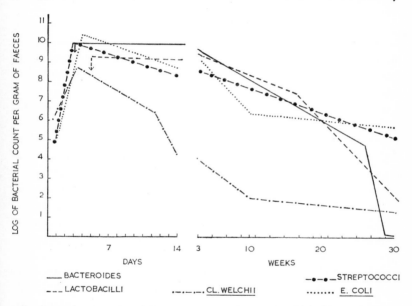

FIG. 1. The development of the faecal bacterial flora of the calf and the changes that occur with age.

be 10,000 times lower than it was in very early life. Some types of lactobacilli and streptococci, including *Strep. faecalis*, behave like *Cl. welchii*, being present in large numbers in early life then decreasing rapidly until they form only a very minor part of the total lactobacillary and streptococcal populations present in later life. Studies on calves of different breeds under different methods of management yield strikingly similar results. During early life, too, the faecal bacterial flora in most species of domestic mammals and man closely resembles that of calves, but considerable differences occur between the species with ageing. In some species there is relatively little difference between the composition of the faecal flora in early and in later life. In others the differences are great either quantitatively, qualitatively or both. The young rabbit, for example, in early life has a similar bacterial faecal flora to that of the young of other mammals but in later life the flora consists almost entirely of bacteroides. By contrast, the adult guinea pig, with a similar digestive tract and diet, has a bacterial flora consisting principally of lactobacilli, a flora which if disturbed by antibiotic administration may result in the death of the host.

Estimation of the bacterial content of the alimentary tract on non-selective media and deliberately planned laboratory experiments do not indicate that any one of the five main bacterial groups is dependent on, or benefited by, the presence of another. Neither do any of the main groups appear to produce substances inimical to the growth of the others. There is, in fact, a surprising lack of evidence of competition between them. If competition does occur, it must be remarkably well balanced because the faecal flora of animals of the same species at the same age is surprisingly similar, quantitatively and qualitatively, and violent fluctuations in the numbers of the main groups is an unusual occurrence. When for some reason or another, an occasional temporary change is noted in the numbers of one of the main groups there is usually no compensating change in any of the others. Again, the slow but large decrease in the total bacterial population of the alimentary tract of the calf that occurs with age is shared by most of the bacterial groups that were predominant in early life. Even in adult animals such as rabbits and guinea pigs in which one bacterial group only is dominant, the actual numbers of organisms present are rarely greater than they were in early life, when the other numerically large groups were also present. In fact, it appears that the numbers of any one main group present at any one period in the life of the host is more dependent on the non-bacterial environmental conditions applying within the tract than upon the numbers of the other groups. The "modes of life" of the main groups are sufficiently dissimilar for one not to be greatly influenced by another.

Within the groups the situation is quite different. Considerable competition may occur between different strains of the same species or between closely related species. Strains of some species, for example *E. coli* and *Cl. welchii*, may produce substances that are bactericidal to other strains of the same species. Competition appears to be particularly intense during the early life of the host and is well illustrated in Table I which shows the fluctuations that occurred from day to day in the relative proportion of different phage types of *E. coli* in the alimentary tract of young calves, the total *E. coli* population of the faeces during this period remaining remarkably constant.

Turning now to the antibiotic aspect, Fig. 2 shows how different antibiotics, all of which possess the common property of being active against *E. coli*, vary in their effects on the *E. coli* population of the alimentary tract of the calf. A single dose by mouth of a bactericidal agent such as streptomycin which is not absorbed from the alimentary tract, reduces the *E. coli* population profoundly. A single dose of one of the tetracyclines, bacteriostatic agents which are excreted in the faeces in appreciable amounts, produces a slight effect or sometimes no observable effect. When given in multiple doses, however, the tetracyclines have a marked effect. Bacteriostatic agents such as chloramphenicol, which are absorbed high up in the intestinal tract (very little, if any, being excreted in the faeces) have only a slight observable effect on the faecal *E. coli* even when given in multiple doses.

As expected from the data obtained from ecological studies, the effect of giving an antibiotic *principally* active against only one of the main groups of bacteria of the alimentary tract (streptomycin or neomycin against the *E. coli* or bacitracin against the *Cl. welchii*), usually results in the depression of the susceptible group followed

by a return in a few days to its previous numerical position. There
is little evidence during this time that any of the other main groups

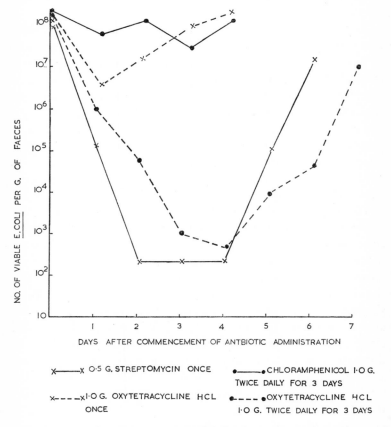

FIG. 2. The effect of oral administration of antibiotics on the *E. coli* population of
the faeces (from Smith and Crabb, 1961).

have increased in numbers and taken over the position previously
occupied by the now greatly depressed groups. Again, as expected
from ecological studies, should there be any resistant strains present

Table I

PHAGE TYPES OF E. *Coli* IN THE FAECES OF HEALTHY CALVES (Smith and Crabb, 1956)

Phage types present in 10 colonies of E. coli isolated on each of the first 12 days after birth

Calf no.	1	2	3	4	5	6	7	8	9	10	11	12
1	2(10)*	2(10)	2(10)	2(9) 51(1)	2(8) 4(1) 60(1)	2(10)	38(10)	38(6) 4(3) 3(1)	4(1) 3(9)	3(10)	3(4) 77(6)	3(3) 77(7)
2	3(1) 38(1) 64(4) 65(4)	4(3) 38(2) 65(4) 69(1)	2(6) 36(2) 69(2)	74(9) 88(1)	74(8) 3(2)	74(3) 3(7)	74(2) 3(2) 77(6)	3(10)	3(8) 74(2)	3(6) 77(4)	3(10)	77(10)
3	71(5) 36(5)	71(2) 2(3) 3(3) 101(2)	71(1) 2(7) 64(2)	71(6) 2(3) 3(1)	1(1) 2(2) 36(4) 63(1) 83(2)	71(9) 1(1)	71(2) 64(2) 63(6)	71(2) 63(4) 2(4)	71(2) 2(8)	71(4) 2(4) 63(1) 60(1)	71(2) 2(6) 80(2)	71(3) 2(4) 80(2) 38(1)

* The number of colonies belonging to each phage type is given in parentheses

belonging to the depressed group, these strains increase rapidly in numbers until they occupy the position previously held by the sensitive strains. On account of this several experiments initially intended for inclusion in Fig. 2 had to be repeated because of the rapid proliferation of resistant *E. coli*. In a number of the experiments, proliferation of resistant Enterobacteriaceae other than *E. coli* occurred. Not only may the change from a predominantly

Table II

EFFECT OF ANTIBIOTIC THERAPY ON THE EMERGENCE OF RESISTANT *E. coli* IN THE FAECES OF CALVES

(Modified from Smith and Crabb, 1960)

Antibiotic (by mouth)	Days after beginning treatment	Log number of E. coli/g. of faeces	
		Resistant	Total
1 dose of 0·5 g.	0	3·0	7·3
streptomycin	1	8·4	8·4
2 doses of 0·5 g.			
oxytetracycline HCl	0	1·0	9·0
(one every 12 hr.)	1	8·7	8·7
4 doses of 1·0 g.	0	1·0	9·8
chloramphenicol	1	1·7	9·4
(one every 12 hr.)	2	10·0	10·0

sensitive to a predominantly resistant group be extremely rapid (Table II), but the stimulus necessary to bring it about may be very slight. Provided resistant strains are present, the change may often be produced with *E. coli* by one dose of chloramphenicol, a treatment which ordinarily has little apparent effect on the numbers of *E. coli* present in the faeces.

As distinct from the narrow-spectrum antibiotics, the broad-spectrum ones such as the tetracyclines are usually active against all the five main groups which comprise the bulk of the alimentary bacterial flora and, for a short period after the beginning of therapy, the bacterial flora is completely disorganized. This situation permits, in some species of animals, the proliferation of resistant bacterial groups that are less well adapted to life in the alimentary tract than the main groups and which, in normal circumstances, form only a very minor part of the total bacterial flora. These groups include *Pseudomonas*, tetracycline-resistant *Staph. aureus*, yeasts and fungi. However, in most animal species, tetracycline-resistant forms of the main groups usually soon proliferate provided administration is continued long enough, and they come to occupy the positions previously held by their tetracycline-sensitive counter-parts. This was well illustrated in a calf (Table III) given 20 mg./kg. oxytetracycline twice daily; faecal bacterial counts were performed at intervals using different types of solid media with and without added oxytetracycline, so that the total numbers of the different bacterial groups and of their tetracycline-resistant components could be estimated. The methods employed were those of Smith and Crabb (1961). No tetracycline-resistant *E. coli* were found in the faeces before administration of oxytetracycline yet in 3 days they had apparently completely replaced the sensitive *E. coli* and in 5 days were present in numbers equal to that of the total *E. coli* flora at the beginning of the experiment. In the meantime, how-ever, tetracycline-resistant Enterobacteriaceae other than *E. coli*, originally present at 10^6 viable organisms/g. faeces had increased to 500 times that figure at 5 days. They then decreased enormously, the decrease coinciding with the increase of the tetracycline-resistant *E. coli*. Tetracycline-sensitive streptococci also were quickly replaced by resistant forms but replacement did not take place in the case of the lactobacilli, bacteroides and *Cl. welchii* until after 5, 7 and 10 days respectively. No yeasts were found before treatment but 10^7/g. were present at 5 days and 10^5 at 7 days; thereafter they were never found. At 10 days, when tetracycline administration was discontinued, the bacterial composition of the faeces closely resembled that of untreated calves of similar age except that all the five main bacterial groups were completely tetracycline-resistant. The mass of the bacteria at 17 days was still

Table III

EFFECT OF OXYTETRACYCLINE ADMINISTRATION ON THE BACTERIAL POPULATION OF THE FAECES OF A CALF

Log$_{10}$ number of viable organisms/g. faeces

Time after starting treatment (days)	Streptococci		E. coli		Cl. welchii		Lactobacilli		Bacteroides		Enterobactereaceae		Yeasts	
	T	R	T	R	T	R	T	R	T	R	T	R	T	R
0	8·9	5·5	8·3	N	6·0	N	9·2	N	9·8	N	6·0	6·0	N	N
3	9·3	9·3	7·2	7·2	N	N	6·0	N	7·0	N	7·0	7·0	N	N
5	9·2	9·2	8·6	8·6	N	N	6·7	6·7	N	N	8·7	8·7	7·0	N
7	9·3	9·3	9·3	9·3	9·0	9·0	8·9	8·9	9·3	9·3	8·4	8·4	5·0	N
10*	9·5	9·5	9·0	9·0	4·7	4·7	9·1	9·1	10·0	10·0	7·7	7·7	N	N
17	7·2	7·2	9·1	9·1	1·7	1·7	9·7	9·7	10·0	10·0	N	N	N	N
24	7·7	7·7	7·2	7·2			9·3	9·3	9·6	9·6	N	N	N	N

T, Total bacterial count; R, Count of oxytetracycline-resistant bacteria; N, not found.

* Oxytetracycline adminstration (20 mg./kg.) twice daily by mouth was discontinued on day 10.

tetracycline-resistant and again resembled the pattern of untreated calves of similar age, the *Cl. welchii* content having decreased greatly and some of the streptococcal species, such as *Strep. faecalis* formed the total streptococcal component. The results of giving oxytetracycline 20 mg./kg. twice daily by mouth to a rabbit and a guinea pig, species in which one bacterial group forms the mass of the faecal flora, are illustrated in Tables IV and V respectively.

Table IV

EFFECT OF OXYTETRACYCLINE ON THE BACTERIAL POPULATION
OF THE FAECES OF A RABBIT

Time after starting treatment (days)	Log_{10} number of viable organisms/g. faeces					
	Sreptococci, Cl. welchii Lactobacilli and E. coli		Bacteroides		Anaerobic spore-formers	
	T	R	T	R	T	R
0	3·0	N	9·3	N	N	N
2	N	N	N	N	6·0	6·0
4	N	N	9·1	9·1	8·0	8·0
7	N	N	9·3	9·3	8·3	8·3
9*	N	N	8·7	8·7	N	N
19	N	N	9·3	9·3	N	N

T, R and *N* as in Table III.

* Oxytetracycline administration was discontinued on day 9.

After two days of treatment with oxytetracycline, bacteroides were completely eliminated from the faeces of the rabbit; after 4 days tetracycline-resistant forms had replaced them. During this time a temporary proliferation of tetracycline-resistant anaerobic spore-forming bacteria occurred, these bacteria disappearing from the faeces when the tetracycline-resistant bacteroides had established themselves as the main bacterial component of the faeces. In contrast to the calf and rabbit, there was no evidence in the guinea pig of a rapid replacement of the faecal bacterial flora following tetracycline administration by a similar but tetracycline-resistant flora. The lactobacilli together with the minority bacteroides flora were eliminated from the faeces, and yeasts and *Proteus vulgaris*

Table V

THE EFFECT OF OXYTETRACYCLINE ADMINISTRATION ON THE BACTERIAL POPULATION OF THE FAECES OF A GUINEA PIG

Log_{10} number of viable organisms/g. faeces

Time after starting treatment (days)	Streptococci		Lactobacilli		Bacteroides		Proteus		Yeasts	
	T	R	T	R	T	R	T	R	T	R
0	N	N	8·6	N	7·6	N	N	N	N	N
2	N	N	N	N	N	N	3·7	3·7	7·3	7·3
4	N	N	N	N	N	N	3·6	3·6	6·7	6·7
6	N	N	N	N	N	N	7·3	7·3	7·5	7·5
10	N	N	N	N	N	N	7·7	7·7	6·4	6·4
17	9·4	9·4	N	N	7·7	7·7	7·5	7·5	N	N
21	8·9	8·9	N	N	7·4	7·4	7·9	7·9	N	N
24*	8·9	8·9	N	N	8·4	8·4	8·2	8·2	N	N
28	8·0	8·0	N	N	9·7	9·7	8·2	8·2	N	N
31	8·4	8·4	N	N	9·7	9·7	7·5	7·5	N	N

T, R and N as in Table III.

* Oxytetracycline administration was discontinued on day 24.

colonized the alimentary tract. At 17 days, streptococci formed the greater part of the bacterial flora, and there were also present fairly large numbers of *Proteus* and *Bacteroides melaninogenicus*. This situation persisted for one week after discontinuing the antibiotic with the exception that large numbers of bacteroides other than *B. melaninogenicus* were then present. This failure of antibiotic-resistant lactobacilli to replace sensitive ones as the main component of the alimentary flora may well be the reason why guinea pigs are unique animals in usually responding adversely to antibiotic administration. Replacement of the alimentary flora with resistant organisms occurred rapidly in the calf and the rabbit, animals which rarely suffer harm from antibiotic administration.

Resistant strains of bacteria also predominate in the alimentary tract of domestic animals given low levels of tetracycline continuously in the food for growth promotion purposes. This has been shown in the case of *E. coli* (Smith and Crabb, 1956; Gordon, Garside and Tucker, 1959; Maclay and Branion, 1960; Fuller *et al.*, 1960), streptococci (Barnes, 1958; Fuller *et al.*, 1960), lactobacilli (Fuller *et al.*, 1960) and *Cl. welchii* (Smith, 1959). There is little information available as to whether or not resistant strains of bacteroides emerge during antibiotic feeding. So far, no reference has been made to the effect of antibiotics on bacteria which form only a minor part of the total faecal flora. Table VI shows the incidence of a tetracycline-resistant *Cl. welchii* faecal flora in piglets weaned at 10 days of age (2 to 8 week group), a period when *Cl. welchii* forms a major part of the faecal flora, and weaned at 8 weeks of age (9 to 30 week group) when it forms only a minor part. A tetracycline-resistant *Cl. welchii* flora was more common in the piglets weaned early than in those weaned late and fed diets containing tetracyclines (58·4 % compared with 17·5 %). Nearly all the *E. coli*, present in large numbers in both groups, were tetracycline-resistant. These results suggest that resistant bacteria are more likely to supplant sensitive ones following tetracycline administration when the bacteria concerned form a major rather

Table VI

THE INCIDENCE OF TETRACYCLINE-RESISTANT *Cl. welchii* IN THE
FAECES OF PIGS FED ON DIETS CONTAINING TETRACYCLINES

(Modified from Smith, 1959)
10 pigs were examined from each herd

		% of faecal specimens in which the Cl. welchii were			
Conditions of herd	Number of faecal specimens	All resistant	Mixed resistant and sensitive	All sensitive	Not found
WEANED AT 10 DAYS					
With tetracyclines	160	58·4	16·7	18·1	6·8
No tetracyclines	160	3·1	41·3	55·0	0·6
WEANED AT 8 WEEKS					
With tetracyclines	240	17·5	7·9	37·1	37·5
No tetracyclines	240	0·4	18·3	75·0	6·8

than a minor part of the total bacterial flora. When they form only a minor part, as *Cl. welchii* does in the older pig, they may frequently have their numbers reduced or be eliminated by prolonged antibiotic administration without being replaced by resistant strains.

REFERENCES

BARNES, E. M. (1958). *Brit. vet. J.*, **114,** 333.
FULLER, R., NEWLAND, L. G. M., BRIGGS, C. A. E., BRAUDE, R. and MITCHELL, K. G. (1960). J. *appl. Bact.*, **23,** 195.
GORDON, R. F., GARSIDE, J. S. and TUCKER, J. F. (1959). *Proc. XV Int. vet. Congr., Madrid*, **2,** 347.
LEV, M., BRIGGS, C. A. E. and COATES, M. E. (1957). *Brit. J. Nutr.*, **11,** 364.
LEV, M. and FORBES, M. (1959). *Brit. J. Nutr.*, **13,** 78.
LUCKEY, T. D. (1959). *In* Goldberg, H. S., *Ed.*, Antibiotics, their Chemistry and Non-medical Uses, New Jersey: D. van Nostrand Co., p. 174.
MACLAY, K. A. and BRANION, H. D. (1960). *Canad. vet. J.*, **1,** 144.
SMITH, H. W. (1959). *J. Path. Bact.*, **77,** 79.
SMITH, H. W. and CRABB, W. E. (1956). *J. gen. Microbiol.*, **15,** 556.
SMITH, H. W. and CRABB, W. E. (1960). *J. comp. Path.*, **70,** 126.
SMITH, H. W. and CRABB, W. E. (1961). *J. Path. Bact.*, **82,** 53.

N-acetyl Muramic acid

Penicillin

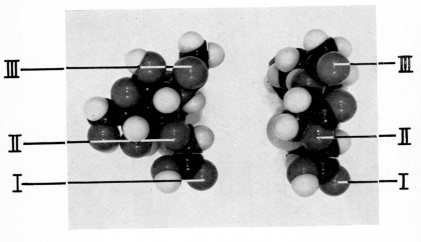

PLATE 4. Solid models of N-acetylmuramic acid and penicillin. The figures in the margin refer to the groups as follows:

Penicillin. I: carboxyl group; II: triply-substituted β-lactam nitrogen; III: carbonyl oxygen of the peptide group in the side-chain.

N-Acetylmuramic acid. I: carboxyl group; II: ether oxygen of the lactyl side-chain; III: carbonyl oxygen of the N-acetyl residue.

To face p. 239

DISCUSSION

M. H. Richmond (*National Institute for Medical Research*): Dr. Pollock mentioned in his contribution that we had grounds for believing there is a certain similarity in structure between penicillin and N-acetylmuramic acid. We thought we might give you a little more detail about this because if it is correct it could give a good reason as to why penicillin is active. In Plate 4 are shown solid models of penicillin and N-acetylmuramic acid. In these rather different molecules, you have at I carboxyl groups with very similar acid dissociation constants (pH 2·7 and 2·6 respectively); at II you have an ether oxygen in N-acetylmuramic acid and a triply-substituted nitrogen in penicillin; and at III you have a carbonyl group in both molecules. When you make an accurate wire model of these two molecules, which you can do from published crystallographic data, you find that with the triply substituted nitrogen (II) of penicillin and the ether oxygen of N-acetylmuramic acid (II) held in the same position in space, the oxygen atoms of the carbonyl groups (III) in the two molecules lie in identical positions. Furthermore, an oxygen atom from the carboxyl group of each molecule (I) will occupy identical positions. Not only do these pairs of groups (I, II and III) occupy similar positions in space, they are capable of taking part in hydrogen bonding. The length, direction and strength of the hydrogen bonds formed by the pairs of groups I, II and III are extremely similar in the two molecules. In addition each of the carboxyl groups (I) will be ionized to the same extent under a given set of conditions and able to take part in ionic bonding in a very similar way.

When molecules associate with the active centres of enzymes, they do so by ionic and by hydrogen bonding. It seems to us that if an enzyme normally concerned with N-acetylmuramic acid were presented with penicillin, the penicillin molecule could well occupy the active centre which is normally occupied by the substrate (N-acetylmuramic acid).

B. Lacey (*Westminster Hospital Medical School*): When one thinks of penicillin toxicity, one is inclined to think it is not toxic for humans, but if it is put intrathecally it is highly toxic. If you are going to carry the analogy to the logical conclusion, you would assume that something like N-acetylmuramic acid might be found somewhere in human CNS tissue.

Richmond: The only compound I know of which has been detected in the CNS is sialic acid or derivatives of sialic acid. Although they have some superficial resemblance even in the solid models, they have their groups in different spatial configurations.

F. L. Rose (Imperial Chemical Industries): Am I not right in thinking that other antibiotics besides penicillin interfere with cell wall substances ? For example does tetracycline bear the same sort of structural resemblance ?

Pollock: I was going to deal with that but I just did not have time. Perhaps I could mention one compound, cycloserine, which causes accumulation of a compound similar to the one which accumulates in the presence of penicillin, but without the two D-alanine residues; it is a "Park" peptide without the D-alanine. This is very interesting because Strominger's thesis (and there is a lot to be said for it) is that cycloserine interferes with some enzymic reaction involving the formation of D-alanine—possibly with alanine racemase, which converts L-alanine to D-alanine—and/or with the actual formation of the dipeptide, D-alanyl-D-alanine which occurs in the "Park" peptide (Strominger, 1962; Strominger *et al.* 1959). In any case, there is a certain structural similarity between cycloserine and D-alanine (Strominger, 1962). Whether or not this is significant I do not know, but here is another compound which interferes with cell wall synthesis, but appears to do it by blocking a completely different reaction for the insertion of the mucopeptide into the whole structure, and it is not so selectively toxic. Cycloserine combines with pyridoxal phosphate and blocks a number of enzymes which depend on pyridoxal phosphate as a coenzyme; for instance, the transaminases as well as the alanine racemases. It is quite a toxic compound to the host, as you would expect. I think it provides indirect support for the general theory that N-acetylmuramic acid is the key molecule for penicillin action. A quite different chemical reaction is concerned in the primary inhibitory effect of cycloserine, but the final result, the absence of formation of the cell wall, is the same.

R. H. Nimmo-Smith (Wellcome Laboratories of Tropical Medicine): I should like to put a point to Dr. Hitchings. I think it is your view that malaria parasites synthesize their own folic acid and do not incorporate exogenous folic acid. Yesterday Dr. Bishop referred to Trager's conclusion that in the infected duck erythrocyte, it is the erythrocyte which is the site of folic acid synthesis. Could you contribute anything to resolve this apparent discrepancy?

Hitchings: The ultimate resolution of this will come from the demonstration of synthesis of folic acid by plasmodia *in vitro* and their inability to take up folic acid, but lacking this ultimate demonstration I think there are some things which might be said. Trager's observation was that duck erythrocyte infected with plasmodia contained more total folic acid than uninfected erythrocytes. From this he concluded that the erythrocyte was doing the synthesis, and I think he perhaps failed to realize the implications of this assumption. The alternative, of course, is that the plasmodium is synthesizing folic acid and excreting it into the erythrocyte, and this is a rather familiar process now. A large number of bacteria synthesize metabolites in excess and excrete them into the medium. Folic acid biosynthesis appears to be a function which was lost way back in the lower orders of the animal tree. It is very difficult to visualize the plasmodium contributing the missing elements of this biosynthetic pathway to the erythrocyte of a species as highly evolved as the duck.

D. D. Woods (Department of Chemical Microbiology, Oxford): Most of the modern work on the coenzyme function of folic acid would seem to suggest that the ultimate coenzyme form is more probably the tetra-hydro-triglutamate derivative and not the monoglutamate. It would therefore seem important in these tests of the antagonistic action of diaminopyrimidines to test the enzymes with the triglutamates as substrates. Folic acid reductase is active with the triglutamates, I think.

It should also be emphasized, in view of recent biochemical work, that the folic acid reductase enzyme system is not only inherent to the *biosynthesis* of folic acid but also to its *function*, because there is evidence that during the carriage of the hydroxymethyl group and its reduction to the methyl group, tetrahydrofolic acid also acts as a reducing agent, being transformed to dihydrofolic acid. This then has to be reduced back again to tetrahydrofolic acid, which involves dihydrofolic acid reductase. There is thus a second point at which the antimetabolite will intervene.

Hitchings: I agree entirely. There is a suggestion in some of our work, which is not yet ready to be presented, that diaminopyrimidines are perhaps more potent inhibitors of the reduction of the monoglutamate than of the triglutamate. There is also the suggestion that the reductase which is synthesized in excess in resistant cells is concerned primarily with the conjugated forms of folic acid.

Lacey: Trager had to supply methionine to his plasmodia when he was growing them in duck erythrocytes. Does that imply that the plasmodia have a total incapacity for synthesizing methionine, even given that they can synthesize folic acid? You have to supply the plasmodia with methionine to grow them *in vitro* even for a few generations.

Boyd: Professor Lacey, are you suggesting that plasmodia can be grown artificially for some generations?

Lacey: Providing you give them methionine, and a suitable ionic environment, and the erythrocytes.

J. D. Fulton (National Institute for Medical Research): I think what Professor Lacey says is quite true. It has been done for at least five generations. During the war, Evans and workers in Chicago confirmed that. He is quite right about methionine. It is the one amino acid which has to be added to grow these plasmodia.

F. Bergel (Chester Beatty Research Institute): I should like to ask Dr. Williams Smith whether he has done any experiments following his antibiotic treatment, with vitamin B complex, and what happens then to the intestinal flora. With antibiotic treatment under clinical conditions clinicians often prescribe B vitamins to follow the antibiotic.

Williams Smith: All I can say is that after 24 days of treatment with tetracycline the guinea pig did not seem to be lacking in anything. We did not give vitamins.

L. G. Goodwin (Wellcome Laboratories of Tropic Medicine): You mentioned the fact that antibiotics are given for increasing the growth rate of animals. As far as we can see, there is merely a changeover from sensitive to resistant flora. What do you think happens to make the animals grow faster?

Williams Smith: It still is a theory. One theory is that they act by depressing *Clostridium welchii.* In older animals this is more of a minority than a majority flora, and you do not find the changeover occurring so quickly in older animals as in younger ones, if at all.

Boyd: Dr. Williams Smith, could I ask you a question which is, perhaps, not wholly relevant. You talked of guinea-pig faeces. My recollection is that they are full of trichomonads and spirochetes, and all sorts of other things. Were these affected by your antibiotic treatment, or did you only examine the things you could plate?

Williams Smith: I confined myself to the things I could plate. These experiments are quite tedious to perform.

Lacey: In the human mouth penicillin produces the same sort of picture as seen in the guinea pig intestine, and presumably for the same reason. The sensitive *viridans* streptococci disappear and are replaced by resistant faecal streptococci, simply because there are no penicillin-resistant *viridans* streptococci. Thus the flora is inevitably changed, and if treatment is continued other organisms grow up and cause stomatitis.

Williams Smith: It is just streptococci being replaced by streptococci in your case then, is it not?

Lacey: Yes, but different species.

Williams Smith: In the guinea pig the lactobacilli were knocked out and that was the end of it. They were not replaced by other lactobacilli.

E. F. Gale (Medical Research Council Unit for Chemical Microbiology, Cambridge): When you have got resistant flora established in your creatures and you stop the antibiotic therapy, how long does it take for the flora to revert to normal, and does it revert to normal? Have you any idea why the guinea-pig is different from other creatures in this type of experiment?

Williams Smith: If an antibiotic has only been used to a small extent in an environment, you can get the change back to sensitive organisms fairly quickly. But if, for example on a pig farm, antibiotics are fed to the pigs for months on end and are then stopped, it may take six months or a year before the sensitive flora returns. The guinea-pig seems to be unique in that it is the only species which cannot stand treatment with antibiotics.

A. C. Cuckler (Merck Institute for Therapeutic Research, Rahway): I should like to ask Dr. Williams Smith if these changes occur even when small levels—a few grams per ton—of the antibiotics are used in the feed of the animals.

Williams Smith: If you feed antibiotics in the levels recommended for growth stimulation these changes will occur in just the same way.

P. C. Elmes (Queens University, Belfast): If you provide the guinea pigs with resistant lactobacilli, can they re-colonize with them?

Williams Smith: That is a thing we have not done, but I should like to try it. At a guess, it probably will not happen, because I think that the guinea pig may have a specific relationship with one particular type of lactobacillus, of which there are no forms resistant to the tetracyclines. There were plenty of resistant lactobacilli in the environment of the guinea-pigs in my experiments.

REFERENCES

STROMINGER, J. (1962). *Fed. Proc.*, **21,** 134.
STROMINGER, J., THRENN, R. H. and SCOTT, S. S. (1959). *J. Amer. chem. Soc.*, **81,** 3803.

THE STRUCTURE OF ANTILEPROTIC DRUGS

F. L. Rose

Imperial Chemical Industries Limited,
Pharmaceuticals Division, Alderley Park

THREE distinct criteria are usually considered in assessing and analysing the chemotherapeutic activity of drugs against infectious diseases: (a) the sensitivity of the causative organism to the drug when exposed to it in the simplest possible culture medium, (b) the therapeutic response as measured in the experimental animal, and (c) the therapeutic response in the clinical form of the disease.

Given data on each of these three parameters, it is sometimes possible to arrange drugs in order of therapeutic efficiency to a comparatively high level of statistical significance, and therefore to consider correlation of such activity with chemical structure. That is certainly not true of drugs which are used in the treatment of human leprosy. *Mycobacterium leprae* of human origin is still one of the organisms which cannot be cultured, except perhaps to a limited extent in tissue cell explants (Morris and Nakamura, 1959), nor has it been transferred to laboratory animals. Clinically, the disease is one of the most difficult to follow in response to medication. Not only does it pursue a protracted course, frequently calling for the observation of patients over periods of many years, but the disease is complicated by allergic manifestations arising from varying degrees of sensitivity of the host tissues to the microorganism which lead to the two distinct forms of the disease, tuberculoid and lepromatous. In these the environment of the bacillus differs, and therefore its likely response to medication also differs. Nor yet can the ultimate measure of therapeutic effect, the complete and final disappearance of the causative organism from the infected tissues, be applied to human leprosy. Superimposed on these uncertainties is the phenomenon of drug resistance, which in the interest of the patient may call for the substitution of one drug for another at a critical point in an investigation.

With these formidable obstacles in mind, it is not surprising that a rational approach to the chemotherapy of human leprosy has not been possible up to the present time. They also account for the virtual impossibility of the task of assessing antileprotic action in terms of chemical structure. At a less ambitious level, however, some such analysis is feasible. Almost all the drugs in use at the present time in human leprosy were selected in the first place because of their activity against the related *M. tuberculosis*, reinforced in some cases by their effect on *M. lepraemurium*, the causative agent of a mycobacterial disease of rodents. It resembles *M. leprae* morphologically; it will not grow in culture but it can be transferred from rat to rat and produces characteristic lesions. It would seem to provide an ideal laboratory counterpart to the human disease. Unfortunately, assessment of drug effect has not proved so simple a matter as might have been supposed; but more serious has been the lack of reliable correlation of therapeutic results obtained in rats (or mice) infected with murine leprosy, with observations in human leprosy. Indeed, murine leprosy is much more closely allied in this respect to murine tuberculosis. In no sense can these inter-relationships be regarded as quantitative. It is commonplace that remedies used in the treatment of leprosy are not necessarily useful as therapeutic agents in tuberculosis, and *vice versa*. At best, the association is of a qualitative nature.

For the purpose of this contribution, attention will be confined to those drugs and classes of drugs which have shown positive effect in human leprosy, but discussion of structure/activity relationships will inevitably be dependent upon studies with murine leprosy, and with the tubercle bacillus *in vivo* and *in vitro*. The agents selected for consideration are listed in Table I.

Table I

ANTILEPROTIC DRUG TYPES

Type	Structure or general formula

Sulphone

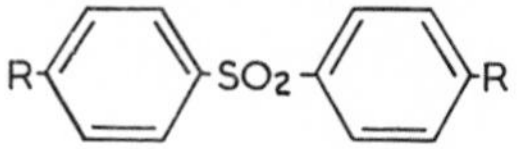

R—〈 〉—SO₂—〈 〉—R

(Sulphoxide)

(- SO -)

Sulphonamide

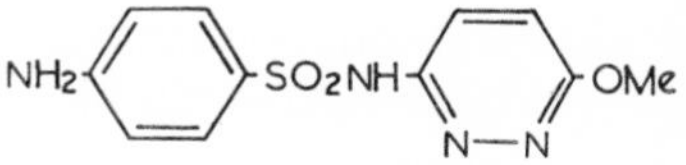

NH₂—〈 〉—SO₂NH—〈 〉—OMe

Thiosemicarbazone

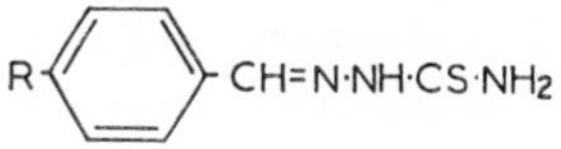

R—〈 〉—CH=N·NH·CS·NH₂

Thiourea

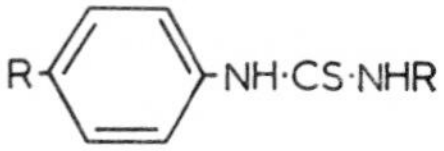

R—〈 〉—NH·CS·NHR

Thiocarbanilide

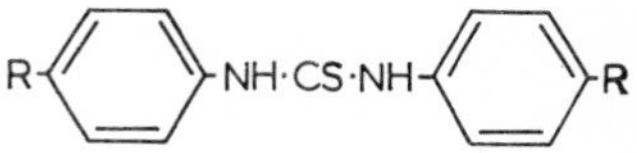

R—〈 〉—NH·CS·NH—〈 〉—R

Thiol

R·SH

Antithyroid
(Methimazole)

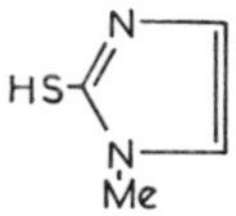

HS—〈 〉
Me

Cycloserine

NH₂·CH—CO
   | NH
   CH₂—O

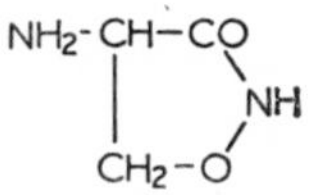

Sulphones

4,4′-Diaminodiphenylsulphone (dapsone) was the first synthetic
agent to exhibit an undisputed beneficial effect in human leprosy
and, as Cochrane (1962) has recently pointed out, still remains the
basic treatment for the disease, despite the fact that some patients

are intolerant to the drug, and others, even after medication with it for many years, are still infective. Initially it came into chemotherapeutic prominence as a development of the early sulphonamide drugs (Buttle *et al.* 1937; Fourneau *et al.*, 1937; Bauer and Rosenthal, 1938). It was more effective than the sulphonamides against experimental streptococcal and pneumococcal infections, but was at first dismissed from clinical use because of its toxicity (Long and Bliss, 1939). Activity against these organisms was antagonized by *p*-aminobenzoic acid, confirming the structural association of the sulphone with its sulphonamide progenitors. A few years later came the announcement of its antimycobacterial activity in rabbits and guinea-pigs, and of its first use in human leprosy (Rist, 1939; Rist, Bloch and Hamon, 1939, 1940; Feldman, Hinshaw and Moses, 1942; Faget *et al.*, 1943).

Most of the chemical variations that have been made on the molecule of diaminodiphenylsulphone have aimed at a reduction of its inherent toxicity; since some aspects of this were attributed to the presence of the anilino residues, much of the effort has concentrated in "blocking" the amino groups. The outcome has been disappointing. Although acute toxicity as measured in the experimental animal has been reduced, this has in general been achieved at the expense of therapeutic effect. It is significant that the most successful preparations have been those in which the blocking group is removed *in vivo* with the regeneration in whole or in part of the parent amine. Prominent among these derivatives are the condensation products of the diamine with aldehyde-bisulphite complexes (Table II).

These agents are very soluble in water and may be injected, although they have been shown to have activity by mouth. In support of the suggestion that they are hydrolysed *in vivo*, when tested *in vitro* under conditions which minimize hydrolysis, their antibacterial activity is less than that exhibited by the parent diamine (Francis and Spinks, 1950; Titus and Bernstein, 1949; Lowe, 1952; Smith, Jackson, Chang and Longenecker, 1949;

Boyer, Troestler, Rist and Tabone, 1950; Boyer, Rist and Saviard, 1949; Floch and Rist, 1952). Additionally, the corresponding bis-methylene sulphonate ($R = -CH_2-SO_3Na$) has been found in our laboratories and by others (Hadler and Ziti, 1956), to be without therapeutic effect against tuberculosis in mice and leprosy in rats, respectively. This accords with the much greater stability of this compound towards hydrolysis.

Table II

WATER-SOLUBLE DERIVATIVES OF DIAMINODIPHENYLSULPHONE

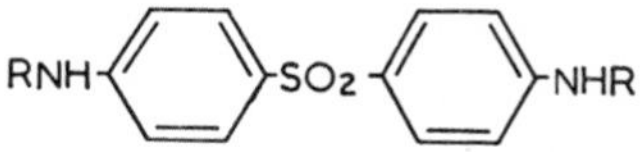

$$RNH-\langle\ \rangle-SO_2-\langle\ \rangle-NHR$$

Name	R group
Promin	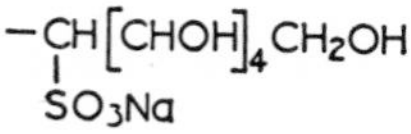 $-CH[CHOH]_4CH_2OH$ with SO_3Na
Diazone	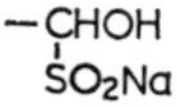 $-CHOH$ with SO_2Na
Sulphetrone	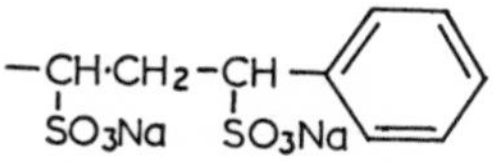 $-CH\cdot CH_2-CH-\langle\ \rangle$ with SO_3Na and SO_3Na
Dapsone acetaldehyde bisulphite	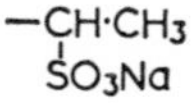 $-CH\cdot CH_3$ with SO_3Na

The mode of action of the sulphone drugs in tuberculostasis, and hence presumably against the leprosy bacillus, seems to involve the same mechanism as that operative in other bacteria. Donovick, Bayan and Hamre (1951, 1952) have shown that p-aminobenzoic acid reverses the bacteriostatic effect of dapsone on the B.C.G. tubercle bacillus. Similar results have been obtained in our laboratories with the same strain, although the reversal is not complete. Donovick observed that the growth-inhibitory action of 4,4'-dihydroxydiphenylsulphone, which *in vitro* is comparable with

9

that of the diamine, was not antagonised by *p*-aminobenzoic acid. In these laboratories (Martin and Wheater, personal communication) we have found the same to hold for the parent diphenylsulphone, which, without any nuclear substitution, still exhibits tuberculostatic action. It thus appears that the antituberculous action of dapsone itself may be made up of at least two components, only one of which involves interference with the utilization of *p*-aminobenzoic acid. Factors not involving *p*-aminobenzoic acid probably account for much of the antibacterial action found *in vitro* amongst a diversity of sulphone structures which contain no amino group, but which have been uniformly inactive *in vivo* (Doub, 1961). The importance of the *para* orientation of the amino and sulphonyl groups in relation to the corresponding disposition of the amino and carboxyl groups in *p*-aminobenzoic acid, is illustrated by the low antituberculous activity *in vitro* of 2,2'- and 3,3'-diaminodiphenylsulphone, and the inactivity of the former (the latter was not tested) in the infected animal (Freedlander and French, 1946). Similar transposition of the *para*-amino group of the sulphanilamide drugs to the position *meta* or *ortho* to the sulphonamide residues abolishes the antistreptococcal action of these agents also, yet again demonstrating the possible similarity of the intrinsic antibacterial mechanisms.

Interest of short duration attached to the clinical use in leprosy of 4,4'-diaminodiphenylsulphoxide (Buu-Hoi, Ba-Khuyen and Dat-Xuong, 1955; Buu-Hoi, 1953). Early enthusiasm was stimulated by the erroneous belief that the sulphoxide was an intermediate in the technical production of the sulphone, and hence should be more readily available. In the event, the sulphoxide now seems to be no more effective and at least as toxic as dapsone (Browne and Davey, 1961). It is still uncertain whether its activity arises from oxidation *in vivo* to the sulphone, or whether the sulphoxide is effective in its own right. Various workers have shown the sulphoxide to be almost without action *in vitro* against pneumococci, haemolytic streptococci and *M. tuberculosis* H37RV, in contrast to the considerable activity of dapsone against these species. The undoubted activity of the compound against these same organisms in the mouse and guinea pig suggested that metabolic oxidation had occurred. The possibility was examined by Levi and Snow (1960) in rabbits, rats and guinea pigs. All three species excreted unchanged drug in the urine together with smaller amounts of dapsone; the poorest conversion occurred in the rabbit. Jardin (1958) showed a similar result in human patients, but the sulphone fraction was so low that he doubted whether its formation could account for the clinical effect of the sulphoxide. No firm conclusions can be drawn, however, until blood and tissue concentrations of the agents have been determined and compared.

Sulphonamides

The sulphonamide drugs, as the first examples of agents found to have unequivocal activity against coccal infections, were logically examined in due course for their action on acid-fast organisms. As early as 1938, Rich and Follis (1938) demonstrated that the tuberculous lesions in infected guinea pigs were less extensive when sulphanilamide was continually administered over periods of 5 to 6 weeks, and their findings were confirmed by many later workers including Smith (1944) who showed in addition a specific bacteriostasis *in vitro* at concentrations around 1:1,000. The therapeutic doses required, even with the later analogues such as sulphathiazole, were in the region of 1 g./kg./day, and in no case were the results good enough to warrant the administration of equivalent massive doses to human tubercular patients. Dharmendra and Bose (1943) showed that both sulphanilamide and sulphapyridine interfered with the viability or infectivity of suspensions of rat leproma, while Krakower, Morales-Otero and Axtmayer (1943) demonstrated the inhibitory effect of sulphanilamide and sulphathiazole on the development of lepromata in rats and mice when the drugs were given in the food in amounts corresponding to

1 g./kg. daily over periods of up to 7 months. In view of these experimental observations, it is not surprising that the sulphonamide drugs have hitherto not been employed in the treatment of leprosy, and indeed Cochrane (1958) has advised against their use for this purpose because they were shown (usually when administered for intercurrent infections) to precipitate lepra reactions. The recent development of long-acting sulphonamides appears to have altered the situation. Schneider, et al., (1960) have obtained very favourable results, especially in tuberculoid cases, by giving 750 mg. doses of sulphamethoxypyridazine every 48 hours. With a view to mass treatment, they tried a suspension of the N^1-acetyl derivative given in 4 g. doses intramuscularly at fortnightly intervals; the treatment was successful and blood levels of 20 to 25 μg./ml. were maintained throughout the intervening periods.

It seems then, that the maintenance of reasonable concentrations of drug in the blood stream might be an especially important factor in determining a therapeutic effect in leprosy; it is perhaps significant that the patterns of absorption, persistence and clearance for sulphamethoxypyridazine and diaminodiphenylsulphone in the mouse and in man (Davey, 1956) are qualitatively similar. In Fig. 1 are shown comparative blood levels obtained in the mouse in experiments in these laboratories carried out by Dr. W. A. M. Duncan using groups of twelve mice, and single oral doses. Values for the sulphones are lower on a dose-for-dose basis than those obtained with the sulphonamide, but this is compensated for by a higher intrinsic antibacterial activity. The corresponding curve for sulphanilamide has been included as typical of a non-persistent sulphonamide drug.

Thioureas

Next to diaminodiphenylsulphone and its congeners, thiourea derivatives, and in particular the thiocarbanilides, have been the most extensively investigated of all therapeutic agents in human leprosy. Interest in these compounds for the treatment of mycobacterial infections was first stimulated by Mayer in 1941, who selected them from amongst known antifungal agents on the basis of the similarity of the taxonomic and host–parasite relationship that existed between infections caused by mycobacteria, and the systemic fungal diseases. Thioureas of two structural series were available, the *N*-monosubstituted, and the *N*,*N*′-disubstituted derivatives. The former usually possessed tuberculostatic activity

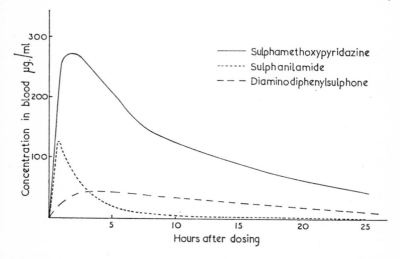

FIG. 1. Concentration in blood of sulphonamide and sulphone drugs after single oral doses in mice of 250 mg./kg.

only *in vitro* and were inactive *in vivo*, while the latter exhibited a still greater effect *in vitro*, associated with marked action against experimental tuberculosis (Mayer, Eisman and Konopka, 1953; Eisman, Konopka and Mayer, 1954; Heubner *et al.*, 1953; Konopka *et al.*, 1954; Konopka, Gisi, Eisman and Mayer, 1955). Numerous representatives from the second group were then tested and found active in murine leprosy, and there are records of three members of the series having been examined subsequently in human leprosy. These are listed in Table III and will be referred to in this text by the code numbers given to them in the original literature.

Su 1380 and Su 1748 were selected for clinical study by Buu-Hoi, Ba-Khuyen and Dat-Xuong (1957), in part because of their comparative ease of synthesis, and shown to be both efficacious and relatively free from toxicity. Administration of the drugs was necessary over prolonged periods. For example, with daily oral doses of Su 1380 beginning at 2 × 100 mg, and rising later to two or three times this amount, a beneficial effect was observed after six to eight months, although there was evidence that bacterial resistance to the drug developed in a proportion of cases. The first

Table III

THIOCARBANILIDE DERIVATIVES IN CLINICAL USE

$$R\text{—}\bigcirc\text{—NH·CS·NH—}\bigcirc\text{—}R'$$

Compound	R	R'
Su 1380	EtO–	EtO–
Su 1748	iso-Am O–	iso-Am O–
Su 1906	n-Bu O–	Me₂N–

clinical trial with Su 1906 was made by Davey and Currie (1956) who selected this compound because of its superior activity against tuberculosis in the mouse and guinea pig, although it was known to be only moderately and irregularly active in murine leprosy. Nevertheless, these workers found it to display marked activity in the human disease at daily doses of 1·5 g. to 3·0 g., and their earlier findings have subsequently been confirmed by further reports from many parts of the world. Unfortunately resistance developed to this drug also, necessitating a change to another drug.

Little is known about the mode of action of the thiourea derivatives. There is only a partial correlation between the antituberculous activities of members of the series as measured *in vitro*, and as observed in the infected mouse. One explanation for this might be the low rate of intestinal absorption of these compounds both in experimental animals and even more noticeably in man (Ellard, 1961). Structural changes would be expected to influence such absorption markedly, but not necessarily in parallel with changes in intrinsic antibacterial activity; and this might lead to seeming anomalies in the *in vitro/in vivo* relationship. Ellard (1961) found that patients who were given doses of 1·5 g. of Su 1906 absorbed only about 10 %, and less than 1 mg. was excreted unchanged in the urine. The antileprotic activity of the drug might therefore be due to the formation of metabolites which were present in much larger quantities in the urine.

However, there is no reason to suppose that the blood and tissue concentrations achieved with Su 1906 are very different from those required to influence the growth of mycobacteria *in vitro*. Moreover, the activity in experimental tuberculosis of a comparatively wide range of structural analogues also lends support to direct action, because although the several hypothetical metabolites would differ from one another in constitution at least as much as do the parent agents, intrinsic activity would need to be accredited to all. In this connection, the surprising observation has been made by Doub *et al.* (1958) that the correlation between antituberculous activity *in vitro* and *in vivo* amongst the thiocarbanilides and related thioureas is much poorer when serum is added to the medium used *in vitro*. These workers also made an extensive study of the influence of structural changes in both series, the results of which accord well with the earlier findings reported by Huebner *et al.* (1953) for the thiocarbanilide series alone.

As already implied, the nature of the R substituents (Table III) can be varied widely without loss of activity, although they must retain the *para* configuration with respect to the thioureido group, and additional nuclear substituents also inactivate. Within these limitations both the R groups can, amongst others, be alkyl or alkoxy; one, but not both, can be amino. The sulphur-containing thiourea residue is essential and activity completely disappears when it is replaced by urea, guanidine or biuret, or even when one hydrogen atom is replaced by alkyl. So far as is known, no hypothesis has yet been advanced to provide a biochemical basis for the activity of the thiocarbanilide drugs, but the configurational requirements do suggest interference with some structurally specific unit associated with the mycobacteria, and which if Mayer's original concept is true, is probably also to be found in the actinomycetes and fungi.

Thiosemicarbazones

This class includes the first synthetic antituberculous drug of high activity both *in vitro* and *in vivo*, and it was logical therefore that this substance (4-acetamidobenzaldehyde thiosemicarbazone; tibione) as well as some of its congeners, should have been tried for the treatment of leprosy. Preliminary results with tibione were encouraging, but later assessments by Lowe (1954) and Davey (1955) showed a deterioration of the therapeutic effects after prolonged treatment, due in part to the emergence of resistant organisms. The development of strains of tubercle bacilli resistant to tibione was also noted by Konopka *et al.* (1955), and equally significant was the cross-resistance that these organisms now exhibited to the thiocarbanilide Su 1906 (Table III). Thiosemicarbazones can be regarded chemically as derived from thiourea, and this is consistent with the suggestion that they act upon similar if not identical biological systems within the mycobacteria. It is for this reason, rather than for their intrinsic chemotherapeutic merit, that the thiosemicarbazones have been included in this review.

Antithyroid agents

Any reviewer of the literature of antileprotic drugs can scarcely fail to notice the frequency with which activity is found in molecules containing organically-bound sulphur. It is true of all the classes of substances mentioned so far in this communication, and applies also to the ethylthiol compounds dealt with below. There is also evidence to support the view that activity against experimental tuberculosis is lost in the non-sulphur containing analogues of these substances, that is, when $C\!=\!S$ is replaced by $C\!=\!O$ or $C\!=\!NH$, or when SO_2 or SO is replaced by CO or CH_2. Only one other biological phenomenon produced by a drug parallels these observations in its dependence upon the presence of sulphur in one form or another in the agent molecule. This is the goitrogenic effect shown by Anderson (1951) to be found amongst an extraordinarily wide range of sulphur derivatives, and which has led to the introduction of several successful compounds for the treatment of clinical thyrotoxicosis. At first sight a connection between two such seemingly unconnected therapies seems improbable, and the chemical relationship mere coincidence, especially in those instances where the antimycobacterial effects *in vivo* could apparently be explained satisfactorily on the basis of a direct action on the organisms. It can be argued that although experimental antithyroid activity has been found in all the classes of thiomolecules to which the antileprotic drugs listed in Table I belong, the individual agents are themselves by no means the most active examples of their types. Indeed such a property has been specifically denied for the thiocarbanilide Su 1906. Publication by O'Byrne (1960) of the results of treatment of human leprosy (236 cases) with antithyroid medicaments over a period of eight years, however, compels consideration of a possible connection between the two effects. O'Byrne was first attracted to this form of therapy following the administration of propylthiouracil to a patient affected simultaneously with thyrotoxicosis and leprosy. At the end of six months both diseases were considerably improved. Led by this observation, by the known effect of iodide on leprous manifestations and by the findings of Hamilton and Werner (1952) that antithyroid drugs decrease protein-bound iodine in the blood, O'Byrne then gave antithyroid preparations in cases of leprosy without thyrotoxicosis. At first they were used as adjuvants to the sulphones and then alone;

recent experience has been gained from the sole use of methimazole (Table I). Cochrane (1962) has drawn attention to the fact that improvement in leprosy occurs within a few weeks of beginning treatment, some months before hypothyroidism would be expected, and that the patients did not become myxoedematous.

No information appears to have been published on the antimycobacterial activity of methimazole *in vitro*, but thiouracil is known to be lethal to bacteria, and it could be assumed in the absence of actual evidence that methimazole exerts a direct action on *M. leprae*. It now seems possible that an additional component in the total therapeutic effect might be contributed through a subliminal action on the thyroid gland of the host. If this were so, then it would be reasonable to suggest that a similar complex of effects comes into play in the treatment of leprosy with at least some of the other sulphur-containing agents.

In an endeavour to link the two conditions of leprosy and thyrotoxicosis, O'Byrne (1960) has drawn attention to a number of relevant facts. Inhabitants of regions of the world where there is a low incidence of endemic goitre are less severely affected by leprosy, and *vice versa*. This can sometimes be related to dietary influences such as the comparatively large iodine intake due to preponderance of fish or iodine-containing algae in the food, or conversely to the consumption of anti-thyroid vegetables such as turnip or rutabaga amongst others, containing " goitrin "(5-vinyl-2-thiooxazolidone). He has also pointed out that in both leprosy and thyrotoxicosis there is a decrease in the serum level of cholesterol, diffusible calcium, urea, glutathione, ascorbic acid and of the alkaline reserve, whereas in both conditions the level of glucose and globulins, as well as the sedimentation rate, are increased.

Ethylthiol

Ethylthiol was first made in 1834, but its antituberculous action was only recently discovered. The first (indirect and unsuspected) observation was by del Pianto (1950) who reported activity in the infected guinea pig for a benzthiazole derivative given together with a source of thiol groups, sodium 5-ethylthiosulphate. In 1953, the same worker noted that ethylthiosulphate was itself active *in vivo* and in due course (del Pianto, 1959) reported an effect in the treatment of leprosy. The therapeutic significance of ethylthiol derivatives was also realized by Brown *et al.* (1954), and by Kushner *et al.* (1955), again on the basis of indirect observations. Del Pianto's first report suggested to us that hydrolytic release of ethylthiol from sodium ethylthiosulphate was the mechanism of its antituberculous activity. Research was concentrated both on the development of a pharmaceutically acceptable precursor of this most objectionable substance, and on determining the extent to which therapeutic activity was a property of other thiol compounds. The results of the more general studies were described by Davies *et al.* (1956) and experience with the preferred compound (diethyldithiolisophthalate; ditophal) against tuberculosis in the mouse by Davies and Driver (1957). The general conclusion of these investigations was that antituberculous activity was unique, apart from trace effects in one or two other thiols, to the ethyl homologue, and that the therapeutic effect of the most active derivatives was comparable with that of isoniazid and streptomycin. Ditophal itself was a stable bland oil, and had the unusual ability to penetrate and be absorbed through the skin. As a result, the percutaneous route of administration was chosen. The outcome of the first trials in leprosy were reported by Davey and Hogerzeil (1959) and Davey (1959). Provided that inunction was adequate (twice weekly), the drug was found to exert a chemotherapeutic action in the first two or three months of treatment. After this time, signs of drug resistance began to appear in some of the patients, and Davey (1959) then instituted standard oral therapy with dapsone or Su 1906, whereupon progress continued to be better than would have been expected had the thiol compound not first been given. It is along these lines that the subsequent use of ditophal has been developed.

The mode of action of ethylthiol has been the subject of considerable research, but it cannot yet be said that it is any more completely understood than that of any of the agents already described. Indeed, there are several most unusual features which still call for investigation. The slight tuberculostatic activity exerted *in vitro* recorded by Davies *et al.* (1956) was no greater than that of the homologous and therapeutically inactive thiols. This led Snow (1957) and Lowe (1960) to search for a possible active metabolite, using first [35]S-, and then ^{14}C-labelled material, converted into and handled as the more convenient disulphide. The chief organic metabolites were ethylmethylsulphone in preponderance, and the corresponding sulphoxide, which are themselves without therapeutic action. A number of hypothetical metabolites which were prepared in the laboratory and tested by Davies *et al.* (1956) were also inactive. A possible mode of action through interference with a biological methylating or thiomethylating system was also studied (Davies and Driver, 1957). In support of this possibility it was found that the antituberculous activity of sodium ethylthiosulphate in mice was antagonized by the corresponding methylthiosulphate. The activities of ethyl thiolbenzoate, diethyldisulphide and ditophal were similarly antagonized by methyl thiolbenzoate. Curiously, dimethyldisulphide did not antagonize the action of either diethyldisulphide or ethyl thiolbenzoate, but this might be due to a different metabolic course pursued by the former. The therapeutic action of ethyl thiolbenzoate was not reduced by cystine, cysteine methionine or glutathione.

Davies and Driver (1958) next examined the effect of ethylthiol against tubercle bacilli growing within monocytes *in vitro* using the method of Suter (1952). Ethylthiol inhibited growth at concentrations of about 10μg./ml. Methylthiol was ineffective, and indeed partially reversed the effect of ethylthiol, in accordance with the observations in mice. Specificity of the effect was shown by the failure of ethylthiol to inhibit the intracellular growth of a strain of bacilli which had become resistant in mice to treatment with thiol esters. It thus seems clear that part at least of the therapeutic action of ethylthiol is a direct one, but through the agency of the monocytes, and is not mediated solely through other defence mechanisms of the host. The development of drug resistance suggests that a chemical agent, presumably derived from ethylthiol itself, is ultimately in contact with the organism and in some manner lowers its virulence towards the infected animal. It would be of great interest to know the structure of this hypothetical substance, but metabolic studies up to the present time have failed to reveal even its presence, let alone its identity. If it exists, it must be an extraordinarily potent agent.

Cycloserine

Cycloserine is included here, not because it is useful in leprosy, but because of the biochemical implications of its distinctive structure. It was discovered almost simultaneously by three American groups (Harris, *et al.*, 1955; Cuckler, Frost, McClelland and Solotorovsky, 1955; Harned, Hidy and La Baw, 1955), who obtained it from various *Streptomyces* species. It is a simple cyclic hydroxamic acid related to serine (Table I). Harned *et al.* (1955) have shown it to be a broad spectrum antibiotic which inhibits the growth *in vitro* of human strains of *M. tuberculosis*. Activity *in vivo* is not detectable in infected mice or guinea pigs, and is low in rabbits and monkeys. Epstein, Nair and Boyd (1955) and Chang (1957) have, however, shown the antibiotic to have antituberculous activity in man; it is less active than streptomycin or isoniazid. The first clinical reports of the use of the drug against leprosy were by De Almeida Neto and De Paula e Silva (1958), and others have followed. Whilst the effects have been definite, and in certain instances quite remarkable, cycloserine is not free from toxic side effects and for this reason, and because of its cost, Cochrane (1962) considers that it is unlikely to replace existing standard treatments to any extent.

Its mode of action is not yet understood. Against certain

non-acid-fast organisms it in some ways resembles penicillin in that there is an interference with the synthesis of cell wall substance. Thus, against *Staph. aureus*, Strominger, Threnn and Scott (1959) have shown that a uridine nucleotide accumulates, and that the effect is antagonized by D-alanine. Similar observations have been made by other workers with respect to *E. coli* and *Strep. faecalis*. There is no evidence, however, that these findings are of relevance to the way in which the drug acts on *M. tuberculosis* or *M. leprae*. Here there may be a relation to the growth factor mycobactin which has been the subject of study in these laboratories (Rose and Snow, 1955). This substance was isolated in the form of its crystalline aluminium complex $C_{47}H_{72}O_{10}N_5Al$ from cultures of *M. phlei*, and was capable of initiating the growth of *M. johnei* on an otherwise synthetic medium. There is reason to believe (Snow, personal communication) that a similar product is present in *M. tuberculosis*. Sutton and Stanfield (1955) showed that the inhibitory effect of cycloserine on the growth of *M. paratuberculosis* was reversed by the addition of mycobactin. The only point of chemical or structural resemblance between these substances relates to the occurrence in the latter of two hydroxamic acid residues. Both are derived from *N*-hydroxylysine, which in one form is believed to present as the cyclized hydroxamic structure. It is tempting to speculate that the interfering action of cycloserine takes place at this latter point in the molecule of the growth factor, although there is as yet no experimental evidence whatsoever to support this view.

As predicted, the relationships between chemical structure and antileprotic activity which can be deduced with existing drugs are uncertain and inconclusive. Success to date in the chemotherapy of human leprosy (which however unsatisfactory has still been sufficient to alter completely the lot of sufferers from the disease) has been entirely dependent on its superficial qualitative correlation with the laboratory form of leprosy and tuberculosis. Susceptibility of natural tuberculosis infections to drugs is even less relevant to leprosy; the use in leprosy of the compounds most effective in tuberculosis namely isoniazid, streptomycin and p-aminosali-cyclic acid, has become obsolete, while dapsone, which has never been seriously considered in the treatment of tuberculosis has now become the antileprotic of choice. As seen by the laboratory worker seeking to devise improved antileprotic drugs, the whole situation is most unsatisfactory. It might well be that he has already to hand agents that could be of value but which he has discarded because of their indifferent performance in the standard antituber-culous screens. An adventurous clinical trial in human leprosy seems to be the only solution in the present state of knowledge, but the objections to this are obvious and substantial. Nor can much assis-tance be expected from a rational approach based on the biochemis-try of the causative organism. Its notoriously low metabolic rate makes the acquistion of biochemical fact tedious or wellnigh impossible and metabolite-antagonists designed therefrom as po-tential drugs would be slow in operation. Considering these circumstances, the therapeutic success achieved so far is perhaps remarkable, so remarkable that it possibly results to a considerable extent from unspecific factors associated with reactions of the host tissues. Here, perhaps, is a clear line for further investigation. If a complex of activity is concerned, made up in part of a component which involves a direct action on the leprosy bacillus, and an equally or more important contribution by the chemical stimu-lation of a host tissue response, there is no reason to suppose that these two effects would be, or need be, at the optimum level in the single therapeutic agent structure. It seems more profitable to study both functions separately in terms of molecular structure, and to devise different compounds which in concert would then pro-vide maximum benefit to the patient, rather than continue with attempts to devise a single agent which at best must repre-sent a compromise. Perhaps a start could be made by a fuller and more direct investigation of the goitrogenic implication amongst the sulphur-containing compounds described in this communication, and it is hoped that this contribution will stimulate such an approach.

[Discussion on this paper was postponed until after the following paper by D. A. Mitchison; see p. 279.]

REFERENCES

ANDERSON, G. W. (1951). Medicinal Chemistry, I, New York:Wiley, p. 1.

BAUER, H. and ROSENTHAL, S. M. (1938). *Publ. Hlth. Rep., Wash.*, **53**, 40.

BOYER, F., RIST, N. and SAVIARD, M. (1949). *Ann. Inst. Pasteur*, **77**, 680.

BOYER, F., TROESTLER, J., RIST, N. and TABONE, J. (1950). *Ann. Inst. Pasteur*, **78**, 140.

BROWN, H. D., MATZUK, A. R., BECKER, H. J., CONBERE, J. P., CONSTANTIN, J. M., SOLOTOROVSKY, M., WINSTEN, S., IRONSON, E. and QUASTEL, J. H. (1954). *J. Amer. chem. Soc.*, **76**, 3860.

BROWNE, S. G. and DAVEY, T. F. (1961). *Leprosy Rev.*, **32**, 194.

BUTTLE, G. A. H., STEPHENSON, D., SMITH, S., DEWING, T. and FOSTER, G. E. (1937). *Lancet*, **i**, 1331.

BUU-HOI, N. P. (1953), *Int. J. Leprosy*, **21**, 567.

BUU-HOI, N. P., BA-KHUYEN, N. and DAT-XUONG, N. (1955). *Bull. Acad. nat. Med., Paris*, **139**, 275.

BUU-HOI, N. P., BA-KHUYEN, N. and DAT-XUONG, N. (1957). *Trop. Dis. Bull.*, **54**, 832.

CHANG, Y. T. (1957). *Int. J. Leprosy*, **25**, 257.

COCHRANE, R. G. (1958). Leprosy in Theory and Practice, Bristol:John Wright, p. 323.

COCHRANE, R. G. (1962). *Practitioner*, **188**, 67.

CUCKLER, A. C., FROST, B. M., McCLELLAND, L. and SOLOTOROVSKY, M. (1955). *Antibiot. and Chemother,*, **5**, 183.

DAVEY, T. F. (1955). *Leprosy Rev.*, **26**, 8.

DAVEY, T. F. (1956). *Leprosy Rev.*, **27**, 6.

DAVEY, T. F. (1959). *Leprosy Rev.*, **30**, 141.

DAVEY, T. F. and CURRIE, G. (1956). *Leprosy Rev.*, **27**, 94.

DAVEY, T. F. and HOGERZEIL, L. M. (1959). *Leprosy Rev.*, **30**, 61.

DAVIES, G. E. and DRIVER, G. W. (1957). *Brit. J. Pharmacol.*, **12**, 434.

DAVIES, G. E. and DRIVER, G. W. (1958). *Nature, Lond.*, **182**, 664.

DAVIES, G. E., DRIVER, G. W., HOGGARTH, E., MARTIN, A. R., PAIGE, M. F. C., ROSE, F. L. and WILSON, B. R. (1956). *Brit. J. Pharmacol.*, **11**, 351.

DE ALMEIDA NETO, E. and DE PAULA E SILVA, D. (1958). *Trop. Dis. Bull.*, **55**, 53.

DEL PIANTO, E. (1950). *Ric. sci.*, **20**, 83; 101.

DEL PIANTO, E. (1953). *Ric. Sci.*, **23**, 1785.

DEL PIANTO, E. (1959), *Leprosy Rev.*, **30**, 23.

DHARMENDRA and BOSE, R. (1943). *Indian J. med. Res.*, **31**, 133.

DONOVICK, R., BAYAN, A. and HAMRE, D. (1951). *XII Int. Congr. Pure and Appl. Chem., Abstracts of Papers*, 301.

DONOVICK, R., BAYAN, A. and HAMRE, D. (1952). *Amer. Rev. Tuberc.*, **66**, 219.

DOUB, L. (1961). Medicinal Chemistry, V, New York:Wiley, p. 363.

DOUB, L., RICHARDSON, L. M., HERBST, D. R., BLACK, M. L., STEVENSON, O. L., BAMBAS, L. L., YOUMANS, G. P. and YOUMANS, A. S. (1958). *J. Amer. chem. Soc.*, **80**, 2205.

EISMAN, P. C., KONOPKA, E. A. and MAYER, R. L. (1954). *Amer. Rev. Tuberc.*, **70**, 121.

ELLARD, G. A. (1961). *Leprosy Rev.*, **32**, 233.

EPSTEIN, I. G., NAIR, K. G. S. and BOYD, L. J. (1955). *Antibiot. Med.*, **1**, 80.

FAGET, G. H., POGGE, R. C., JOHANSEN, F. A., DINAN, J. F., PREJEAN, B. M. and ECCLES, C. G. (1943). *Publ. Hlth. Rep.,Wash.*, **58**, 1729.

FELDMAN, W. H., HINSHAW, H. C. and MOSES, H. E. (1942). *Amer. Rev. Tuberc.*, **45**, 303.

FLOCH, H. and RIST, N. (1952). *Rev. brasil. Leprol.*, **18**, 111. (*Chem. Abstr.*, **47**, 7659).

FOURNEAU, E., TRÉFOUËL, J., NITTI, F., BOVET, D. and TRÉFOUËL, T. J. (1937). *C.R. Acad. Sci. Paris*, **204**, 1763.

FRANCIS, J. and SPINKS, A. (1950). *Brit. J. Pharmacol.*, **5**, 565.

FREEDLANDER, B. L. and FRENCH, F. (1946). *Proc. Soc. exp. Biol., N.Y.*, **63**, 361.

HADLER, W. A. and ZITI, L. M. (1956). *Arzneimittel-forsch.*, **6**, 534.

HAMILTON, H. B. and WERNER, S. C. (1952). *J. clin. Endocr.*, **12**, 1083.

HARNED, R. C., HIDY, P. H. and LA BAW, E. K. (1955). *Antibiot. and Chemother.*, **5**, 204.

HARRIS, D. A., RUGER, M., REAGAN, M. A., WOLF, F. S., PEEK, R. L., WALLICK, H. and WOODRUFF, H. B. (1955). *Antibiot. and Chemother.*, **5**, 183.

HUEBNER, C. F., MARSH, J. L., MIZZONI, R. H., MULL, R. P., SCHROEDER, D. C., TROXELL, H. A. and SCHOLZ, C. R. (1953). *J. Amer. chem. Soc.*, **75**, 2274.

JARDIN, C. (1958). *Sem. Hôp. Paris*, **34**, TH 611.

KONOPKA, E. A., EISMAN, P. C., MAYER, R. L., PARKER, F. and ROBBINS, S. L. (1954). *Amer. Rev. Tuberc.*, **70**, 130.

KONOPKA, E. A., GISI, T., EISMAN, P. C. and MAYER, R. L. (1955). *Proc. Soc. exp. Biol., N.Y.*, **89**, 388.

KRAKOWER, C., MORALES-OTERO, P. and AXTMAYER, J. H. (1943). *J. infect. Dis.*, **72**, 1.

KUSHNER, S., DALALIAN, H., BACH, F. L. (Jr.), CENTOLA, D., SANJURJO, J. L. and WILLIAMS, J. H. (1955). *J. Amer. chem. Soc.*, **77**, 1152.

LEVI, A. A.and SNOW, G. A. (1960). *Brit. J. Pharmacol.*, **15**, 160.

LONG, P. A. and BLISS, E. A. (1939). The Clinical and Experimental Use of Sulfanilamide, Sulfapyridine and Allied Compounds, New York: Macmillan, p. 21.

LOWE, J. (1952). *Leprosy Rev.*, **23**, 4.

LOWE, J. (1954). *Lancet*, **ii**, 1065.

LOWE, J. S. (1960). *Biochem. Pharmacol.*, **3**, 163.

MAYER, R. L. (1941). *Rev. med. franc.*, **9**, 393.

MAYER, R. L., EISMAN, P. C. and KONOPKA, E. A. (1953). *Proc. Soc. exp. Biol., N.Y.* **82**, 769.

MORRIS, J. A. and NAKAMURA, K. (1959). *J. infect. Dis.*, **105**, 73.

O'BYRNE, A. (1960). *Int. J. Leprosy*, **28**, 401.

RICH, A. R. and FOLLIS, R. H. (1938). *Bull. Johns Hopk. Hosp.*, **62**, 77.

RIST, N. (1939). *C.R. Soc. Biol.*, Paris, **130**, 972.

RIST, N., BLOCH, F. and HAMON, V. (1939). *C.R. Soc. Biol.*, Paris, **130**, 976.

RIST, N., BLOCH, F. and HAMON, V. (1940). *Ann. Inst. Pasteur*, **64**, 203.

ROSE, F. L. and SNOW, G. A. (1955) Ciba Foundation Symposium on Experimental Tuberculosis, Churchill: London, p. 41.

SCHNEIDER, J., LANGUILLON, J., CLARY, J., BOISSAN, R. and PICARD, P. (1960). *Bull. Soc. Path. exot.*, **53**, 173.

SMITH, C. R. (1944). *Amer. Rev. Tuberc.*, **50**, 163.

SMITH, M. I., JACKSON, E. L., CHANG, Y. T. and LONGENECKER, W. H. (1949). *Proc. Soc. exp. Biol., N.Y.*, **71**, 23.

SNOW, G. A. (1957). *Biochem. J.*, **65**, 77.

STROMINGER, J. L., THRENN, R. H. and SCOTT, S. S. (1959). *J. Amer. chem. Soc.*, **81**, 3803.

SUTER, E. (1952). *J. exp. Med.*, **96**, 137.

SUTTON, W. B. and STANFIELD, LaV. (1955). *Antibiot. and Chemother.*, **5**, 582.

TITUS, E. and BERNSTEIN, J. (1949). *Ann. N.Y. Acad. Sci.*, **52**, 719.

THE PHARMACOLOGY OF ISONIAZID IN MAN

D. A. MITCHISON

Medical Research Council's Unit for Research on Drug Sensitivity in Tuberculosis, Postgraduate Medical School, London

ISONIAZID (isonicotinyl hydrazide) is the most effective and widely used chemotherapeutic drug in the treatment of tuberculosis; it has the advantage of a cost considerably lower than either of the other two standard drugs. In the developing countries, where tuberculosis if often a particularly prevalent disease, the amount of money that can be spent on the treatment of each patient is limited, so that it is common practice to use isoniazid alone. The merits of different regimens of isoniazid alone have therefore been investigated in clinical studies carried out at the Tuberculosis Chemotherapy Centre, Madras, under the auspices of the Indian Council of Medical Research, the Madras State Government, the World Health Organization and the British Medical Research Council. It is to the staff of the Centre that the credit for the work reported here must be given.

In the first study (Tuberculosis Chemotherapy Centre, 1960), patients with newly diagnosed and previously untreated pulmonary tuberculosis were treated for one year in their homes with three regimens of isoniazid alone and one of isoniazid together with *p*-aminosalicylic acid. The dosage used in the regimens of isoniazid alone is set out in Table I. Patients in the "H" series received 4·5 mg./kg. body weight a day, divided in to 2 daily doses, that is to say, 2 doses of 100 mg. each for a patient weighing 100 lb or more. In the "HI-2" regimen, 2 doses a day were also given, but the individual dose was doubled so that a patient weighing 100 lb or more received 200 mg. isoniazid twice a day. The patients in the

"HI-1" series received the same total dose as those in the "HI-2" series, but this was given in a single daily dose, 400 mg. a day for a patient of 100 lb or more. The dosage was adjusted to the weight of the patient.

The results of the first study indicated that improved therapeutic results were obtained with increasing dosage of isoniazid, though the two higher dosage regimens were accompanied by the occurrence of toxicity in the form of peripheral neuritis. The second

Table I

REGIMENS OF TREATMENT WITH ISONIAZID ALONE

Treatment regimen	Single dose of isoniazid (mg./kg.)	No. of doses a day	Total daily dose of isoniazid (mg./kg.)	Number of patients
X	13·8	1	13·8	51
HI-1	8·7	1	8·7	69
HI-2	4·4	2	8·7	67
H	2·2	2	4·5	86

study (Tuberculosis Chemotherapy Centre, 1962) was then carried out in which an even higher dosage of isoniazid was used (a single daily dose of 13·8 mg./kg.; Table I) and in which various supplements were tried to see whether they would reduce the incidence of peripheral neuritis. The supplements had little or no influence on toxicity, so that the study may be taken to demonstrate the therapeutic effectiveness and the toxicity of this high dose of isoniazid alone.

During the course of the studies the concentration of isoniazid in the serum of the patients was determined and on this basis they were classified as slow or rapid inactivators of isoniazid. Reported here is the evidence obtained in the manner in which therapeutic efficacy and toxicity are related to dose and also to certain measures of the time-concentration curves. From these findings practical conclusions can be drawn about dosage schedules which are likely to produce maximal therapeutic benefit with a minimal risk of toxicity.

Rate of inactivation

Isoniazid is metabolized in the body principally to its acetyl derivative, to hydrazones and to isonicotinic acid (Hughes, Schmidt and Biehl, 1955; Vivien and Grosset, 1961). None of these compounds, with the possible exception of some of the hydrazones, are active against tubercle bacilli. Considerable differences exist between patients in the rate at which isoniazid is inactivated (Bönicke and Reif, 1953; Hughes, 1953). They can be divided into two fairly distinct groups of slow and rapid inactivators (Biehl, 1956; 1957, Mitchell, Riemensnider, Harsch and Bell, 1958; Evans, Manley and McKusick, 1960). The serum concentrations of microbiologically active isoniazid obtained in these groups after an intramuscular dose, are shown in Fig. 1. The rate of inactivation appears to be linked with a single gene (Knight, Selin and Harris, 1959; Evans, Manley and McKusick, 1960; Sunahara, Urano, and Ogawa 1961).

Patients in the clinical studies were classified as slow or rapid inactivators by giving them an intramuscular injection of 3 mg./kg. isoniazid followed by a microbiological assay (Mandel, Cohn, Russell and Middlebrook, 1956) of the serum isoniazid concentration $4\frac{1}{2}$ hours later. Patients with serum concentrations of $0 \cdot 58$ μg./ml. or more were classified as slow inactivators, and those with concentrations less than this as rapid inactivators (Gangadharam, Bhatia, Radhakrishna and Selkon, 1961). About 60% of the Indian patients were found to be slow inactivators.

Serum concentrations during treatment

Serum isoniazid concentrations were also studied in patients receiving their prescribed regimen of treatment (Gangadharam, Deradatta, Fox, Nair and Selkon, 1961). A supervised dose of isoniazid was given in the amount used for treatment, and microbiological assays were done on serum samples obtained at intervals thereafter. Groups of 3 to 7 slow inactivators, and similar numbers of rapid inactivators in each treatment series, were so examined.

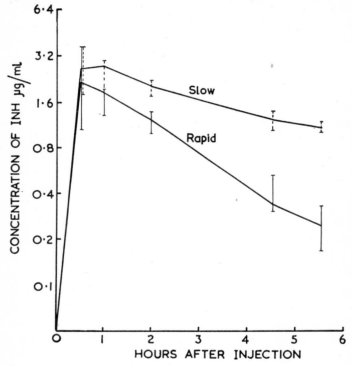

FIG. 1. Serum concentrations of isoniazid in slow and rapid inactivators following an intramuscular injection of 3 mg. isoniazid/kg.

The concentrations of free isoniazid are shown in Fig. 2. Two particularly important measurements were made from these curves. The peak isoniazid concentration was estimated as the point of intersection of the extrapolated ascending line joining the 0 to 1 hour concentrations and the extrapolated descending line joining

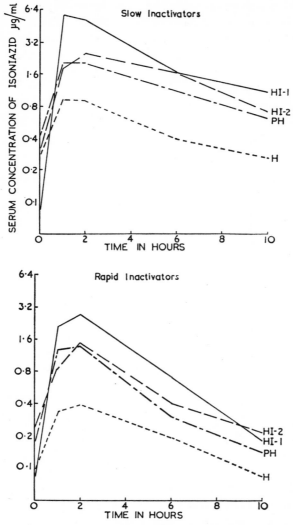

FIG. 2. Mean serum concentrations of isoniazid in patients receiving single doses of isoniazid. HI-1, 8·7 mg./kg.; HI-2, 4·4 mg./kg.; H, 2·2 mg./kg.; PH, 2·2 mg./kg. *plus* 230 mg./kg. of sodium *p*-aminosalicylate.

the 2 and 6 hour concentrations. The period during which 0·2 μg./ml. isoniazid was present in the serum was also estimated as a measure of coverage by a low bacteriostatic concentration of the drug.

Therapeutic efficacy related to dosage and serum concentrations

One of the best measures of therapeutic efficacy of a chemo-therapeutic regimen is the proportion of patients whose disease

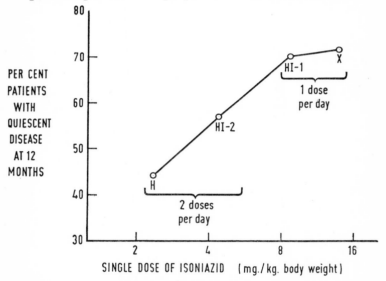

Fig. 3. Proportion of patients with bacteriologically quiescent disease at 12 months related to the dosage of isoniazid.

attains bacteriological quiescence. The disease has been termed quiescent if not more than one culture among the 7 to 9 cultures obtained from each patient during the last 3 months of the year's treatment was positive (in the majority of these patients all of the cultures were negative).

The proportions of patients who had quiescent disease at one year is related to the size of a single dose of isoniazid in Fig. 3. The response in patients treated with a single daily dose of 8·7 mg./kg. (HI-1) was significantly better than the response of patients treated with the same daily dose divided into two single doses of 4·3 mg./kg. (HI-2). This finding suggested that it is more appropriate to relate response to the size of the single dose, as in Fig. 3, than to the total daily dose.

The response to isoniazid was found to improve with increase in dosage, but the improvement was very small when the dose was increased from 8·7 to 13·8 mg./kg. Furthermore, it is probable that the improvement noted on increasing the dose from 2·2 to 4·4 mg./kg. may have been less than is indicated in Fig. 3. The proportion of patients who showed deterioration sufficient to warrant a change of treatment, a further important measure of response, was slightly higher in the HI-2 than in the H series. There were also differences in the pretreatment virulence of the organisms in these two series, and when allowance was made for these differences, the response of the two series became more nearly equal. Thus it is possible that the curve relating dose to response may be sigmoid in shape.

Data on the relationship between serum isoniazid concentrations in the samples of patients taking their prescribed regimens, and the response in the three treatment series (HI-1, HI-2 and H) in which an increase in dose influences response, are set out in Table II.

Table II

RESPONSE TO TREATMENT FOR I YEAR RELATED TO PEAK SERUM
CONCENTRATIONS AND DURATION OF COVERAGE

Treatment regimen	Rate of inactivation of isoniazid	Number of patients	Patients with quiescent disease (%)	Peak serum concentration of isoniazid ($\mu g./ml.$)	Duration of coverage with $0·2\ \mu g./ml.$ isoniazid (hours)
HI-1	Slow	32	72	6·6	> 26
	Rapid	29	66	4·2	12–18
HI-2	Slow	35	59	2·6	> 26
	Rapid	23	56	1·9	24–26
H	Slow	38	48	1·2	> 26
	Rapid	33	44	0·7	4–12

Since slow and rapid inactivators differ less in the peak concentrations attained than in the duration of coverage with a low concentration of isoniazid, an analysis of the relationship between various measures of the concentration-time curve and the response of the patients was possible. A good association exists between response and the peak serum concentration. However, response does not appear to be related to the duration of coverage with 0·2 μg./ml. isoniazid, nor is there a good association with other measures of the concentration-time curves (not tabulated here) such as the duration of a concentration of 1 μg./ml. isoniazid in the serum or the concentrations found at 6 hours after the dose.

In each treatment series the proportion of patients who attained quiescent disease was slightly higher for the slow than for the rapid inactivators. The difference is approximately equal to that achieved by an increase in dose of 50 %.

Toxicity related to dosage and serum concentrations

The main type of toxicity to isoniazid was the occurrence of peripheral neuritis (Devadatta et al., 1960; Tuberculosis Chemotherapy Centre, 1962). Biehl and Vilter (1954) have shown that isoniazid increases the urinary excretion of pyridoxine and it is thought that peripheral neuritis may result from a deficiency of this vitamin. The incidence of peripheral neuritis in the patients in the two clinical studies is set out in Table III. Peak concentrations of isoniazid in the serum of patients in the second (X) study are not yet available and have been estimated from the values obtained in the first study, assuming that the peak serum concentrations increased proportionately to log. dose from the HI-1 dose to the X dose, as they did from the HI-2 to the HI-1 doses. In Table III these values are given in parentheses. It is evident that the incidence of toxicity increases with the dose of isoniazid but that the association with peak serum concentrations is poor. Examination of the slow and rapid inactivator groups within each treatment series

reveals that the incidence of toxicity is higher in the slow inactivators than would be expected from the values of the peak serum
concentrations.

It is reasonable to assume that toxicity is related not only to
concentration of isoniazid in the tissues but also to the period of
exposure to the drug. A purely empirical attempt was therefore
made to relate the incidence of toxicity not only to peak serum
concentrations, but also to the difference between slow and rapid

Table III

INCIDENCE OF PERIPHERAL NEURITIS RELATED TO PEAK SERUM CONCENTRATIONS

Treatment regimen	Rate of inactivation of isoniazid	Number of patients	Patients with peripheral neuritis		Peak serum concentration of isoniazid ($\mu g./ml.$)
			No.	%	
X	Slow	21	11	52	(10·5)
	Rapid	34	2	6	(6·7)
HI-1	Slow	39	11	28	6·6
	Rapid	32	2	6	4·2
HI-2	Slow	44	6	14	2·6
	Rapid	28	0	0	1·9
H	Slow	50	0	0	1·2
	Rapid	36	0	0	0·7

inactivators in the period that isoniazid was present in the serum,
and to the frequency of dosage. A function P/Kt was calculated for
rapid and slow inactivators in each treatment series, where P is
peak serum comcentration, K is the descending slope of the line
joining the 2 hour and the 6 hour serum isoniazid concentrations
on a logarithmic scale ($K_{slow} = 0·100$ and $K_{rapid} = 0·198$) and t is
the period in hours between the doses of isoniazid (12 for the H and
HI-2 series, 24 for the H and X series). Values for P/Kt show a fairly
good association with the incidence of toxicity (Table IV). The
function P/Kt only serves the purpose of a very approximate
correction for the time element in the time-concentration curves.
There are reasons for supposing that the deficiency of vitamin B_6, or

any other factor responsible for peripheral neuritis, is unlikely to be strictly proportional either to K or to t.

Barclay, Koch-Weser and Ebert (1954) showed that the maximal adsorption of radioactively-labelled isoniazid on to isoniazid-sensitive tubercle bacilli occurred in 16 to 24 hours, and that the amount adsorbed by the bacilli increased with the concentration of isoniazid in the medium, according to Freundlich's equation. The bacilli in the lesions of the patient are unlikely to be able to multiply to any considerable extent once chemotherapy has been

Table IV

INCIDENCE OF PERIPHERAL NEURITIS RELATED TO AN
EMPIRICAL CONCENTRATION–TIME FUNCTION

Treatment regimen	Rate of inactivation of isoniazid	Patients with peripheral neuritis (%)	P/Kt
X	Slow	52	4·38
HI-1	Slow	14	2·75
HI-2	Slow	14	2·17
X	Rapid	6	1·41
H	Slow	0	1·00
HI-1	Rapid	6	0·88
HI-2	Rapid	0	0·80
H	Rapid	0	0·29

started. It is reasonable to assume that the isoniazid bound by the bacilli increases with each dose of the drug given to the patient, and tends towards a maximal value determined by the highest concentration present in the lesions, a concentration that will be proportional to the peak serum concentration. Thus, the concept that the amount of bound isoniazid determines the antibacterial activity of the drug is consistent with the finding that the response of patients shows a good association with the peak serum levels attained and not with other measurements of the time-concentration curves.

The practical implications of the relationship between isoniazid dosage and therapeutic efficacy are as follows:

(1) An initial period of treatment with frequent high doses of isoniazid might be of value in causing binding of large amounts of the drug by the tubercle bacilli. Only a short time, perhaps 1 to 2 weeks, should be necessary.

(2) Following this initial period, maintenance of the bound isoniazid might be attained by a moderate dose given less frequently than usual. The greater efficacy of a single moderate dose of isoniazid given once a day (the HI-1 regimen) over the same total divided into 2 doses a day (the HI-2 regimen) indicates that one dose a day is likely to be at least as effective as the more usual practice of giving 2 or 3 doses a day.

(3) When a single dose of isoniazid is given each day, there is little advantage to be gained by increasing its size above 400 mg. However, if this dose were to be given less frequently, a larger dose might be necessary to maintain adequate binding of isoniazid by the bacilli. Further work is necessary to investigate the potentialities of widely spread dosage rhythms.

In contrast to these findings on therapeutic efficacy, the incidence of toxicity to isoniazid appears to be related to the length of time that the drug is present in the serum as well as to the highest concentration attained. Such a relationship is compatible with the view that isoniazid combines with pyridoxal, leading to its excess excretion. Whatever the chemical mechanism involved, a spacing out of the dosage with isoniazid would be likely to decrease the incidence of toxicity. Thus, giving the drug at less frequent intervals would be expected to have the advantages of good therapeutic response and of low toxicity.

It might be argued that conventional dosage schedules with low divided doses of isoniazid need no improvement since Crofton (1960), Thomas *et al.* (1960) and Johnston, Smith, Lockhart and Ritchie (1961), have all claimed sputum conversion in 100% of

their patients with such regimens. In each of these series, streptomycin was given with the isoniazid but the use of streptomycin in
domiciliary treatment is expensive and difficult to arrange in
countries with limited resources. When isoniazid in conventional
dose is given with p-aminosalicyclic acid or with thiacetazone, both
of which can be taken by mouth, failures of treatment occur in
about 10 % of patients (Tuberculosis Chemotherapy Centre, 1959,
1960; East African/British Medical Research Council, 1960). Thus,
there is still scope for better therapeutic results when combined
treatment with isoniazid and either of these two drugs is envisaged.

REFERENCES

BARCLAY, W. R., KOCH-WESER, D. and EBERT, R. H. (1954). *Amer. Rev. Tuberc.*,
    70, 784.
BIEHL, J. P. (1956). *Trans. XV Conf. Chemother. Tuberc.*, p. 279, Washington:
    Veterans Administration.
BIEHL, J. P. (1957). *Trans. XVI Conf. Chermother. Tuberc.*, p. 108, Washington:
    Veterans Administration.
BIEHL, J. P. and VILTER, R. W. (1954). *Proc. Soc. exp. Biol. Med., N.Y.,* **85,** 389.
BÖNICKE, R. and REIF, W. (1953). *Arch. exp. Path. Pharmakol.,* **220,** 321.
CROFTON, J. (1960). *Brit. med. J.* **ii,** 370.
DEVADATTA, S., GANGADHARAM, P. R. J., ANDREWS, R. H., FOX, W., RAMA-
    KRISHNAN, C.V., SELKON, J. B. and VELU, S. (1960). *Bull. Wld Hlth Org.,* 1960,
    23, 587.
EAST AFRICAN/BRITISH MEDICAL RESEARCH COUNCIL (1960). *Tubercle, Lond.,*
    42, 399.
EVANS, D. A. P., MANLEY, K. A. and MCKUSICK, V. A. (1960). *Brit. med. J.* **ii,** 485.
GANGADHARAM, P. R. J., BHATIA, A. L., RADHAKRISHNA, S. and SELKON, J. B.
    (1961). *Bull. Wld Hlth Org.,* **25,** 765.
GANGADHARAM, P. R. J. DEVADATTA, S., FOX, W., NAIR, C. N. and SELKON,
    J. B. (1961). *Bull. Wld Hlth Org.,* **25,** 793.
HUGHES, H. B. (1953). *J. Pharmacol. exp. Ther.,* **109,** 444.
HUGHES, H. B., SCHMIDT, L. H. and BIEHL, J. P. (1955). *Trans. XIV Conf.
    Chemother. Tuberc.*, p. 217, Washington: Veterans Administration.
JOHNSTON, R. N., SMITH, D. H., LOCKHART, W. and RITCHIE, R. T. (1961). *Brit.
    med. J.,* **i,** 105.
KNIGHT, R. A., SELIN, M. J. and HARRIS, H. W. (1959). *Trans. XVIII Cong.
    Chemother. Tuberc.* p. 52, Washington: Veterans Administration.
MANDEL, W., COHN, M. L., RUSSELL, W. F. and MIDDLEBROOK, G. (1956). *Proc.
    Soc. exp. Biol. Med. N.Y.,* **91,** 409.

MITCHELL, R. S., RIEMENSNIDER, D. K., HARSCH, J. R. and BELL, J. C. (1958). *Trans. XVII Conf. Chemother. Tuberc.*, p. 77, Washington: Veterans Administration.

SUNAHARA, S., URANO, M. and OGAWA, M. (1961). *Science*, **134**, 1530.

THOMAS, H. E., LUNDTZ, G. R. W. N., FORBES, D. E. P., ROSS, H. J. P., MORRISON-SMITH, J. and SPRINGETT, V. H. (1960). *Lancet*, **ii**, 1185.

TUBERCULOSIS CHEMOTHERAPY CENTRE, MADRAS (1959). *Bull, Wld Hlth Org.*, **21**, 51.

TUBERCULOSIS CHEMOTHERAPY CENTRE, MADRAS (1960). *Bull. Wld Hlth Org.* **23**, 535.

TUBERCULOSIS CHEMOTHERAPY CENTRE, MADRAS (1962). *Bull. Wld Hlth Org.*, in press.

VIVIEN, J. N. and GROSSET, J. (1961). *Progr. Explor. Tuberc.*, **11**, 45.

DISCUSSION

J. D. Fulton (National Institute for Medical Research): Did I understand Dr. Rose to say that the action of etisul (diethyldithiolisophthalate) finally depended on the formation of ethylmercaptan, or does it go further to give something like hydrogen sulphide from etisul in the skin?

Rose: The evidence that ethylmercaptan is formed from etisul in the tissues is indirect, largely based on the fact that the metabolites are the same as when you give ethylmercaptan itself or the diethyldisulphide. We never actually isolated ethylmercaptan from the tissues, to the best of my knowledge.

Is there an active metabolite? The metabolism of ethylthiol has been studied extensively in our laboratories, labelling both the carbon and the sulphur. The main organic metabolite excreted in the urine is ethyl-methylsulphone. There are also related compounds, perhaps the vinyl-methylsulphone. Labelled CO_2 is exhaled and labelled sulphate ion is excreted in the urine. We have examined these metabolites and they have no antitubercular activity. We have gone further than this. We have also prepared about twenty possible metabolites, and these all have no antitubercular activity whatsoever. At the moment, I am afraid the mode of action of ethylthiol is a mystery. It is certainly not brought about by a metabolite which we have been able to find.

B. Lacey (Westminster Hospital Medical School): May I ask Dr. Rose if he has compared the metabolism of etisul in tasters and non-tasters of phenylthiourea? I ask this in relation to his interesting suggestion of a possible association between chemotherapy and goitrogenic activity. In Liverpool there was shown an interesting association between the type of goitre which people develop and their ability to taste phenylthiourea, as well as their sex, of course.

Rose: That is a most interesting suggestion. I am pretty certain it has not been looked into and I will bear it in mind.

D. D. Woods (Department of Chemical Microbiology, Oxford): I should like to make one suggestion about the possible mode of action of diaminodiphenylsulphone. There is some evidence that the pathway of folic acid synthesis in the tubercle bacillus may be different from that in other bacteria. There were Japanese workers (Katunuma, 1957; Katunuma, Shoda and Noda, 1957) who found evidence with cell-free extracts for an initial reaction between *p*-aminobenzoic acid and glutamic acid, giving *p*-aminobenzoylglutamic acid as the primary reaction product. Whereas, in other bacteria, the first reaction is now known to be between *p*-aminobenzoic acid and reduced pteridine (Brown, 1962) and this reaction is inhibited by sulphonamides. It is possible therefore that in the tubercle bacillus the primary reaction involving *p*-aminobenzoic acid which is interfered with is in fact a different one. This may explain the relative lack of activity of the traditional sulphonamides. It would be interesting to make a glutamic acid analogue of a sulphonamide and see if it had activity against tubercle.

Rose: That is a very interesting suggestion.

G. A. H. Buttle (School of Pharmacy, London): Could I ask Dr. Mitchison if he has any information about the administration of isoniazid to large numbers of people? I think it has been done in drinking water. Is there a very great incidence of peripheral neuritis or of drug-resistant organisms?

Mitchison: I am afraid I would not be able to speak with any confidence on this subject. There is a suggestion that the incidence of peripheral neuritis in the Indian patients was considerably higher than the incidence found in other countries. The Indian population is nutritionally deficient, and their deficiency of B group vitamins may well be more severe than in other areas in the world.

F. M. Sullivan (Guys Hospital Medical School): Dr. Mitchison, I find it a bit difficult to understand how it would be possible to devize a

regimen with a low incidence of peripheral neuritis but a good therapeutic effect. From the data it appeared very much as though they go
hand in hand. At a level of $0 \cdot 2$ μg./ml. in the blood there did not
seem to be any correlation with therapeutic effect; on almost all
regimens this level was exceded for several hours each day. I think
one of the difficulties is in knowing what, in fact, is the antibacterial
level of isoniazid in the blood. *In vitro*, isoniazid inhibits in concentrations of $0 \cdot 01$ μg./ml. If you add a high concentration of serum to
the medium, then the tubercle bacilli stop growing anyway. I think, in
fact, that the antibacterial concentration of isoniazid in serum is probably
higher than $0 \cdot 2$ μg/ml.

Dr. Rose raised the question of drug-resistance in leprosy. I think that
this is very interesting because resistance to sulphones is extremely rare.
In patients treated with sulphones alone, I think that it is very unusual
to get any resistance, whereas with some of the newer drugs such as
etisul resistance develops extremely rapidly. This is where you get a
breakdown in the story between leprosy and tuberculosis. In tuberculosis all the drugs we know produce drug-resistance quite rapidly if used
alone, but the sulphones seem to be wonderful drugs, inhibiting the
development of resistance in some way. Are sulphones different from all
other drugs, both for tuberculosis and leprosy, in not allowing resistance
to develop?

Mitchison: Dr. Sullivan said that we do not know the minimal
bacteriostatic concentration of isoniazid in the serum, nor do we know
what it is in the lesions. However, if you measure the duration of any
concentration, up to as high as 1 μg./ml., it is still true that there is no
relationship between therapeutic efficacy and the duration for which that
concentration is maintained. It is possible that we could get as good
results with a single daily dose of 100 mg. of isoniazid as with three doses
of 100 mg. a day. That is to say, we may be over-using our drugs
immensely, and in the process of over-using them, we may be introducing unnecessary toxicity.

Rose: Drug resistance and leprosy? It is true, of course, that if you
write down all the drugs which are active you can arrange them in an
approximate order of the speed at which resistance is induced. Etisul
and the thiocarbanilides come quite high on the list. Diaminodiphenylsulphone and its derivatives come low down on the list. I doubt whether

10

it is correct to say that resistance to sulphone therapy has never occurred. You cannot, as things stand at the moment, relate the ease with which resistance develops to any particular structural features. If there is any relationship at all, I should imagine it is to the speed of action of the particular compound. Etisul is notable, for example, for the immediate effect which it seemingly has on the leprosy bacillus. The bacterial index falls dramatically, and quite rapidly also with the thiocarbanilides. With diaminodiphenylsulphone it is a much slower process. That is the only relationship I can think of on the spur of the moment.

A. S. Alving (*University of Chicago*): We have found that we can abolish clinical haemolysis with primaquine by giving three or four times the daily dose of drug once a week. I am wondering if you have tried intermittent isoniazid therapy with larger doses at longer intervals. Primaquine used to be given for malaria three times a day, and then once a day, and finally three or four times the dose was given once a week—and it worked better with less toxicity. It might be worth trying.

Mitchison: I think that is a perfectly logical development, to be tried out.

Rose: In leprosy the regimen differs from drug to drug. N^1-Acetyl sulphamethoxypyridazine is given parenterally once every fourteen days. Thiocarbanilides, on the other hand, need to be given daily because they are metabolized and excreted with considerable speed.

Mitchison: The relationship between peak serum concentrations of isoniazid and therapeutic efficacy appears to be related to its binding by the bacilli. Nobody knows how long the drug is bound for, and information on this subject might be of value in determining optimal spacing of doses.

A. C. Cuckler (*Merck Institute for Therapeutic Research, Rahway*): Is there any relation between a large single dose and repeated doses to the development of resistance to isoniazid in tubercle?

Mitchison: There is a relationship between the degree of resistance and size of a *single* dose of isoniazid. The larger the single dose, the higher the degree of resistance. From the point of view of timing—that is to say, the length of time before resistant strains appear—there is very little difference between the regimens. By about five months virtually all tubercle bacilli which are culturable from the patients are resistant to isoniazid.

H. J. Barber (May and Baker): There is a point I should like Dr. Rose to clarify. Did I understand him to say that he thought there was some correlation between the *speed* of action of a drug and the tendency for resistance to develop? He said that ethylmercaptan was rapid in action and diaminodiphenylsulphone was slow acting, and he correlated rapidity of action with tendency to produce drug resistance. We are now dealing with bacteria, but if he harks back to yesterday's protozoa, precisely the reverse argument was used to explain why it was extremely difficult to produce strains resistant to berenil, because it acted with great rapidity as compared with other antiprotozoal drugs.

Rose: I was asked if I could find a relationship, and I did my best. Those are the facts as they stand. Whether there is a causal relationship is another matter; I would not like to say. There may be other reasons which are nothing to do with speed of onset of action.

H. Smith (Microbiological Research Establishment, Porton): I should like to take up a point regarding the testing of compounds against tubercle or leprosy bacilli, or in our own work *Brucella*, growing intracellularly. There is a difficulty which I want to emphasize. In the test system, to make certain that the organism is growing intracellularly, the external environment must contain antibiotic or normal serum to make it bactericidal. It is very, very difficult to tell whether the drug is, in fact, affecting the monocyte or polymorph, so that the bactericidal mixture goes in and kills the organism, or whether the drug is acting in its own right.

Rose: In the case of ethylmercaptan, although the action is seemingly indirect, there must in fact be a direct action. If you take organisms which have become resistant to ethylmercaptan *in vivo*, they are still resistant in monocyte preparations.

Lacey: Dr. Mitchison, is the distribution of rapid and slow inactivators the same in tuberculous patients as in the normal population? Second, would it not be logical, if you wished to raise the peak value of isoniazid to the limit and minimize toxicity, to give a large dose of isoniazid and follow it the next day with an enormous dose of something like pyridoxine, which would counteract the toxicity?

Mitchison: The answer to the first part of the question is, yes. As far as is known, the distribution is the same for tuberculous and non-tuberculous patients.

The answer to the second point is that you can prevent isoniazid toxicity by giving pyridoxal or pyridoxine, but there is some doubt as to whether this may interfere with its antitubercular action.

Lacey: Given simultaneously. Has it ever been tried alternately?

Mitchison: Not as far as I know.

E. F. Gale (Medical Research Council Unit for Chemical Microbiology Cambridge): I should like to ask Dr. Rose a general question which, perhaps, will help me in my summing up this afternoon. In the course of these contributions we have heard a number of examples where you have taken a structure and you have modified it and you have made a better drug as a result of modifying it. You, Dr. Rose, have done this with particular success. What I would like to ask you—and, perhaps, Dr. Barber as well—is how do you decide what structures you are going to start with?

Rose: Dear, dear, dear! We might have a symposium on this one later on.

Let me answer it somewhat obliquely. In the British Pharmacopoeia there are about a couple of hundred synthetic drugs. If you go back into the history of these—ten years, twenty years, fifty years, or even a hundred years ago, you nearly always come to a time when an observation was made about a clinical, pharmacological, or therapeutic effect of a compound of known constitution. If may perhaps have been a natural product whose structure was sometimes not known completely when the biological observation was made. For example, you find that characteristic features of the quinine structure were being incorporated into synthetic antimalarials long before the complete structure of the alkaloid was known. The chemist must have a starting point of this kind (I hope Dr. Barber will agree with me on this) after which an experienced man can very soon pep up the activity by judicious modification of the molecule. He endeavours to find out which parts of the prototype structure are responsible for the activity and those which are superfluous, and builds anew from this.

G. H. Hitchings (The Wellcome Research Laboratories, Tuckahoe): There is an alternative, I think: that is to start with a metabolite and try and produce an antimetabolite which will produce a specific biochemical block and to work from there to its exploitation in a chemotherapeutic situation.

Rose: Yes, that is quite true, and drugs have been developed in this way. However, generally speaking, the original lead is a chance observation; but development is still based on a known structure. It may be a substance with a positive biological action or it may be, as you say, an essential metabolite. You must have a picture in front of you.

Barber: One could refer to emetine, a natural product on which chance observations were made many centuries ago. It inspired a considerable amount of work, notably by Pyman, to try and find new antiamoebic drugs, but the work was based on the wrong structure of emetine. Then about ten years ago the correct structure of emetine was found, and this stimulated further work.

REFERENCES

BROWN, G. M. (1962). *J. biol. Chem.*, **237**, 536.

KATUNUMA, N. (1957). Special Lecture to *XXXII Congr. Japanese Biochem. Assoc., Kyoto City.*

KATUNUMA, N., SHODA, T. and NODA, H. (1957). *J. Vitaminology, Japan*, **3**, 77.

Session 4: Viral Infections

CHAIRMAN: E. F. Gale

ANTIVIRAL CHEMOTHERAPY WITH ISATIN β-THIOSEMICARBAZONE AND ITS DERIVATIVES

P. W. SADLER

Courtauld Institute of Biochemistry,
Middlesex Hospital Medical School, London

THE activity of isatin β-thiosemicarbazone (I) against vaccinia virus was first observed by Thompson *et al.* (1953) and was further studied by Bauer (1955). Activity against alastrim has also been demonstrated in the N-ethyl derivative (Bauer and Sadler, 1960*b*) and in a number of derivatives against variola major (Bauer *et al.*, 1962).

In the studies which are to be reported, the tests for chemotherapeutic activity in mice infected with vaccinia, alastrim and ectromelia viruses were performed by Dr. D. J. Bauer at the Wellcome Laboratories of Tropical Medicine. Experiments with animals infected with variola major were carried out in collaboration with Miss P. Fox-Hulme and Dr. K. R. Dumbell in the Department of Bacteriology of Liverpool University.

As a first step, systematic structural modification was undertaken to determine which parts of this molecule are essential for retention of the antiviral activity (Bauer and Sadler, 1960*a*). N-Acetylindoxyl β-thiosemicarbazone (II), which lacks the carbonyl group in the 2-position, and N-methyl-β-formyloxindole thiosemicarbazone (III), a closely related molecule in which the side chain has been lengthened by one carbon atom, are both inactive. Therefore, structural modifications in positions 2 and 3 are incompatible with the retention of high activity against neurovaccinia, which leaves positions 1, 4, 5, 6, and 7 available for further investigation.

Substitution in the aromatic ring was tackled systematically to give a range of steric, electronic, and mesomeric effects. The complete series of chloroisatin β-thiosemicarbazones was synthesized and the effects of alkyl, trifluoromethyl, nitro, carboxyl and methoxyl substituents were investigated. To determine whether substituent effects were essentially chemical or physical, an examination was made of the infrared spectra. Comparison of shifts in the frequencies of the functional groups with changes in biological activity demonstrated that the substituent effects were almost entirely physical (Sadler, 1960, 1961a). Large substituents in the 5- and 6-positions seriously decrease the activity (Table I) and there is a gradation of antiviral activity with increasing van der Waals radii of the substituents. The fluorine atom, which has the smallest radius apart from hydrogen, decreases antiviral activity the least. Compounds with other large substituents, such as the naphthisatins, in which another ring is fused to the 4,5-, 5,6- or 6,7-positions are completely inactive. The 4- and 7-positions are less susceptible to substituent effects than the 5- and 6-positions but all

Table I

RELATIONSHIP OF RADII OF RING SUBSTITUTED
ISATIN β-THIOSEMICARBAZONES TO ANTIVACCINIAL ACTIVITY

Substituent	Radii (Å)	5-position	6-position
None	1·2	100	100
Fluoro	1·35	35·5	43·1
Chloro	1·80	4·2	11·7
Bromo	1·95	3·1	10·5
Methyl	2·0	0	0·3
Iodo	2·15	0	3·9

structural modifications in these positions result in a diminution of antiviral activity. In general, these substituent effects are additive so that any polysubstituted derivative containing large 5- or 6-substituents is inactive.

The situation with respect to position 1 is very different. Here there is almost endless scope for modifying the physical properties

Table II

ANTIVIRAL ACTIVITY OF N-SUBSTITUTED ISATIN β-THIOSEMICARBAZONES

Substituent	Antiviral activity
None	100
Methyl	202
Ethyl	286
Isopropyl	44
Propyl	28·5
Pentyl	3·4
Hydroxymethyl	42
2-Hydroxyethyl	204
Acetyl	87
Ethoxycarbonylmethyl	0
Diethoxycarbonylmethyl	0

of the molecule and a series of compounds with a very wide range of antiviral activity has been obtained. Table II shows the antiviral activities of a selection of the N-substituted isatin β-thiosemicarbazones which have been prepared.

The simple alkyl substituents produce a marked rise in activity with a maximum at ethyl, tailing off again to the pentyl derivative which has only 3·4% of the activity of the parent compound. Similarly in the series of hydroxylated compounds maximum activity is obtained with the hydroxyethyl compound. The N-acetyl derivative is quite active, but those with ester groupings are not. In general, most strongly polar groupings such as cyanoethyl or carboxymethyl abolish activity and the useful range of compounds is restricted to the alkyl and hydroxyalkyl derivatives. This poses many problems from the point of view of chemotherapy because all the derivatives which are readily water-soluble are

Table III

RELATIONSHIP BETWEEN ANTIVIRAL ACTIVITY OF SUBSTITUTED
ISATIN β-THIOSEMICARBAZONES AND THEIR SOLUBILITY IN CHLOROFORM

Substituent	Antiviral Activity	Solubility in chloroform (mg./100 ml)
7-Carboxy	0	0
5-Methoxy	0·03	3
4-Methyl	3·4	8
4-Chloro	8·6	10
6-Fluoro	39·8	16
7-Chloro	85	29
None	100	32

inactive (Sadler, 1961b). For example, the sodium salt of 7-carboxy-isatin β-thiosemicarbazone and a quaternary derivative of the most active compound, N-2-(2,3-dioxoindolinyl)ethylpryidinium bromide 3-thiosemicarbazone (IV) show no activity; which is probably because they do not reach the neurotropic virus used in the *in vivo* assay method. There is, in fact, some correlation between lipid solubility and activity in the simple derivatives (Table III). When a wider range of compounds is considered and the logarithms of the solubilities are plotted against antiviral activity a correlation coefficient of 0·775 is obtained.

The compounds which exhibit pronounced activity against neurovaccinia are also active against cowpox, rabbitpox (Bauer and Sheffield, 1959), and alastrim (Bauer and Sadler, 1960b) but they show no activity against the closely related virus ectromelia. This is a very surprising finding, since one is always led to believe that an antiviral agent is necessarily a substance which interferes with some enzyme or substrate which is present in the host cell and is required by the virus. In the specific case of vaccinia and ectromelia infections of mouse brain the host cell is the same, with the same complement of enzymes and substrates, and only the virus is

different. It is difficult to believe that such a closely related virus as ectromelia requires enzymes or substrates which are different from those required by vaccinia, which implies that the compound is acting against the virus itself. This view is strongly supported by the discovery of a related group of compounds the isatin β-4′,4′-dialkylthiosemicarbazones (V) which are highly active against ectromelia but are not active at all against vaccinia (Bauer and Sadler, 1961).

A range of 4′,4′-dialkyl derivatives was prepared from isatin, N-methylisatin, and N-ethylisatin. Compounds with mixed alkyl groups and with cyclic groups such as piperidine, pyrollidine and morpholine were also prepared, and structural modifications made to the 1-position and the aromatic ring. The introduction of one or more alkyl substituents into the side chain completely abolishes antivaccinial activity, but compounds bearing identical alkyl substituents on the terminal nitrogen atom (V, R′ = alkyl) show a wide range of activity against ectromelia. The most active compound is isatin β-4′,4′-dimethylthiosemicarbazone (V, R=H, R′=CH$_3$) and activity is progressively reduced in the diethyl, dipropyl and dibutyl analogues. The effect of alkylation in the 1-position is to reduce activity, which is in direct contrast with the situation in the antivaccinia compounds, where substitution of alkyl groups in the 1-position enhances activity. The effect of substitution in the aromatic ring has disclosed another striking difference from the structure-function relationships of the anti-vaccinia compounds, for substitution in the 5-position is very damaging to antivaccinial activity, but with the antiectromelia compounds substitution of large groups in the 5-position is tolerated with only moderate loss of activity. These results could indicate that there is no general solution to the problem of antiviral chemotherapy, and that each virus must be treated as a problem on its own, but this is not necessarily the case, as N-methylisatin β-4′,4′-dibutylthiosemicarbazone which shows moderate activity against ectromelia also possesses high activity against type 2 poliovirus in the quite unrelated group of enteroviruses (O'Sullivan and Sadler, 1961). This compound which in tissue culture provides over 2 log units of protection against type 2 infection, shows approximately the same activity as 2-α-hydroxybenzylbenzimidazole (VI).

In the case of isatin β-thiosemicarbazones certain possibilities as to the mode of action have been eliminated. The compounds do not cyclize *in vivo* to form indolothiotriazines (Sadler, 1961c), and when these are prepared chemically they have no antiviral activity. Nor are the compounds hydrolysed *in vivo* to release the parent isatin which by virtue of its dehydrogenase activity could remove an essential metabolite, for a series of isatin β-thiosemicarbazones showed no correlation between antivaccinial activity and the dehydrogenase activities of the substituted isatins (O'Sullivan and Sadler, 1957). Certainly the thioamide group is essential in the isatin β-thiosemicarbazone series, but this does not apply to the benzimidazole derivatives. However, there is a superficial steric resemblance between VI and N-methylisatin β-4',4'-dibutyl thiosemicarbazone (V, R=CH₃, R'=C₄H₉) inasmuch as both contain five-membered heterocycles attached to hydrogen-bonded rings. This suggests that the ability to chelate may be an essential feature of these antiviral agents, for there are no compounds with high anti-pox virus activity which lack the imino and carbonyl groups involved in the formation of a strong *intra*molecular bond, and the same would appear to be true in the benzimidazole derivatives with activity against poliomyelitis infection (O'Sullivan and Sadler, 1961).

The pox virus which is of the greatest interest is, of course, smallpox, for although the disease has been eradicated from Europe, outbreaks are always liable to occur from an imported case. In countries such as India and Burma where the disease is endemic and where vaccination is carried out repeatedly and on a large scale, many thousands of cases nevertheless occur every year (Annual Epidemiological and Vital Statistics, 1956). Vaccination protects against the disease for only a short time, and after a year immunity is already declining. The failure of vaccine prophylaxis in smallpox is presumably due to the administrative impossibility of maintaining adequate immunity in an Eastern population which is exposed to serious risk of infection all the time. Vaccination after exposure to smallpox is not very effective, and it is common in such cases for the patient to develop both smallpox and a vaccination reaction at the same time. Also the use of vaccinia hyperimmune gamma-globulin has only limited application in the prophylaxis of smallpox (Kempe *et al.*, 1961). So there is a very real need for an effective antiviral chemotherapeutic agent both for the prophylaxis and treatment of the disease. Such an agent would have an important advantage over smallpox vaccine, for in cases of exposure to infection, it would confer protection as soon as it entered the bloodstream.

Whether or not adequate blood levels of N-methylisatin β-thiosemicarbazone (compound 33T57) can be achieved in smallpox patients remains to be seen, but the results so far would appear to be encouraging.

[Discussion of this paper was postponed until after the paper by G. Belyavin; see p. 330.]

REFERENCES

ANNUAL EPIDEMIOLOGICAL AND VITAL STATISTICS (1956). pp. 474–479 Geneva: World Health Organization, 1959.

BAUER, D. J. (1955). *Brit. J. exp. Path.*, **36**, 105.

BAUER, D. J., DUMBELL, K. R. FOX-HULME, P. and SADLER, P. W. (1962). *Bull. Wld Hlth Org.*, in press.

BAUER, D. J. and SADLER, P. W. (1960*a*). *Brit. J. Pharmacol.*, **15**, 101.

BAUER, D. J. and SADLER, P. W. (1960*b*). *Lancet*, **i**, 1110.

BAUER, D. J. and SADLER, P. W. (1961). *Nature, Lond.*, **190**, 1167.

BAUER, D. J. and SHEFFIELD, F. W. (1959). *Nature, Lond.*, **184**, 1496.

KEMPE, C. H., BOWLES, C., MEIKLEJOHN, G., BERGE, T. O., ST. VINCENT, L., SUNDARA BABU, B. V., GOVINDARAJAN, S., RATNAKANNAN, N. R., DOWNIE, A. W. and MURTHY, V. R. (1961). *Bull. Wld Hlth Org.*, **25**, 41.

O'SULLIVAN, D. G. and SADLER, P. W. (1957). *Arch. Biochem.*, **65**, 243.

O'SULLIVAN, D. G. and SADLER, P. W. (1961). *Nature, Lond.*, **192**, 341.

SADLER, P. W. (1960). *Chem. Rev.*, **60**, 575.

SADLER, P. W. (1961*a*). *J. chem. Soc.*, 957.

SADLER, P. W., (1961*b*). *J. org. Chem.*, **26**, 1315.

SADLER, P. W. (1961*c*). *J. chem. Soc.*, 243.

THOMPSON, R. L., MINTON, S. A., OFFICER, J. E. and HITCHINGS, G. H. (1953). *J. Immunol.*, **70**, 229.

INTERFERON—SOME ASPECTS OF PRODUCTION AND ACTION

D. C. BURKE

Department of Biological Chemistry,
Marischal College, Aberdeen

INTERFERON was discovered in the course of a study of viral interference by Isaacs and Lindenmann (1957). Viral interference describes the action of a virus, either live or inactivated, when it inhibits the growth of a second, challenge virus. If the two viruses infect the same cell simultaneously either dual infection, interference, or genetic recombination may result, depending on the dosage and the system used. In studies of viral interference it has been common to add the challenge virus some time after the first virus; in this way maximum viral interference is usually obtained (Schlesinger, 1959a). The two viruses may be quite unrelated to each other, and the mechanism is not an immunological one.

It is clear, however, that there are several factors which, either alone or together, may be responsible for the induction of viral interference. Interference induced by an infective cytopathic virus may be due to depletion of metabolic intermediates or to actual destruction of the host cell. In contrast, the interference induced by non-cytopathic viruses is probably due to interferon, and is discussed in detail later. It has proved more profitable to study interference induced by an inactivated virus, since with this system the complications due to concomitant viral mutiplication and interference can be avoided. Henle and Henle (1943) were the first to show that ultraviolet-inactivated influenza virus could induce interference, and this system has been extensively studied. Since the interfering virus does not multiply, multiplicities of about one (one virus particle/cell) have to be used in order to obtain complete interference. It has also been observed that high multiplicities of ultraviolet-inactivated Newcastle disease virus can induce interference with homologous virus by destruction of cellular receptors (Baluda, 1959). This effect is a rapid one, which gradually breaks down as new receptors are synthesized by the host cell (Stone, 1948). However, since interference can be induced by heat-inactivated influenza virus which has no action on cellular receptors (Isaacs and Edney, 1950) and since interference induced by influenza virus is effective against viruses which do not share the cellular receptors of the influenza group (Schlesinger, 1951) destruction of cellular receptors cannot be the only mechanism operating. Interference by heat-inactivated influenza virus requires several hours to become established, and has been shown by later studies to be clearly intracellular (Henle, 1950). It was during a study of this system that interferon was discovered (Isaacs and Lindenmann, 1957).

Isaacs and Lindenmann found that, following incubation of heat-inactivated influenza virus with chick chorioallantoic membranes, a new substance, which they named interferon, was formed within the cells and was subsequently released in to the fluid. This substance could induce interference in fresh cells, and appeared to be the mediator of the viral interference. Interference due to the action of interferon is characterized by (i) activity against a wide variety of viruses, including such unrelated viruses as vaccinia, influenza (Isaacs, Lindenmann and Valentine, 1957), polyoma (Allison, 1961) and the arbor viruses (Isaacs and Westwood, 1959b; Wagner, 1960); (ii) absence of activity against extracellular virus or on virus adsorption to cells (Wagner, 1961); and (iii) the need for several hours' incubation at 37° before maximum interference is induced.

Interferon is produced by a wide variety of viruses in a number of different types of cells. The interferons produced in different cells do, however, differ in some way as discussed below.

Interferon, produced by the interaction of ultraviolet-inactivated influenza and chick chorioallantoic membranes, is a protein of molecular weight 63,000; it has been purified and shown to be free of nucleic acids (Burke, 1961). As yet, nothing is known of its detailed structure, and only preliminary comparisons have been made with interferons produced in other systems.

Study of the production and action of interferon has aroused wide interest, not only because it appears to be involved in the normal host defence mechanisms against viral infections, and therefore offers some hope as a potential viral antibiotic, but also because an increased understanding of its production and action is bound to increase our understanding of the nature of viral multiplication in general. Recent work on the production and action of interferon is discussed in the sections that follow.

Production of interferon by inactivated myxoviruses

Interferon was first obtained by the interaction of heat-inactivated influenza virus and chick chorioallantoic membranes, and a close correlation was observed between the ability of the virus to induce interference and its ability to produce interferon (Isaacs and Lindenmann, 1957). Ultraviolet-inactivated influenza virus is known to be a more efficient interfering agent than heat-inactivated virus (Henle, 1953), and was found to be a much better producer of interferon. Here again the correlation between induction of interference and production of interferon was observed (Lindenmann, Burke and Isaacs, 1957). Incubation of ultraviolet-inactivated virus with chick chorioallantoic membranes has proved to be a convenient method of preparing interferon relatively free of impurities, and has been used for large-scale production (Andrews, and Dudgeon, 1961). Interferon prepared using infective virus in the allantoic cavity, as described by Wagner (1961), is a good deal less satisfactory in this respect. Henle, Henle, Deinhardt and Bergs (1959) showed that addition of ultraviolet-inactivated mumps, Newcastle disease and Sendai viruses to cultures of MCN cells led to the production of interferon. Cantell (1960) has also reported interferon production by ultraviolet-inactivated mumps virus in HeLa cells. These viruses are all close relatives of influenza and despite a number of attempts, which are discussed below, interferon production has not been observed to be initiated by any other heat- or ultraviolet-inactivated virus. The reason for this is not known, but it may be that in the majority of viruses, it is not possible to damage the viral nucleic acid without also damaging the viral component responsible for the initiation of interferon production.

Production of interferon by infective myxoviruses

Tyrrell (1959) was the first to observe production of interferon by an infective myxovirus. Calf kidney cells infected with influenza A virus were found to produce virus in a cyclical manner, cells producing virus for about two days and then ceasing to do so. After a few more days virus was again produced, and this effect continued for some months. During the time that the cells were not producing virus they were resistant to superinfection, and were found to be producing interferon. This cyclical effect had been predicted by Wagner (1960) in a discussion of persistent viral infection of cells. Burke and Isaacs (1958b) and Wagner (1960) also observed the formation of interferon after infection with influenza virus of chorioallantoic membranes and whole eggs, respectively. No interferon was produced during the 24 hours following infection, when virus production was at its peak, but it appeared later, when virus production was declining. These results are consistent with an earlier observation that interferon was not produced during a 24 hour incubation of infective influenza virus on the chick chorion (Burke and Isaacs, 1958a). The late production of interferon may well be due to accumulation of thermally inactivated virus, since influenza virus, partially inactivated at $37°$, has been shown to produce interferon more rapidly after infection than fully infective virus does (Burke and Isaacs, 1958b). Gresser (1961a) has prepared interferon by infecting monkey kidney cells, human amnion cells and human leucocytes with Sendai virus. Hsuing (1962) has shown that an interferon-like inhibitor is produced by DA virus, a myxovirus belonging to the parainfluenza group.

De Maeyer and Enders (1961) have described the production of an interferon during the growth of measles virus in human amnion or HeLa cells maintained in tissue culture. They found that production and release of the inhibitor were broadly coincident with that of infective virus. It has also been found that attenuated strains of measles virus produce more interferon than do virulent strains (Enders, 1960).

Henle, Deinhardt, Bergs and Henle (1958) have studied stable cell cultures which were persistently infected with Newcastle disease and other viruses. The cells, which produced only a small amount of virus, showed no spontaneous degeneration and were resistant to superinfection with vesicular stomatitis virus. This resistance to superinfection fulfils all the criteria of virus interference, and similar resistance could be induced by treating cells with ultraviolet-irradiated Newcastle disease virus (Bergs, Henle, Deinhardt and Henle, 1958). However, the cultures contained insufficient virus particles to account for the interference, fewer than 10% of the cells contained even a single myxovirus particle, and this suggested the presence of another interfering agent, apart from the myxovirus itself. Henle et al. (1959) were able to demonstrate the presence of small amounts of interferon in infected cell cultures, and the authors suggested that interferon plays a role in the establishment and maintenance of these persistently infected cultures. Chany (1961) has shown that interferon is produced by cultures of KB cells persistently infected with parainfluenza 3, and he too suggested that interferon may play a role in the establishment and possibly in the maintenance of the persistently infected culture.

The interferons produced by the different inactivated and infective myxoviruses in any given cell type appear to be similar, although possibly not identical, substances. Interferons produced by the same virus in different host cells must differ, since they usually show maximum activity in the cells of the type in which they are produced, and often little activity in cells from other species. Apart from this difference in biological activity, which has not yet been related to any difference in physical properties, the interferons have broadly similar physicochemical properties. They are all unaffected by viral antiserum, and are not sedimented by high speed centrifuging. They are non-dialysable and moderately heat stable, the minor differences in heat stability possibly being due to the variation of heat stability with pH. With the exception of measles interferon, which has not been tested, they are all stable over the pH range 2 to 8. They are proteins, as indicated by inactivation by trypsin and by resistance to the action of ribonuclease and deoxyribonuclease. Measles interferon, in contrast to ultraviolet-inactivated influenza interferon, was not completely inactivated by shaking with chloroform-octanol, but this may have been due to the protective effect of the large amount of protein present in the measles interferon solution. Measles and parainfluenza 3 interferons, in contrast to ultraviolet-inactivated influenza interferon (Lindenmann et al., 1957), were unaffected by treatment with ether. Again the protein in the medium was probably exerting a protective effect, since ultraviolet-inactivated influenza interferon was unaffected by treatment with ether when protein (10 % w/v) was added before, but not after, the ether treatment (Burke, unpublished results).

Production of interferon by poliomyelitis virus

Ho and Enders (1959a, b) found that during the growth of a chick embryo-adapted strain of poliomyelitis virus in primary human kidney and amnion cell cultures, a factor appeared in the medium which inhibited the growth of several different viruses. The medium prepared in this way was named "virus inhibitory fluid" by the authors, and the factor resembles interferon in many ways. Its activity is unaffected by viral antiserum or by high speed centrifuging, it is non-dialysable, fairly heat stable, and unaffected by treatment with ribonuclease, but it is destroyed by incubation with trypsin. Neither interferon nor the factor of Ho and Enders have any effect on virus adsorption, and the factor appears to inhibit viral mutliplication at an intracellular level. The factor is less well adsorbed than interferon and only acts effectively when it is retained in the system. The highest concentrations of factor were found shortly after infection with the virus, which grows only poorly in this system. However, no virus inhibitory factor was produced after treatment of cells with heat or ultraviolet-inacti-vated virus, and it appears that some virus multiplication is needed to stimulate the factor's production. Drake (1958) found that inter-ference induced by poliomyelitis virus against heterotypic polio-myelitis virus was not induced by ultraviolet-inactivated virus. Although interferon production can be initiated by a number of infective viruses, only in the case of the myxoviruses is heat or ultraviolet-inactivated virus effective. Ho and Enders found evi-dence for the involvement of the inhibitory factor in two persis-tently infected cell lines, and they suggested that interferon and similar factors may play a part in the mechanism of resistance to viral infections.

Production of interferon by arbor viruses

Arthropod-borne animal (arbor) viruses are viruses which infect mammals and birds, and also multiply in the bodies of arthropods, the viruses being carried from vertebrate to vertebrate by the vector. Interferon is produced by a number of arbor viruses.

Tick-borne encephalitis virus. Chick embryo cells infected with tick-borne encephalitis virus showed very little evidence of a cytopathic effect, and were found to be resistant to superinfection with Western equine encephalomyelitis virus (Vilček, 1960). Cells infected with tick-borne encephalitis virus release an interferon very similar to the interferon produced by ultraviolet-inactivated virus in chick cells. The inhibitory agent is unaffected by viral antiserum or high speed centrifuging, is stable at pH 2, is quite stable to heat, unaffected by irradiation with ultraviolet light, and inactivated by trypsin (Vilček, 1961, Žemla and Vilček, 1961*b*). Like the interferon produced by infectious influenza, the agent is formed late in the course of the viral infection, but its formation cannot be initiated by heat or ultraviolet-inactivated virus (Vilček, 1961). Addition of acetone at $-$ 10 to $-$ 15° led to precipitation of the inhibitory agent, with some purification (Žemla and Vilček, 1961*a*).

Sindbis virus. Ho (1961*a*) has shown that in chick embryo cells infected with Sindbis virus (a virulent virus which produces rapid cytopathic action and grows to high titre in these cells), an interferon was produced which was unaffected by virus antiserum or high speed centrifuging but was destroyed by incubating with trypsin. A greater yield of interferon was obtained by infecting with a mixture of thermally inactivated and infective virus. Ho suggests that interferon production may be a general phenomenon of viral infections, optimum production being partially determined by the primary action of non-infective virus particles. It is still possible that the interferon produced during the multiplication of infective virus could be caused by the presence of virus inactivated during incubation; a closely related arbor virus, Semliki Forest virus, is known to be rapidly inactivated by heat (Cheng, 1961). A detailed kinetic analysis of the production of interferon and of virus might clarify the problem.

Other arbor viruses. Doherty (1958) and Lockhart (1960) have described cell lines persistently infected with other arbor viruses. It is not known whether or not they produce interferon.

Interferon production by other viruses

Polyoma virus. Polyoma virus was found by Deinhardt and Henle (1960) to interfere with the growth of several unrelated viruses, and

Allison (1961) has shown that an inhibitory substance with properties similiar to those of interferon was obtained during growth of polyoma virus in mouse embryo cells. The inhibitor was produced at about the same rate as infective virus, was resistant to polyoma antiserum and to treatment at pH 2 but, like interferon, was destroyed by incubation with pepsin.

Vaccinia virus. Nagano and Kojima (1958) reported that the supernatant obtained after repeatedly centrifuging a product derived from vaccinia-infected rabbit skin inhibited the growth of vaccinia virus. A similar effect was shown by ultraviolet-inactivated vaccinia. The protective effect did not appear to be caused by antibody. The inhibitor was non-dialysable, fairly heat stable and was unaffected by ultraviolet irradiation. It has been partially purified (Nagano, Kojima and Sukuzi, 1960) and the preparation of an antibody has been reported (Nagano and Kojima, 1960). Using similar methods Burke and Isaacs (1960) were unable to demonstrate formation of antibody to chick interferon.

Polyoma virus and vaccinia virus are the only DNA-containing viruses which have been shown to produce interferon.

Rabies virus. Non-cytopathic strains of rabies virus have been shown to interfere with Western equine encephalitis (Kaplan, Wecker, Forsek and Koprowski, 1960). An interferon unaffected by high speed centrifuging and viral antiserum was produced.

Vesicular stomatitis virus. Virus stocks of vesicular stomatitis virus obtained by serial undiluted passage contain a non-infective component capable of inducing homotypic interference (Cooper and Bellett, 1959). The agent may be an interferon or an incomplete virus (Bellett and Cooper, 1959).

Foot-and-mouth disease virus. Dinter (1960) has reported the appearance of a virus inhibitor during the growth of foot-and-mouth disease virus in calf kidney cells. The inhibitor was unaffected by viral antiserum, high speed centrifuging or dialysis at pH2. It was destroyed by incubation with trypsin.

Production of interferon by virus components

Interferon may be part of the virus, may be formed in the host cell from an inactive precursor, or may be newly synthesized in the host cells. All the available evidence favours the third possibility. Interferon production is stimulated by such different viruses as polyoma and influenza, and it is very unlikely that they both contain an interfering component with similar properties. It is also difficult to see why interferon production stimulated by ultra-violet-inactivated influenza virus should continue for 48 hours (Burke and Isaacs, 1958b) unless it is newly synthesized. The cell specificity of interferon, discussed below, shows that part of the active molecule is controlled by the host. Finally, an attempt to prepare interferon from an inactivated virus failed (Burke and Isaacs, 1958a).

If interferon is synthesized in the host cell, what component of the virus is responsible for stimulation of its production? An obvious choice is viral nucleic acid, and such evidence as exists favours this suggestion. When influenza virus is irradiated with ultraviolet light, the primary site of damage is the nucleic acid (Hollaender and Oliphant, 1944; Tamm and Fluke, 1950) and infectivity is quickly lost. The product is an efficient interfering agent, and since it can take part in genetic recombination (Gotlieb and Hirst, 1956), the nucleic acid must still be partially functional. Further irradiation of the virus causes extensive damage to nucleic acid and leads to loss of its ability to interfere (Burke and Isaacs, 1958a). However, when the effect of monochromatic ultraviolet light of different wavelengths on the destruction of interfering power was examined, the action spectrum had a broad maximum at 2600–2800 Å, rather than the sharp maximum at 2600 Å shown by loss of virus infectivity (Powell and Setlow, 1956). The action spectrum was similar to that of a protein containing aromatic amino acids, or associated with a small amount of nucleic acid. It did not represent nucleic acid as did the infectivity action spectrum.

This evidence suggests that, although the viral nucleic acid may be involved in induction of interference, other viral components are also involved. These components have not been identified.

There is some biological evidence for the involvement of nucleic acid. This was obtained with incomplete virus, prepared by serial undiluted passage, and known to contain less nucleic acid than fully infective virus (Ada and Perry, 1956). Paucker and Henle (1958) found that, after ultraviolet-inactivation, incomplete influenza virus was a less efficient interfering agent than an equivalent amount of fully infective virus. On the other hand, Burke and Isaacs (1958a) found that incomplete virus produced more interferon in the first 24 hours after infection than did fully infective virus. A possible interpretation of these results is that incomplete influenza virus, like virus inactivated at 37°, produces interferon earlier than does fully infective virus (Burke and Isaacs, 1958b), but that ultraviolet irradiation damages an already deficient nucleic acid so that it becomes a less efficient producer of interferon. If this were so the interfering power of ultraviolet irradiated incomplete virus would be destroyed more rapidly by further ultraviolet irradiation than the interfering power of fully infective virus, but no comparisons have been made.

Paucker and Henle (1958) were unable to induce interference by exposing the cells to the internal nucleoprotein soluble antigen of influenza virus, and Isaacs and Burke (unpublished work) also failed to induce interference with hot and cold phenol extracts of ultraviolet irradiated virus. However no infective nucleic acid has been obtained from influenza virus by phenol extraction, and it would be more relevant to test phenol extracts of viruses, such as the arbor viruses, which are known to yield infective nucleic acids and also to initiate interferon production.

Kinetics of interferon production

The kinetics of interferon production have been examined in several systems but only in detail in the case of initiation by heat-inactivated influenza virus (Isaacs and Lindenmann, 1957). Interferon was first detected in the cells at about 5 hours after infection, and was then rapidly released into the surrounding fluid. If the virus eclipse phase is largely made up of the time necessary for the action of messenger ribonucleic acid and for synthesis of new enzymes, then synthesis of a new protein, interferon, might take about as long as synthesis of viral proteins. Interferon in fact appears at about the same time as new virus antigens.

The situation in the case of infective virus is more complex, since production of interferon may either follow or be coincident with maximum virus production, depending on the system studied. The difficulty is that it is not known whether the interferon produced is due to the action of the fully infective virus, or to the inactivated virus that accumulates in the system, or to both. If interferon production were largely due to the effect of inactivated virus, maximum interferon production would be expected later than maximum virus production; this occurs with influenza virus and tick-borne encephalitis virus. But with measles virus, chick-adapted poliomyelitis virus and polyoma virus, the production of the inhibitor is broadly coincident with that of the virus. Neither measles nor chick-adapted poliomyelitis virus were well adapted to the host cell used, and since this is a factor favouring interferon production (see below), it may well explain the relatively early production of interferon in these two instances.

Production of interferon in different host cells

Interferon production has been observed in many but not all virus-host cell systems. Why should one such system produce interferon and another not? Schlesinger (1959b) points out that "autointerference is characteristic especially of viruses which are not fully adapted to the experimental host or which are mixtures of particles with different properties". This generalization seems to be true of interferon production too; there are numerous examples of interferon production by poorly adapted virus—the inactivated myxoviruses, measles virus, chick-adapted poliomyelitis in human kidney cells, the non-cytopathic strain of rabies. There are also several instances of interferon production by mixtures of particles with different properties, for the infective myxoviruses certainly consist of a mixture of particles with different properties at the time when interferon is being produced. This is true also of the mixture of infective and heat-inactivated Sindbis virus that was used for interferon production (Ho, 1961a, b). The generalization does not appear to be true of the production of interferon by infective Sindbis within the first 24 hours after infection (Ho, 1961a), although here too thermally inactivated virus may play some role.

There are several reports of interferon production by a virus, either infective or inactivated, in cells which are unable to support the growth of the fully infective virus. Lindenmann, Burke and Isaacs (1957) found that interferon was produced in approximately equal amounts by inoculation of inactivated virus on to the chorionic or the allantoic surface of the chick chorioallantoic membrane although only the allantoic surface was able to support influenza virus multiplication (Isaacs and Fulton, 1953). It was also found that interferon could be produced by incubating infective or inactivated virus with cells which had been previously treated with inactivated virus, and which were unable to support virus multiplication (Isaacs and Burke, 1958). Infection of human amnion cells with Sendai virus leads to interferon production although the virus cannot multiply in these cells (Gresser, 1961b), and a similar effect with mumps virus in HeLa cells has been observed by Cantell (1960). A possible explanation is that, in these cells, the viral nucleic acid is unable to complete the synthesis of either viral protein or of viral nucleic acid, but only of a protein interferon.

Interferon has been produced in chick chorioallantoic membranes (Isaacs and Lindenmann, 1957) and such primary tissue culture cells as those of calf kidney (Tyrrell, 1959), monkey kidney (Burke and

Isaacs, 1958b), mouse embryo (Allison, 1961), chick embryo (Vilček, 1961), human kidney (Ho and Enders, 1959a) and human amnion (Sutton and Tyrrell, 1961). It has also been prepared in a number of cell lines including HeLa cells (De Maeyer and Enders, 1961; Cantell, 1960), MCN cells (Henle *et al.*, 1959), and KB cells (Chany, 1961). No comparisons of the yields of interferon in these different cell systems are possible because of the different assay systems used.

The interferons produced in these different cells are not identical. Tyrrell (1959) found that interferon prepared in calf kidney cells was not active in chick chorioallantoic membranes and *vice versa*, and Wagner (1960) demonstrated a similar effect with interferons made in chick and duck cells. A similar species-specificity was found by Issaacs and Westwood (1959a) with rabbit and chick cells, although Andrews (1961) reported some overlapping of activity. The subject was more thoroughly examined by Sutton and Tyrrell (1961), who found that interferon prepared in rhesus monkey kidney tissue cultures was active in all cultures in which it was assayed (calf, monkey and several human cultures). In contrast interferon prepared in human amnion cultures was only active in the homologous cultures. Interferon prepared in calf kidney and cultures of human adult thyroid tissue occupied an intermediate position.

Biochemical changes in the host cell during interferon production

During virus interference, synthesis either of virus protein or nucleic acid, or of both, is blocked and some effect would be expected on the synthesis of host protein or nucleic acid. Henle, Henle and Kirber (1947) showed that injection of ultraviolet-inactivated influenza into fertile hens' eggs slowed down further growth of the embryo and the chorioallantoic membrane. There is also evidence that cells persistently infected with Newcastle disease virus, and therefore producing interferon, grow more slowly than normal cells (Henle, *et al.*, 1958), but this may be an effect caused by the small amount of virus produced, rather than by the establishment of interference. Apart from the reports of the effects of interference on the growth rate of the cells, there is also a little information on intracellular changes during interferon production. Tyrell and Tamm (1955) showed that 2,5-dimethylbenzimidazole, an antimetabolite of nucleic acid, inhibited the interfering action of heat-inactivated influenza virus. The antimetabolite probably acts by affecting host nucleic acid metabolism, suggesting that the host nucleic acids are involved in the establishment of interference and production of interferon. This is not an unexpected result in view of the connection between nucleic acids and protein synthesis. Burke and Buchan (unpublished work) found that chick embryo cells, kept in a maintenance medium, became better producers of interferon over a period of about 5 days. The change was paralleled by an increase in the host cell ribonucleic acid content suggesting a connection between ribonucleic acid synthesis and interferon production. On the other hand, Schlesinger and Kuske (1958) failed to find any inhibition by ribonuclease of interference induced by ultraviolet-inactivated virus.

Kilbourne (1957) and Smart and Kilbourne (1961) have shown that cortisone inhibits not only the establishment of interference by inactivated virus but also the production of interferon and viral multiplication. It presumably functions by affecting some stage common to these processes.

The action of interferon—variation of cell susceptibility

Interferon is most effective in the cell in which it is formed, and the role of interferon in virus-induced autointerference has already been discussed. Interferon, produced *in situ*, probably also plays a part in the mechanism of resistance to natural virus infections. However, interferon is released very easily from the cells. Two reports (Henle, *et al.* 1959; Burke and Isaacs, 1960) have shown that on testing serial two-fold dilutions of ultraviolet-inactivated

influenza for interfering ability and interferon production, interferon production has an end-point about one or two dilutions
before induction of interference. This difference is partly a function
of the sensitivity of the assays, but also probably indicates that very
small doses of inactivated virus can induce interference without
release of interferon, that is, no excess interferon is produced.

Although interferon is released freely from cells, it is adsorbed
rather slowly by new cells in the only two systems for which data
are available—chick chlorioallantoic membranes (Lindenmann
et al., 1957) and chick embryo cells (Wagner, 1961). Differences in
the rate of interferon adsorption may account for variations in cell
susceptibility: for differences between cells of different species and
for differences in the same species between cells derived from malignant tissue and from primary cells. Ho and Enders (1959b) and
Chany (1961) observed that cells derived from cancer tissues
(HeLa cells and KB cells) produced interferon, but showed a lower
sensitivity to its antiviral action than did primary cells of the same
species. Isaacs, Porterfield and Baron (1961) found that HeLa cells
were much less susceptible to the action of interferons than normal
human thyroid cells, while Cantell (1960) reported that HeLa cells
were susceptible to the action of interferon although no comparisons with other cells were made. These differences are partly due
to the use of different strains of HeLa cells (Cantell, 1960), but until
radioactive interferon is available it may be difficult to decide
whether the difference in cell susceptibility is due to different rates
of adsorption or to intracellular factors.

The comparative resistance to interferon of many cell lines will
be a handicap to biochemical work on the action of interferon, and
studies will probably have to continue to be carried out in primary
tissue culture cells.

Histology of the resistant cell

Interferon inhibits viral protein and nucleic acid synthesis, but
it appears to have very little effect on the growth and multiplication

of host cells. Wagner and Levy (1960) examined chick fibroblasts which had been treated with interferon and subsequently infected with Eastern equine encephalomyelitis. The distribution of nucleic acids was normal and mitotic figures were observed. The formation of multinucleate cells occurred, although it was not determined whether this effect was due to the action of interferon alone, or in combination with the superinfecting virus. Baron and Isaacs (1962) examined the effect of interferon on growing cultures of human and mouse cells, and found no gross difference between the growth of treated and control cultures. Gresser (1961a) has reported that interferon prepared in several different cell cultures of human origin induced marked morphological changes in primary cultures of human amnion cells. The effect was reversible and its extent and duration depended on the initial concentration of interferon. An interferon preparation made in monkey kidney cells produced little effect in human amnion cells, although it markedly inhibited virus growth; it is possible that the effect was due to the presence of another factor, especially since the interferon preparations had not been purified in any way.

The reported lack of effect of interferon on the growth and multiplication of host cells is difficult to explain, particularly in view of the effect of ultraviolet-inactivated influenza on cell multiplication (Henle *et al.*, 1947). The effect of interferon must be a very specific one.

Metabolic changes induced by interferon in the host cell

Interferon does not produce its maximum effect within the host cell until after several hours' incubation at 37°. The reason for this delayed action is not known; possibly it is due to transformation of interferon to another protein, which is the actual antiviral factor. The cell is not likely to be susceptible to the action of interferon during only part of the mitotic cycle, since the pieces of chorio-membrane used in much of the earlier work were surviving and not multiplying tissues. Wagner (1961) has shown that interferon is bound rapidly and irreversibly after adsorption.

In the presence of interferon chick embryo cells show an increased aerobic glycolysis, increased uptake of oxygen, decreased uptake of inorganic phosphate and decreased oxidation of glucose *via* the pentose phosphate cycle (Isaacs, Klemperer and Hitchcock, 1961). Some of these changes are similar to those produced in tissue culture cells after infection by many viruses. Virus infection is often followed by increased aerobic glycolysis (Levy and Baron, 1957; Fisher and Ginsberg, 1957; Becker, Grossowicz and Bernkopf, 1958; Klemperer, 1961), and since the increase is found shortly after infection, it is probably a reflection of changes due to the early stages of virus synthesis, rather than of cell breakdown. It is therefore unlikely that the action of interferon is due to increased glycolysis. It would be interesting to discover if the increase in aerobic glycolysis caused by interferon parallels the development of virus resistance, for glycolysis levels have only been measured after interference has already become established.

In contrast to the action of interferon, infection of chick embryo cells with influenza virus causes an increased oxidation of glucose by way of the pentose phosphate cycle (Klemperer, 1961), suggesting that the antiviral effect might be due to inhibition of ribose production and consequent suppression of viral nucleic acid synthesis. However, the antiviral effect of interferon was unaltered when glucose in the medium was replaced by ribose and pyruvate; the action of interferon cannot therefore be due to inhibition of ribose formation and it is not clear how its effect on glucose oxidation should be interpreted.

The metabolic changes caused by interferon are due to changes in glucose metabolism through glycolysis, the tricarboxylic acid cycle and the terminal respiratory chain and may well be connected with its antiviral action. The changes are similar to those produced by agents such as dinitrophenol which uncouple oxidative phosphorylation. Dinitrophenol also inhibits virus growth, although preincubation with the cells is not necessary and it is not a very effective interfering agent. Several other points of similarity between the action of interferon and dinitrophenol have been observed (Isaacs, Klemperer and Hitchcock, 1961). Both caused an increase in oxygen uptake, an increase in phosphate release and an inhibition of oxidation *via* the pentose phosphate cycle, although in all three situations concentrations of dinitrophenol, having 2% (or less) of the antiviral activity of an interferon preparation, produced greater metabolic changes. Dinitrophenol, sodium azide, dicoumarol and Janus green, all uncoupling agents, were more effective inhibitors of the growth of Sendai virus than of Newcastle disease virus. Interferon was also more effective against Sendai virus than against Newcastle disease virus, although the ratio of the sensitivities was greater with interferon than with dinitrophenol.

The effect of dinitrophenol on the two viruses suggested that the multiplication of Sendai virus was more dependent on oxidative processes than was Newcastle disease virus, and the same conclusion was reached by a study of the effect of oxygen tension on viral multiplication (Baron, Porterfield and Isaacs, 1961). The viruses most sensitive to the action of interferon were those most dependent on oxygen for growth, and the antiviral action of interferon was increased by decreased oxygen tension (Isaacs, Porterfield and Baron, 1961).

Dinitrophenol, in doses which inhibit myxovirus growth in normal cells, had no effect on the growth of poliomyelitis virus in HeLa cells (Gifford and Blakey, 1959), presumably because HeLa cells obtain most of their energy from glycolytic processes. Interferon produced in HeLa cells was found to be active in primary human cells but not in HeLa cells (Ho and Enders, 1959*b*) and this has been suggested as another similarity between the action of interferon and that of dinitrophenol (Isaacs, Klemperer and Hitchcock, 1961). HeLa cells have been found to vary in their sensitivity to interferon (Cantell, 1960), and it would be interesting to compare the sensitivity to interferon and the effect of dinitro-

reports indicate that interferon may be one of the other factors involved. Isaacs and Hitchcock (1960) infected mice with influenza virus and assayed the lungs and sera for virus, viral antibody and interferon. The interferon content of the lungs followed closely the peak of virus titre, but antibody was not detected until a week later. The authors concluded that interferon might play a significant role in the recovery of mice from influenza virus infection. Link and Raus (1961) have also reported production of interferon in the mouse lung previously infected with influenza virus. Porterfield and Hitchcock (1961) infected mice intracerebrally with an arbor virus and determined the amount of infective virus and interferon in the brain at daily intervals. They found that a rapid rise in virus titre was followed by a rise in interferon titre which remained high until the end of the experiment although, by this time, virus yield was declining. They suggested that this drop in virus titre was due to interferon and that the balance between the production of infective virus and the production of interferon may be a factor influencing the speed of adaptation of a virus to a new tissue or host. Sawicki, Baron and Isaacs (1961) showed that increased oxygen tension, known to decrease the antiviral action of interferon, led to earlier appearance of lethal pneumonia and to an increased final mortality rate in mice infected with influenza virus. This finding may be connected with the effect of interferon *in vivo*. Vainio, Gwatkin, and Koprowski (1961) compared the production of virus and interferon in the brains of genetically resistant and susceptible strains of mice infected with West Nile virus, and found that the yield of virus and of interferon was much lower in the brains of resistant mice than in the brains of susceptible mice. The authors suggested that interferon plays no role in the resistance of the genetically resistant mice to West Nile virus. The role of interferon in the maintenance of the chronic virus infection in tissue culture has already been discussed. If such chronic infections exist *in vivo*, then possibly interferon plays part in their control.

The antiviral action of interferon has been demonstrated on the dropped chorioallantoic membrane of the egg (Isaacs, Burke and Fadeeva, 1958) and in the whole egg (Wagner, 1961). A comparison of the susceptibility to virus infection of chick embryos of varying ages with their susceptibility to the antiviral action of interferon revealed a close correlation (Baron and Isaacs, 1961) suggesting that interferon may be involved in recovery from infection *in ovo*.

There have been two reports of the demonstration of an antiviral effect of interferon in mice. Hitchcock and Isaacs (1960) found that intraperitoneal inoculation of mouse interferon into mice gave a slight but significant protection against an encephalitis virus, and Pollikoff, Donikian and Liu (1961) reported slight protection of partially immunized mice treated with chick interferon and infected with influenza virus, and also a similar slight protection of non-immune mice treated with monkey kidney interferon.

Experiments in larger animals have been restricted to demonstration of the antiviral action of interferon against local infections in rabbit skin (Isaacs and Westwood, 1959b; Andrews, 1961), in rabbit eye (Cantell and Tommila, 1960) and in monkey skin (Andrews, 1961). Baron and Isaacs (1962) have demonstrated the absence of interferon in lungs from fatal cases of influenza in man and have suggested that this absence may be significant.

Interferons are produced by a number of virus–host cell systems The products are generally similar, although the species-specificity shows that interferons produced in different cells must differ in some way, as yet unknown. Interferon production appears to be characteristic of viruses which are not fully adapted to the host, or which are mixtures of particles with different properties. It is not yet clear whether fully infective virus can produce interferon. Little is yet known about the viral components responsible for the initiation of interferon production, or of biochemical changes within the host cell.

Interferon acts after virus adsorption and before virus maturation. It appears to have little effect on growth and multiplication of host cells and its effect must be a very specific one. Interferon does, however, induce a number of changes in the host cell which are probably connected with its antiviral action. These changes suggest that interferon acts by inhibiting some oxidative processes of the host necessary for virus synthesis, possibly in the terminal respiratory chain. Interferon appears to be involved in recovery from viral infections *in vivo* and offers real possibilities in protection against local viral infections and possibly against systemic infections.

[Discussion on this paper was postponed until after the following paper by G. Belyavin; see p. 330.]

REFERENCES

ADA, G. L. and PERRY, B. T. (1956). *J. gen. Microbiol.*, **14**, 623.
ALLISON, A. C. (1961). *Virology*, **15**, 47.
ANDREWS, R. D. (1961). *Brit. med. J.*, **i**, 1728.
ANDREWS, R. D. and DUDGEON, J. A. (1961). *Biochem. J.*, **78**, 564.
BALUDA, M. A. (1959). *Virology*, **7**, 315.
BARON, S. and ISAACS, A. (1961). *Nature, Lond.*, **191**, 97.
BARON, S. and ISAACS, A. (1962). *Brit. med. J.*, **i**, 18.
BARON, S., PORTERFIELD, J. S. and ISAACS, A. (1961). *Virology*, **14**, 444.
BECKER, Y., GROSSOWICZ, N. and BERNKOPF, H. (1958). *Proc. Soc. exp. Biol., N.Y.*, **97**, 77.
BELLETT, A. J. D. and COOPER, P. D. (1959). *J. gen. Microbiol.*, **21**, 498.
BERGS, V. V., HENLE, G., DEINHARDT, F. and HENLE, W. (1958). *J. exp. Med.*, **108**, 537.
BURKE, D. C. (1961). *Biochem. J.*, **78**, 556.
BURKE, D. C. and ISAACS, A. (1958a). *Brit. J. exp. Path.*, **39**, 78.
BURKE, D. C. and ISAACS, A. (1958b). *Brit. J. exp. Path.*, **39**, 452.
BURKE, D. C. and ISAACS, A. (1960). *Acta virol.*, **4**, 215.
CANTELL, K. (1960). *Arch. ges. Virusforsch.*, **10**, 510.
CANTELL, K. and TOMMILA, V. (1960). *Lancet*, **ii**, 682.
CHANY, C. (1961). *Virology*, **13**, 485.
CHENG, P. Y. (1961). *Virology*, **14**, 124.
COOPER, P. D. and BELLETT, A. J. D. (1959). *J. gen. Microbiol.*, **21**, 485.
DEINHARDT, F. and HENLE, G. (1960). *J. Immunol.*, **84**, 608.
DE MAEYER, E. and ENDERS, J. F. (1961). *Proc. Soc. exp. Biol., N.Y.*, **107**, 573.
DE SOMER, P., PRINZIE, A., DENYS, P. and SCHONNE, E. (1962). *Virology*, **16**, 63.
DINTER, Z. (1960). *Acta path. microbiol. scand.*, **49**, 270.

DOHERTY, R. L. (1958). *Virology*, **6**, 575.

DRAKE, J. W. (1958). *Virology*, **6**, 244.

ENDERS, J. (1960). *Trans. Coll. Phycns. Philad.*, **28**, 68.

ERMOLIEVA, Z. V., FURER, N. M., BALESINA, T. I., FADEEVA, L. L. and NEMIROV-SKAYA, B. M. (1961). *Antibiotiki (U.S.S.R.)*, **6**, 196.

FISHER, T. N. and GINSBERG, H. S. (1957). *Proc. Soc. exp. Biol., N.Y.*, **95**, 47.

FRIEDMAN, R. M. and BARON, S. (1961). *J. Immunol.*, **87**, 379.

GIFFORD, G. E. and BLAKEY, B. R. (1959). *Proc. Soc. exp. Biol., N.Y.*, **102**, 268.

GOTLIEB, T. and HIRST, G. K. (1956). *Virology*, **2**, 235.

GRESSER, I. (1961a). *Proc. nat. Acad. Sci., Wash.*, **47**, 1817.

GRESSER, I. (1961b). *Proc. Soc. exp. Biol., N.Y.*, **108**, 303.

GROSSBERG, S. E. and HOLLAND, J. J. (1961). *Fed. Proc.*, **20**, 442.

HENLE, W. (1950). *J. Immunol.*, **64**, 203.

HENLE, W. (1953). Advances in Virus Research, p. 142, New York: Academic Press.

HENLE, G., DEINHARDT, F., BERGS, V. V. and HENLE, W. (1958). *J. exp. Med.*, **108**, 537.

HENLE, W. and HENLE, G. (1943). *Science*, **98**, 87.

HENLE, W., HENLE, G., DEINHARDT, F. and BERGS, V. V. (1959). *J. exp. Med.*, **110**, 525.

HENLE, W., HENLE, G. and KIRBER, M. W. (1947). *Amer. J. med. Sci.*, **214**, 529.

HITCHCOCK, G. and ISAACS, A. (1960). *Brit. med. J.*, **ii**, 1268.

HO, M. (1961a). *Fed. Proc.*, **20**, 442.

HO, M. (1961b). *Proc. Soc. exp. Biol., N.Y.*, **107**, 639.

HO, M. and ENDERS, J. F. (1959a). *Proc. nat. Acad. Sci., Wash.*, **45**, 385.

HO, M. and ENDERS, J. F. (1959b). *Virology*, **9**, 446.

HOLLAENDER, A. and OLIPHANT, J. W. (1944). *J. Bact.*, **48**, 447.

HSUING, G. D. (1962). *Proc. Soc. exp. Biol., N.Y.*, **108**, 357.

ISAACS, A. and BURKE, D. C. (1958). *Nature, Lond.*, **182**, 1073.

ISAACS, A., BURKE, D. C. and FADEEVA, L. (1958). *Brit. J. exp. Path.*, **39**, 447.

ISAACS, A. and EDNEY, M. (1950). *Aust. J. exp. Biol. med. Sci.*, **28**, 219.

ISAACS, A. and FULTON, F. (1953). *J. gen. Microbiol.*, **9**, 132.

ISAACS, A. and HITCHCOCK, G. (1960). *Lancet*, **ii**, 69.

ISAACS, A., KLEMPERER, H. G. and HITCHCOCK, G. (1961). *Virology*, **13**, 191.

ISAACS, A. and LINDENMANN, J. (1957). *Proc. roy. Soc. B.*, **147**, 258.

ISAACS, A., LINDENMANN, J. and VALENTINE, R. C. (1957). *Proc. roy. Soc. B.*, **147**, 268.

ISAACS, A., PORTERFIELD, J. S. and BARON, S. (1961). *Virology*, **14**, 450.

ISAACS, A. and WESTWOOD, M. A. (1959a). *Lancet*, **ii**, 324.

ISAACS, A. and WESTWOOD, M. A. (1959b). *Nature, Lond.*, **184**, 1232.

KAPLAN, M. M., WECKER, E., FORSEK, Z. and KOPROWSKI, H. (1960). *Nature, Lond.*, **186**, 821.

KILBOURNE, E. D. (1957). *J. exp. Med.*, **106**, 863.

KLEMPERER, H. (1961). *Virology*, **13**, 68.

LEVY, H. B. and BARON, S. (1957). *J. infect. Dis.*, **100**, 109.
LINDENMANN, J., BURKE, D. C. and ISAACS, A. (1957). *Brit. J. exp. Path.*, **38**, 551.
LINK, F. and RAUS, J. (1961). *Nature, Lond.*, **192**, 478.
LOCKHART, R. Z. Jr. (1960). *Virology*, **10**, 198.
MAYER, V., SOKOL, F. and VILČEK, J. (1961). *Acta virol.*, **5**, 264.
NAGANO, Y. and KOJIMA, Y. (1958). *C.R. Soc. Biol., Paris*, **152**, 1627.
NAGANO, Y. and KOJIMA, Y. (1960). *C.R. Soc. Biol., Paris*, **154**, 2172.
NAGANO, Y., KOJIMA, Y. and SUKUZI, T. (1960). *C.R. Soc. Biol., Paris*, **154**, 2166.
PAUCKER, K. and HENLE, W. (1958). *Virology*, **6**, 198.
POLLIKOFF, R., DONIKIAN, M. A. and LIU, O. C. (1961). *Bact. Proc.*, 158.
PORTERFIELD, J. S. and HITCHCOCK, G. (1961). *Virology*, **13**, 363.
POWELL, W. F. and SETLOW, R. B. (1956). *Virology*, **2**, 337.
SAWICKI, L., BARON, S. and ISAACS, A. (1961). *Lancet*, **ii**, 680.
SCHLESINGER, R. W. (1951). *Arch. ges. Virusforch.*, **4**, 501.
SCHLESINGER, R. W. (1959*a*). Viral and Rickettsial Diseases of Man, 3rd Ed., p. 145, Philadelphia: Lippincot.
SCHLESINGER, R. W. (1959*b*). The Viruses, III, 169, New York: Academic Press.
SCHLESINGER, R. W. and KUSKE, T. T. (1958) *quoted in* The Viruses, III, 187, New York: Academic Press.
SMART, K. M. and KILBOURNE, E. D. (1961). *Fed. Proc.*, **20**, 441.
STONE, J. D. (1948). *Aust. J. exp. Biol. med. Sci.*, **26**, 49.
SUTTON, R. N. P. and TYRELL, D. A. J. (1961). *Brit. J. exp. Path.*, **42**, 99.
TAMM, I. and FLUKE, D. J. (1950). *J. Bact.*, **59**, 449.
TYRRELL, D. A. J. (1959). *Nature, Lond.*, **184**, 452.
TYRRELL, D. A. J. and TAMM, I. (1955). *J. Immunol.*, **75**, 43.
VAINIO, T., GWATKIN, R. and KOPROWSKI, H. (1961). *Virology*, **14**, 385.
VILČEK, J. (1960). *Acta virol.*, **4**, 308.
VILČEK, J. (1961). *Acta virol.*, **5**, 278.
VILČEK, J. and RADA, B. (1962). *Acta virol.*, **6**, 9.
WAGNER, R. R. (1960). *Bact. Rev.*, **24**, 151.
WAGNER, R. R. (1961). *Virology*, **13**, 323.
WAGNER, R. R. and LEVY, A. H. (1960). *Ann. N.Y. Acad. Sci.*, **88**, 1308.
ŽEMLA, J. and SCHRAMEK, S. (1962). *Virology*, **16**, 204.
ŽEMLA, J. and VILČEK, J. (1961*a*). *Acta virol.*, **5**, 129.
ŽEMLA, J. and VILČEK, J. (1961*b*). *Acta virol.*, **5**, 367.

ADVENTURES OF A VIRUS IN THE HOST WONDERLAND

G. BELYAVIN

Department of Bacteriology,
University College Medical School, London

I MUST confess at the outset that the light-hearted title I have chosen for this communication is no more than a literary conceit. This paper could perhaps be more properly entitled "A survey of the kinetic problems of virus chemotherapy", a title although more accurate, at the same much more forbidding.

Virus chemotherapy has been studied so far along the lines of specific metabolic inhibition as pioneered in the classical field of bacterial chemotherapy. This brief account of the adventures of a virus in the host wonderland and the conclusions that may be deduced from it, suggest alternative lines of therapy applicable in the intact and integrated host which may at least be of interest, if not ultimately of practical value.

Pathways of virus spread in host tissues

All adventures must have a beginning, and as far as a virus is concerned, the adventures we are interested in begin with the entry of a virus particle into the tissues of the susceptible host. If this is followed by general dissemination of the virus to many diverse tissues, certain stages in this dissemination process may be postulated (Fig. 1).

With many virus infections of man, these stages are more inferred than proved. Investigation of experimental laboratory infections, such as the classical work of Fenner on ectromelia and myxomatosis

(Fenner, 1948; Fenner and Woodroofe, 1953), has indicated that these steps in the spread of virus infection in the body can and do occur in this way. Nevertheless we can recognize important restrictions on this overall pattern. Thus it seems clear that natural influenzal infection in man and experimentally induced influenza in the ferret involve virus infection of the superficial respiratory epithelium alone, with no evidence of deeper spread. Similarly it is likely that the great majority of human poliomyelitis infections are

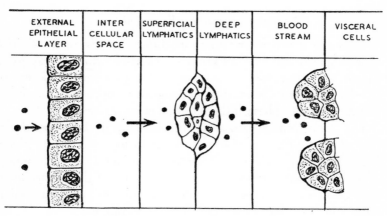

| EXTERNAL EPITHELIAL LAYER | INTER CELLULAR SPACE | SUPERFICIAL LYMPHATICS | DEEP LYMPHATICS | BLOOD STREAM | VISCERAL CELLS |

FIG. 1. Pathway of virus spread in the host.

localized infections of the gut epithelium, with deeper spread limited to the mesenteric lymph nodes. This is in contradistinction to a disease like smallpox where generalized spread is almost invariable—at least subclinical cases with a limited spread of infection are not commonly recognized.

Throughout these stages we can recognize that at all times the virus may exist in the host both intracellularly or extracellularly. Furthermore, as spread of infection proceeds in the organized host, we have innumerable transfers from extracellular to intracellular phase, followed by the formation of more virus and transition back

from intracellular phase to extracellular again. Any one such cycle
may be summarized in the brief steps of virus behaviour thus:

(1) Adsorption of virus onto cell surface
(2) Penetration of adsorbed virus through cell surface
(3) Intracellular virus replication
(4) Release of new virus into extracellular phase

Suppression of any one of these stages must lead to a chemotherapeutic effect.

Suppression of intracellular replication

A great deal of work has been concentrated on this aspect of virus
chemotherapy and I do not propose to consider this topic at great
length. It is clear that as virus replication proceeds in the intracellular phase, any chemical agent designed to suppress it must itself
be present in this phase at the requisite concentration.

The rate at which such an agent builds up in the intracellular
phase is dependent on its concentration in the extracellular phase
at that time and on the rate of transfer through the cell membrane.

Both these conditions apply to those parts of the intracellular
phase which are accessible to material present in the extracellular
phase; the boundary of separation is cell membrane.

There is one point worth noting with regard to this important
restriction. Intracellular phase which is readily accessible to the
chemical agent is probably equally accessible to virus, and *vice-
versa*. The important exceptions here are the superficial epithelia,
which *may* be more readily accessible to external virus than to agent
in the extracellular phase, and special internal tissues such as brain
tissue, where transfer from circulating blood is poor.

Nevertheless, it is clear as a generalization that the maintenance
of high blood levels of chemotherapeutic substance may not achieve
an adequate effect in a virus infection if the rate of diffusion into
the intracellular phase is low. While parenteral administration can
overcome inefficient initial absorption into the extracellular phase,

a slow rate of diffusion into the cell may be much more difficult to overcome, and may be decisive in the face of a rapidly multiplying virus. This seems to me to be one of the important potential limitations of this particular approach to viral chemotherapy.

The intracellular distribution of chemotherapeutic agent within the cell and the relationship of this distribution to the cytoplasmic regions which are essentially concerned in virus synthesis must be a second factor with important implications for "intracellular chemotherapy" of virus infection. Apart from this, an efficient chemotherapeutic substance must be capable of suppressing virus synthesis without grossly disorganizing the metabolic activity of the infected cell. This presupposes a high functional specificity for the virus-manufacturing process. Regarded in a superficial light, most viruses consist principally of protein and nucleic acid and one would suppose that these must be synthesized through the normal cellular channels involved in the production of the same basic cellular constituents under normal conditions. One would predict that even if all the problems of introducing the compound into the cell were overcome, any interference with virus synthesis would affect the metabolic efficiency of the cell as a whole. One must admit however, that as the total weight of virus material synthesized must be only a very small fraction of the total output of the cell, considerable suppression of virus formation could perhaps be achieved at the cost of only a small loss in total metabolic turnover. Sheffield (1962) has shown that the replication of rabbitpox virus in embryo rabbit kidney (ERK) cells can be almost completely suppressed by isatin β-thiosemicarbazone with virtually little change in total protein synthesis over a period of 5 days. These problems I think are fascinating to a degree, and merit a symposium on their own.

"Surface blocking" agents

We must now consider those potentially chemotherapeutic processes which are dependent on the concentration of active agent in the extracellular phase only. These involve the compounds which must act either directly on the surface of free extracellular virus or on the surface of the susceptible cell—the "surface blocking" agents. The former are agents which will interfere with the specific processes by which a virus adsorbs to the host cell surface and the latter materials capable of blocking the mechanisms of virus transfer through the cell membrane, whatever these may be. This may of course affect either penetration into the cell, or escape out of

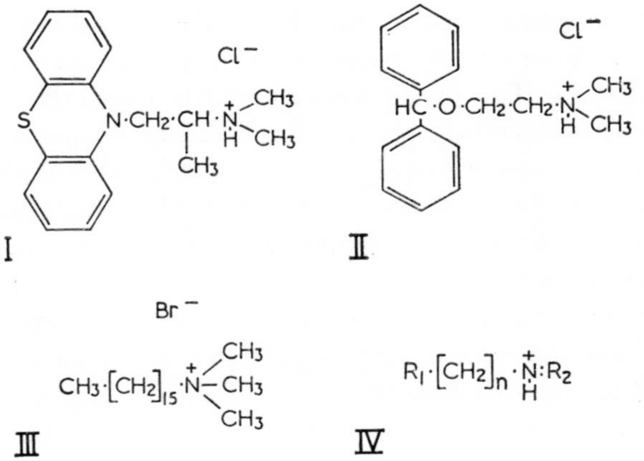

FIG. 2. Amphipathic compounds.
I: Promethazine; II: Diphenhydramine; III: Cetyltrimethylammonium bromide
IV: General formula.

the cell. To take these particular processes first, one can say that little is known about virus penetration and egress. Rees and his collaborators have shown that diphenhydramine (benadryl) or promethazine (phenergan) will protect rats against liver necrosis induced by carbon tetrachloride, and that this effect appears to be determined by the ability of the compounds to control the increased permeability of the liver cell induced by carbon tetrachloride poisoning (Bangham, Rees and Shotlander, 1962).

Inspection of the molecular formulae of these compounds shows that they belong to the general class of "amphipathic" compounds (Fig. 2) which are active in changing the pressure of lipid films in the Langmuir trough (Table I). It was shown that the amphipathic activity of the cationic compounds was closely linked with ability

Table I

PROTECTIVE EFFECTS AND PHYSICAL PROPERTIES OF COMPOUNDS
AGAINST LIVER NECROSIS IN RATS POISONED WITH CARBON
TETRACHLORIDE

Compound	Dose $\mu moles/kg.$ bodyweight at 0 hr., half dose at 6 hr.	Degree of necrosis 24 hr. after CCl_4	Molar concentration raising the surface pressure of lipid film from 20 to 35 dynes
Nil	—	+ + + +	—
Sodium hexadecyl sulphate	70	+ + + +	1×10^{-6}
Sodium dodecyl sulphate	85	+ + + +	$8 \cdot 9 \times 10^{-6}$
Sodium phenobarbitone	100	+ + + +	$\varDelta \pi$ 10 dynes at 10^{-3}
Diphenhydramine hydrochloride	85	+ +	$2 \cdot 5 \times 10^{-3}$
Mepyramine maleate	77	+ +	$3 \cdot 7 \times 10^{-3}$
Promazine hydrochloride	77	+	$1 \cdot 4 \times 10^{-4}$
Promethazine hydrochloride	77	+	$1 \cdot 7 \times 10^{-4}$
Cinchocaine hydrochloride	65	+	$3 \cdot 5 \times 10^{-4}$
Chlorpromazine hydrochloride	70	+	$5 \cdot 5 \times 10^{-5}$
Docosanyl pyridinium bromide	27	——★	$4 \cdot 3 \times 10^{-6}$
Stearylamine	55	——★	$5 \cdot 1 \times 10^{-7}$
Cetyl trimethyl ammonium bromide	14	+	$5 \cdot 9 \times 10^{-7}$

★ These drugs could not be assessed against necrosis because of potent side effects;
+ + + + denotes an active necrosis with areas of eosinophilic coagulative necrosis of liver cells.

(Modified from Bangham, Rees and Shotlander, 1962)

to protect against liver necrosis; it was concluded that these substances acted by altering the permeability of lipid membrane structures, either at the cell surface or in the cytoplasm. Such a hypothesis suggests that virus entry into (or release from) the cell may be influenced by compounds of this type, thus limiting the spread of virus through the intracellular and extracellular phase.

It is interesting to note that Judah and his collaborators at the

Wistar Institute (Vainio, Judah and Bjotvedt, 1962) have shown that benadryl can protect mice against death from infection with murine hepatitis virus and my colleague, Dr. Stevenson, has obtained some evidence suggesting that promazine can partially suppress plaque formation by Type I poliovirus in ERK cell monolayers.

As a long term view, this may be one of the most promising avenues of virus chemotherapy to explore, for many of these "amphipathic" compounds are comparatively readily absorbed into the extracellular phase, and are active on lipid films in the Langmuir trough at a concentration of 10^{-4}M or less.

Virus surface blocking agents

An excellent example of a virus "surface blocking" agent is of course, specific antibody. The molecules of antibody bind on to antigenic receptor sites on the surface of the virus particle and in this way interfere with its capacity to adsorb on to the surface of the host cell.

In the case of the influenza viruses it is believed that the receptor site on the cell surface which links with the virus particle is a sialic acid-substituted oligosaccharide residue. There are a number of substances in the sera of many animal species, in mucous secretions, in saliva and similar materials, which will bind on to many strains of influenza virus and not only interfere with their capacity to adsorb on to fowl red cells and agglutinate them, but also their ability to infect the appropriate cells of a host animal. These are the so-called haemagglutination inhibitors of influenza viruses, and by virtue of their activity against many antigenically dissimilar strains, they are designated as non-specific, in contradistinction to antibody.

The considerable infectivity-neutralizing potency of many of these materials makes them of interest as potential chemotherapeutic substances, and my colleagues and I have spent some years studying their biological, chemical and physical properties.

Most of the non-specific haemagglutination inhibitors which

have been isolated in a sufficiently pure state to be chemically studied have been shown to contain varying amounts of sialic acid, oligosaccharides, amino sugars and amino acid residues. They are therefore mucoproteins. The presence of sugar residues and sialic acid suggests that these inhibitors carry the chemical homologue of the cell receptor site, and it is this which renders them able to bind on to the virus surface.

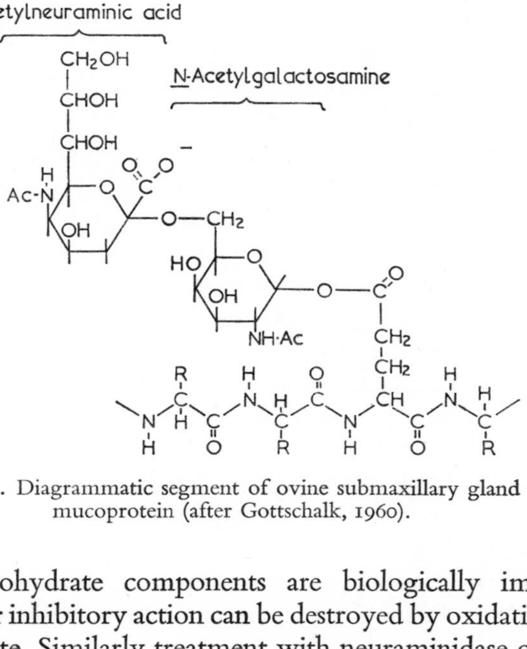

FIG. 3. Diagrammatic segment of ovine submaxillary gland mucoprotein (after Gottschalk, 1960).

The carbohydrate components are biologically important because their inhibitory action can be destroyed by oxidation with metaperiodate. Similarly treatment with neuraminidase of *Vibrio cholerae* will destroy the potency of those non-specific inhibitors which are classed as the α inhibitors. This is presumed to be the result of splitting off the sialic acid prosthetic group.

Sheep submaxillary gland mucoprotein has been obtained in a purified form, and a chemical constitution (Fig. 3) has been proposed for it by Gottschalk (1960). This substance is not a very active haemagglutination inhibitor. On the other hand, Tamm and his co-workers (Tamm and Horsfall, 1952) in the States have worked on a mucoprotein isolated from human urine by fractional salt precipitation and have shown that in the pure state this material is both a haemagglutination inhibitor and an active infectivity neutralizer of certain influenza virus strains, notably the A_1 strains. Under the electron microscope this material can be seen to consist of long threads up to 2,000 Å in length, and it is very tempting to infer that a coiled polypeptide chain is the basic structural skeleton of these molecules. In fact, this type of general chemical structure may be common to most of the inhibitory mucoproteins.

Two haemagglutination inhibitors are of immediate interest here, because of their strong neutralizing potency. The first is collocalia mucoid, originally described by Howe and his collaborators in the States (Howe, Rose and Lee, 1960; Howe, Lee and Rose, 1961), and extracted in a fairly pure state from the nest substance of the cave-dwelling swift, *Collocalia esculenta*. The crude nest material is used by the Chinese for the making of soup, and is strongly advocated by them for its aphrodisiac properties. A hot water extract of this material yields an active haemagglutination inhibitor in almost pure form and Dr. Biddle and I have studied it chemically, physically and biologically.

Its most striking property is the fact that 10 μg. of this material will neutralize over 500 EID_{50} of A_1 strain influenza virus and about the same challenge dose of a representative A_2 strain. This of course represents the results of *in ovo* titrations and we know nothing at the moment of its activity in an experimental animal such as the mouse.

Chemical and physical data, as they stand at the moment, indicate a molecular weight of about 200,000 with about 56% of amino acid residues, the rest being made up of carbohydrate and sialic acid. Such a qualitative constitution suggests a possible similarity with the structure proposed for ovine submaxillary gland mucoprotein.

The second substance which is of great interest is the haem-agglutination inhibitor present in horse serum. This is one of the most active neutralizing inhibitors known to us, and it has been found (Cohen and Belyavin, 1959) that horse serum diluted 1/300 will neutralize about 1,000 EID_{50} of Asian influenza virus (A/Singapore variant strain). My colleague, Dr. Cohen, has been able to demonstrate that intranasal administration of horse serum to mice will protect them from severe spreading infection with a mouse-adapted Asian influenza strain, even when administered 48 hours before challenge. Intranasal administration up to 6 hours after challenge with 100 LD_{50} of mouse-adapted virus will still confer some protection on the mice (Cohen, 1960).

We have as yet little information on the exact chemical nature of this horse serum substance, but it is readily inactivated by meta-periodate, and contains sialic acid; to this extent it has some chemical affinities with other inhibitory mucoproteins.

Limitations on the use of virus surface blocking agents

Antibody is secreted by the cells of the immune host, and thus gains ready access to the extracellular phase. In the case of large molecular substances such as the neutralizing non-specific inhibitors I have just discussed, these may of course be present in the extracellular phase in the course of nature. Where they may be used for chemotherapeutic purposes in a species that does not normally carry them in the extracellular phase, the problem of passing the intact molecule into this phase and keeping it there may be considerable. Collocalia mucoid has an estimated molecular weight of about 200,000 and urinary mucoprotein, another neutralizing inhibitor, about 7×10^6. The absorption of these substances in their native form through epithelial barriers into the extracellular phase would seem extremely difficult. Parenteral administration would seem inadvisable; collocalia mucoid for instance, is certainly antigenic and immune sensitization of the host is a very likely outcome of this form of administration.

On the other hand, although high concentrations may be required to achieve sufficient neutralizations in surface layers of fluid, where these are covering superficial epithelia it is practically easier to achieve such concentrations. Experimental work on the protection of mice with intranasal horse serum indicates the feasibility of such an approach.

Greater knowledge of the essential chemistry of these neutralizing inhibitors may permit chemical modifications to render them more easily absorbed and less antigenic, and therefore more practicable as chemotherapeutic materials.

We feel that these "surface blocking" agents, whether they act primarily on the virus surface or on the host cell surface, may provide a solution to the problem of virus chemotherapy.

REFERENCES

BANGHAM, A. D., REES, K. R. and SHOTLANDER, V. (1962). *Nature, Lond.*, **193,** 754.
COHEN, A. (1960). *Lancet*, **ii,** 791.
COHEN, A. and BELYAVIN, G. (1959). *Virology*, **7,** 59.
FENNER, F. (1948). *J. path. Bact.*, **60,** 529.
FENNER, F. and WOODROOFE, G. M. (1953). *Brit. J. exp. Path.*, **34,** 400.
GOTTSCHALK, A. (1960). *Nature, Lond.*, **186,** 949.
HOWE, C., LEE, L. T. and ROSE, H. M. (1961). *Arch. Biochem. Biophys.*, **95,** 512.
HOWE, C., ROSE, H. M. and LEE, L. T. (1960). *Nature, Lond.*, **188,** 251.
SHEFFIELD, F. W. (1962). *Brit. J. exp. Path.*, **43,** 59.
TAMM, I. and HORSFALL, F. L. (1952). *J. exp. Med.*, **95,** 71.
VAINIO, T., JUDAH, J. D. and BJOTVEDT, G. (1962). *Exp. mol. Path.*, **1, 15.**

DISCUSSION

C. E. D. Taylor (Central Public Health Labaratories, Colindale): Interferon is a protein and although it has a molecular weight of only 63,000 it is reasonable to suppose that it is probably antigenic. What, if anything, is known of the antigenic properties of interferon? How might this problem of antigenicity be overcome—as it surely would have to be overcome—if interferon were to be used as a therapeutic agent?

Burke: The evidence we have so far is that if interferon is antigenic, it is poorly antigenic. We have been unable to demonstrate the formation of an antibody in injected rabbits using the normal adjuvant methods, which would have shown up a highly antigenic substance. An antigen would be very useful for many studies, and I think it would be worth looking for one.

B. Lacey (Westminster Hospital Medical School): I know a great deal of energy has gone into trying to make an antibody, but what has been your test system? Has it involved looking for an inactivater of interferon?

Burke: I think it is a weakness of the work we have done, that we did not have purified material. The only way we could test this was to see if it inhibited the antiviral action of interferon. If we could get pure material then we could look for precipitin lines.

J. S. K. Boyd (The Wellcome Trust): Can I ask Dr. Sadler if he has any experience of the clinical use of the thiosemicarbazones?

Sadler: Perhaps Dr. Bauer could answer.

D. J. Bauer (Wellcome Laboratories of Tropical Medicine): Since the end of December there have been some thirty or forty cases of smallpox in England and Wales, and there have also been a much larger number of cases of complications due to vaccination on account of the concomitant vaccination campaign. These cases have offered an opportunity of carrying out a preliminary clinical evaluation of one of the compounds about which Dr. Sadler has told you. The one we selected for trial was the N-methylisatin β-thiosemicarbazone, otherwise known as compound 33T57.

The first case, a Pakistani, was not treated until about the fourth or fifth day of the rash, at the time when it was vesicular and becoming pustular. One would have thought at the time that the virus infection was dying out. It was a typical case of malignant confluent smallpox, and Dr. Marsden tells me that the course of the disease was not modified in any way by the treatment. The patient died after twelve days.

The strain of the virus which was isolated from him was tested by Dr. Dumbell of Liverpool University, and he found that the strain was fully sensitive to chemotherapy; either the patient was treated too late or else the dosage or the route of administration was inadequate. That is a point which we are trying to work out at the moment.

A patient in South Wales was treated with the compound. He again was got very late. He was treated on the sixth day of illness, and he recovered quite well though he had a very severe attack. Dr. Thomas, who was treating, him was gratified by his recovery, but I personally do not feel inclined to ascribe the recovery of this patient to the drug.

The third patient to be treated was a man aged about 50 who was last vaccinated ten years previously with unknown results, possibly favourable; he developed a very severe prodromal attack with a very high fever which went on for five days. There was a generalized prodromal morbilliform eruption and a petechial eruption of "bathing-drawers" distribution which is a very grave prognostic sign. He was treated with the compound on the fourth day of pyrexia. After the second dose of the compound his temperature came down by crisis from 103 · 5 to 98° F and remained at that level in the subsequent course of the illness. When his rash came out it was very sparse and the lesions failed to mature. He made an uninterrupted recovery.

The fourth patient treated was a pathologist who had done an autopsy on a child who died in the infectious stages of smallpox but who was diagnozed as having malaria and tuberculosis. He developed a very severe form of smallpox. It was a malignant confluent smallpox. He was treated with the compound quite early in the course of pyrexia. Evolution of the rash was very greatly delayed and it was modified; the lesions were soft and took nine days to reach the vesicular stage. One could possibly claim that the compound had modified the development of the rash and had modified its appearance and subsequent course. However, one does not know at the moment what a smallpox rash looks like while it is being affected by specific chemotherapy, but one must be cautious here because in malignant confluent smallpox the evolution of the rash may be greatly delayed and its appearance may be unusual. Therefore, I think with this particular case that we must leave outrselves with an open mind. This patient unfortunately died of myocarditis on the twelfth day of illness.

Quite a number of patients suffering from vaccinia have been treated. They have been suffering mostly from eczema vaccinatum—21 infants and 5 adults—and also there have been cases of ectopic primaries. In all these cases the patients have recovered, and there has been strong evidence that the compound has cured them. However, this, of course, must rest upon clinical impressions and, furthermore, in many cases the patients have had specific therapy with antivaccinial gamma-globulin. Apart from that there have been one or two cases from which that can be excluded and it is possible the compound has produced a therapeutic effect.

We have here in the audience Dr. Barlow who has used this compound with favourable effect, and he may be inclined to say something about it. Dr. Turner of Burnley has had a favourable result in the treatment of a case of eczema vaccinatum.

A. J. E. Barlow (Royal Infirmary, Huddersfield): I have recently had occasion to use compound 33T57 in a case of Kaposi's varicelliform eruption in a child of three-and-a-half. The drug was not given until the thirteenth day; two grams were then given daily for seven days. There were no toxic signs whatever. The child improved very rapidly and was clear about ten days later. It is difficult to say how far improvement was a result of the drug or of a natural resolution of the condition, but my impression, compared with other cases which were not similarly treated, was that the resolution was quicker than I would have expected.

L. Dickinson (Boots Pure Drug Co., Nottingham): Could Dr. Sadler or Dr. Bauer clarify two points? I take it that these compounds were assayed intracerebrally in mice. Are the ectromelia-positive compounds also active against generalized ectromelia in mice; and are the vaccinia-positive ones active against vaccinia on the back of the rabbit?

The other problem was about lipid solubility. Does the correlation with activity occur also in tissue culture studies with vaccinia?

Bauer: Yes, that is correct. Ectromelia virus was inoculated into the sole of the foot, and then the animal was treated with an anti-ectromelia compound; multiplication of the virus was arrested in the same way.

Dickinson: Have you any views as to why that should be, why it should not be active when the virus is given intraperitoneally?

Bauer: We have not tried that.

F. W. Sheffield (Wellcome Laboratories of Tropical Medicine): Generally speaking, the *in vivo* results with vaccinia run in parallel with the *in vitro* results and are therefore correlated with lipid solubility.

F. L. Rose (Imperial Chemical Industries): I was very interested in Professor Belyavin's paper because about ten or twelve years ago we were walking along the same path and examining inhibitors of the haem-agglutination effect on chick embryonic erythrocytes. We found inhibitory activity in a wide range of polysaccharides, most of which we obtained from Professor Stacey in Birmingham. We also studied poly-anionic and polycationic compoinds, and eventually we found activity in polyvinyl alcohol, of all things. We even had the idea that we might perhaps protect audiences in cinemas and theatres during influenza epidemics, by spraying polyvinyl alcohol.

Belyavin: We have not got round to the idea of using polyvinyl alcohol. We have been examining one or two of the simpler amphipathic com-pounds such as benadryl, promazine and promethazine. However, we are going to try CTAB which is very active in protecting rats against liver necrosis induced by carbon tetrachloride. If there is anything in the idea CTAB should be very effective in protecting cells against certain infections such as plaque formation of polio virus in ERK cells or pos-sibly influenza virus infection in mice. We are at present testing this possibility.

P. C. Elmes (Queens University, Belfast): Why did Professor Belyavin go to such obscure things as Chinese birds' nests to get mucoproteins? He will find very similar substances in such a mundane source as human spit. I wonder whether these compounds have been produced in response to previous stimulation by specific viruses and whether they are not perhaps as non-specific as he implied. Perhaps he should be investigating human spit to see whether the content of virus inhibiting agents depends on the previous experience of the patient with respect to viruses. There has been some work done on this subject by Burnet's group.

Belyavin: We considered the possibility of using good, honest human spit, but the main problem was to produce a very large quantity of good, honest human spit! We found that in practice it was very much simpler to go to the Hong Kong Emporium off Shaftesbury Avenue to purchase the requisite amount of birds' nest soup rather than to go round with little beakers and slices of lemon! The reason we chose this source was mainly one of availability and ease of extraction.

Broadly speaking, I do not think that the substances in saliva are formed in response to influenzal infections. I cannot vouch for the fact that the *Collocalia esculenta* does not catch influenza, but we can obtain inhibitory substances from the sera of species which are more or less refractory to influenza.

These substances have very few of the characteristics of antibody.

They are relatively—I do say this advisedly—non-specific and fairly catholic in their tastes with regard to the antigenic configuration of the viruses which they inhibit, which makes them rather unlike antibodies.

W. Jacobson (Strangeways Research Laboratory, Cambridge): You mentioned that the polyoma virus causes interferon formation. Have you any views on the mechanism of tumour formation in connection with this process?

Burke: I have no views. The work was done by Allison and reported in *Virology* last year (Allison, 1961). He speculated on the possibility of a connection between interferon production and the establishment of a stable cell-virus interaction, but I do not think there is any evidence for this.

Jacobson: There is no correlation then between tumours induced by polyoma virus and the synthesis of interferon?

Burke: Allison grew polyoma virus in tissue culture where it transforms cells but does not form tumours. He speculated on the *transformation* of cells.

Shulman (Department of Physiology, Melbourne): Dr. Sadler suggested that isatin compounds and possibly imidazole compounds may act by metal complex formation. In Melbourne we (Harris, Shulman and White, unpublished) have had occasion to test metal complexes against a wide range of organisms, including viruses, and we find that some are highly active against influenza, vaccinia and poliomyelitis viruses, both in tissue culture cells and in membranes. This applies particularly to influenza virus on chick chorioallantoic membrane. The metal complexes have two separate effects. One is to inactivate sites on influenza virus concerned with its adsorption to the host cell. The other, concerned with compounds which penetrate allantoic cells, is exerted during the eclipse phase. This is shown by giving such compounds three hours after infection of the chorioallantoic membrane with influenza virus. All doses of compound which inhibit virus multiplication also inhibit respiration of allantoic cells, and this respiratory depression is progressive. The compound starts to act in about twenty minutes, and its activity in the case of ruthenium complexes must be a function of the metal complex itself because they are extraordinarily stable. They cannot be decomposed by heating with concentrated acids and alkalies, and radioactive complexes in intact animals pass through completely unchanged. Consequently, inhibition of virus multiplication must occur by a physicochemical mechanism because the metal complex can only act in this way.

Professor Belyavin suggested that phenothiazine compounds exert their effect by alteration of membrane permeability. I referred yesterday to the work of Koch and Gallagher (1959) which shows that selected ruthenium complexes of 1,10-phenanthroline alter membrane permeability of liver mitochondrial preparations. It seems possible that phenothiazine acts in the same way because Borg (1961) has shown that phenothiazine can form complexes with a variety of metals. Furthermore, you may have here, as before, the formation of a charged compound which inhibits virus multiplication, either intracellularly or extracellularly.

N. Larin (Pfizer Laboratories): I should be grateful if Dr. Bauer could tell us at what dose level he uses his thiosemicarbazones.

Bauer: Five grams a day. That is somewhere around 100 mg./kg. but in experiments in mice the active dose level is far below that. It is active at 2·5 to 5 mg./kg. in repeated doses. Against a very sensitive virus, such as alastrim or rabbitpox it is active down to 0·25 mg./kg.

As far as the toxic dose is concerned, we do not know what it is. I myself have taken 10 g. of this compound by mouth without any ill effects whatsoever, and my colleague, Dr. Goodwin, and I also took 5 g. a day for seven days, also without any ill effects. So I think that the ratio between the toxic dose and the therapeutic dose has not yet been determined.

REFERENCES

ALLISON, A. C. (1961). *Virology*, **15,** 47.
BORG, D. C. (1961). *Fed. Proc.* **20,** Suppl. 10, part II, 104.
KOCH, J. H. and GALLAGHER, C. H. (1959). *Nature, Lond.*, **184,** 1039.

PERSPECTIVES

E. F. GALE

Medical Research Council Unit for Chemical Microbiology,
Department of Biochemistry, University of Cambridge

THE contributions in this Symposium have ranged widely and diversely within the terms defined by its title and my task is now to try to draw some general conclusions from our deliberations. The papers have been organized around the four main groups of "infecting organism" and this division, apart from reflecting the state of research in this subject as a whole, also reflects the problems which are peculiar to the organisms that are being studied; problems that are so esoteric that, very often, workers with one group of organisms do not realize the particular difficulties with which workers in other fields are faced.

In our first session we learned something of the treatment of helminths, and even those of us who are more familiar with the common or garden variety, could see that there is something about the physiology of the worm which is peculiar to itself and provides sites of chemotherapeutic or selective attack. We heard from Drs. Bueding and Broome of the neuromuscular mechanism and of the oral sucker; two structures which can be paralysed specifically and whose paralysis leads to the expulsion of the parasite from the environment which gives it so much comfort and us so much interest. Dr. Pollock has given us a very illuminating survey of the specific structures in the cell wall of some bacteria, structures whose function or synthesis we have learned to impair. Where we find such specific structures which we can attack selectively, then we can attain a high degree of selectivity and we are led to the position where, in some cases, it almost seems that we can afford to ignore the third party to the triangle—the host—and concentrate on the nature of this selective toxicity towards the parasite. Here our path appears to be comparatively simple. However, we must admit that knowledge of these specific structures has not been gained by brilliant deduction from fundamental experiments but by painful extraction from years of probing of the results of the action of the drugs on the organisms. Once we have obtained this knowledge, then the way seems to be much clearer and enables Drs. Bueding and Pollock to predict that it will be possible to base a rational chemotherapy upon the biochemistry and genetics of the organisms with which we are concerned.

With other organisms we have problems additional to those simply of selective toxicity. Dr. Rose has shown us some of the difficulties associated with work on the leprosy bacilli, and many of the organisms in the other two main groups which we have studied pose particular biological problems. Biochemically speaking, the virus is the simplest of the organisms we have studied but its simplicity results in, or arises from—depending upon how you look at it—a necessity to use part of the host's mechanisms for the reproductive process. Consequently, if we hope to interfere selectively with this process, we are faced with the singularly difficult problem of interfering in a host/parasite relationship in which part of the host's mechanisms are used for replication of the parasite. However, Professor Belyavin has suggested that we need not worry too much about this since there are other ways in which we can approach the problem. Before the virus can replicate, it must enter the host cell and this provides us with further sites of attack. We can consider blocking the surface of the virus itself; we can consider blocking the membranes of the host cell through which the virus has to pass in and out; and Professor Belyavin has made suggestions which could be exploited along these lines.

Our fourth group of organisms—the protozoa—appear to be so complex and so fragile that direct experiment has in many cases proved almost impossible. Much of the work, particularly on pathogenic protozoa, has to be interpreted by inference and analogy with other systems. Dr. Weitz and Dr. Bishop have told us something of the difficulties which arise in connection with the antigenicity and drug resistance of these organisms, and have indicated that even the basis of resistance has yet to be experimentally established for many of them. In these cases where there seems to be such a close relationship between the host and the parasite, it looks as though we may have to base our selective interference on fine differences in the properties of receptors and enzymes between host and parasite. Professor Alving has described one of these very fine differences: the sensitivity to oxidation of certain enzyme systems in the malaria parasite and the erythrocyte.

Where the balance is so finely adjusted, we must expect a magnificent interplay of factors between the host, the parasite and the drug. We had this interplay brilliantly displayed before us in Mr. Whiteside's absorbing account of life among the veterinarians and entomologists of Africa. His artistic skill showed us the maze of ways relating the three components of our Symposium; the maze of ways of which, in the laboratory, we tend to select only two or three, and he told us from his experience of some of the errors into which we may be led by such a selection.

We have heard of a number of different types of attack on the central problem. Ehrlich, in the beginning, wrote, "It is safest and best for the development of chemotherapy ... to start with such substances as are known to destroy the parasite", and we have had some fine examples of this classical approach, the approach which Ehrlich himself started with his studies on the modification of the arsenicals. Dr. Gönnert has shown us the effect in schistosomiasis of modification of the thioxanthone structure. Professor Alving modified the aminoquinoline structure to obtain its best antimalarial effect. Dr. Sadler dealt with isatin β-thiosemicarbazone and its derivatives as antiviral agents, and we have heard something of the beginnings of their use in clinical practice. Dr. Rose presented us with a galaxy of formulae in the development of antileprotic drugs, while Dr. Barber gave us a positively pyrotechnic display of structures which are effective as antiprotozoal molecules.

Here is the happy hunting ground of the chemist. It has, of course, been a remarkably successful happy hunting ground, and we are all of us—whether patients or biochemists—eternally indebted to the chemists for what they have done in this field. It leads

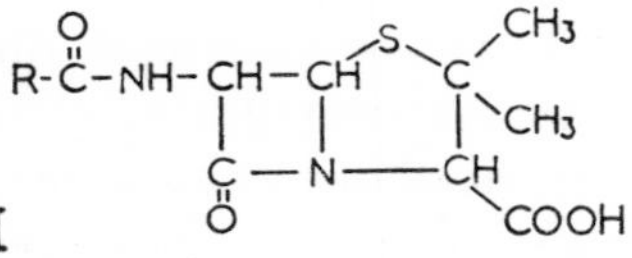

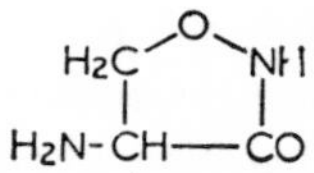

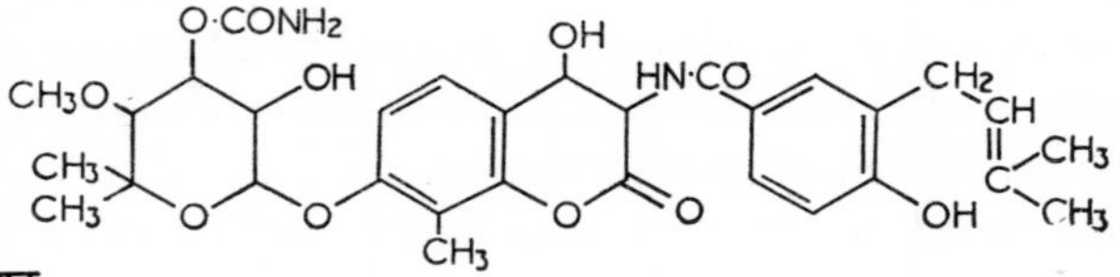

FIG. 1. Substances which impair the synthesis of the wall of the bacterial cell. I: Penicillin; II: Oxamycin; III: Bacitracin; IV: Novobiocin.

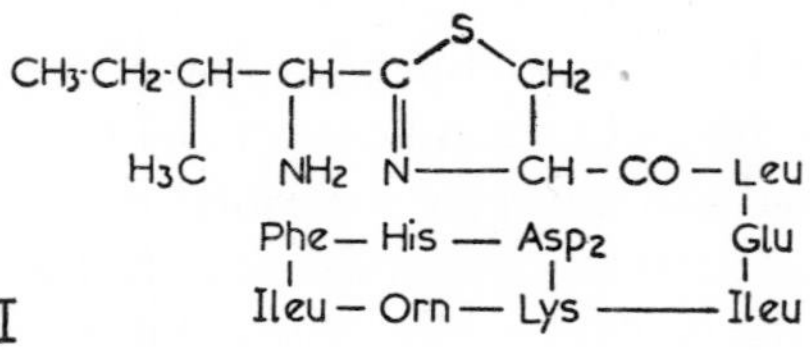

Dr. Gönnert to tell us that "chemotherapy is predominantly an empirical science". Dr. Barber writes "It has to be recognized, albeit with humility, that analogical chemistry has yielded results in the form of useful drugs which are far in advance of the state of our knowledge of how they achieve these results." He showed us a display of formulae—not exactly blackboard chemistry; it has been far to effective to call it that—but what one might call "black magic" chemistry, almost daring us to try to find a mode of action in such a chemical complexity. Of course, those of us who work in that side of the field must find the mode of action of these materials. We must not be deterred by the chemical complexity of their

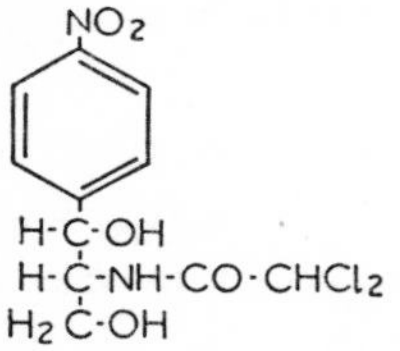

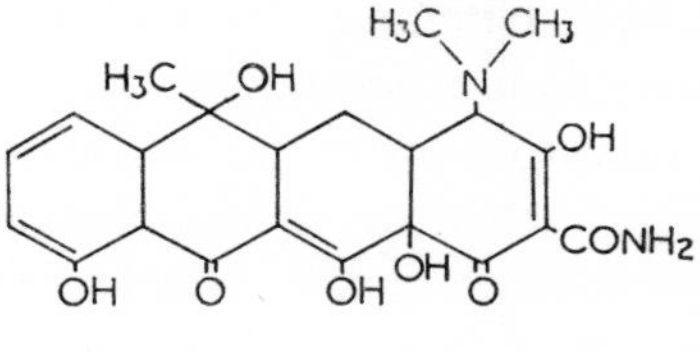

FIG. 2. Antibiotics which inhibit the synthesis of protein in bacteria. V: Chloramphenicol; VI: Tetracycline; VII: Erythromycin.

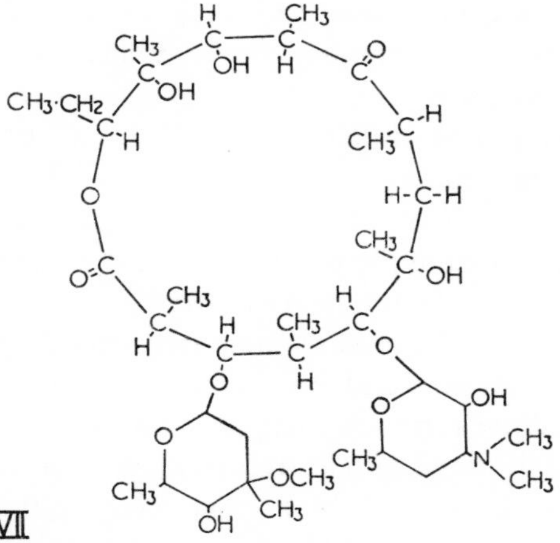

structures, nor by the fact that so many different chemical formulae seem to yield similar effects. Look at the formulae of substances which we know impair the synthesis of the wall of the bacterial cell (Fig. 1); or look at the structures of the antibiotics which inhibit the synthesis of protein in bacteria (Fig. 2). By simply looking at their structures no one could venture a guess that the substances within each group work in the same general way. We cannot find a guide in chemical structure at present, but take the drugs by name and press on with trying to find their mode of action on a biochemical basis. Once the mode of action is indicated, even very generally, then, as Dr. Hitchings has told us, much can be accomplished by enlightened empiricism.

Dr. Rose told me in the course of the discussion, that the search for drugs starts from chance observations. I think that all of us in this Symposium look forward to the time when we can take the chance out of that situation, and provide the chemists with deliberate and experimentally-founded suggestions from which they can start their chemical tricks.

I am a confirmed biochemist, and I believe that a rational development of chemotherapy is going to be possible. Once we can define the mode of action of some of these agents, then we can go ahead with the development of better molecules on a rational basis, and we can even begin to think in terms of control. The contributions that we have had from Drs. Pollock, Hitchings, Bueding and Newton have shown us the profits that come from an investment in the study of comparative biochemistry.

The chemists amongst us do not need encouragement. They speak with the authority and the modesty of success. Therefore, for the rest of the time at my disposal, I would like to try to draw together such of the bases of selective toxicity as can be extracted or deduced from the contributions that have been made to this Symposium, and then have a look at some of the possibilities for further investigation.

The Bases of Selective Toxicity

1. *Reaction of the chemotherapeutic agent with a specific essential component of the organism or of the host.*

Where this component is completely specific, unique to the infecting organism, then we have complete selectivity. Dr. Pollock has shown us the relationship between N-acetylmuramic acid as a component of the bacterial cell wall, and the action of penicillin in impairing the synthetic mechanism whereby that component is inserted into the mucopolysaccharide composing the cell wall substance. Mammalian cell walls do not contain muramic acid and their formation is consequently not affected by penicillin. Other antibiotics display almost the same degree of selectivity and our atitude towards this subject has now come to the stage where, when we meet an antibiotic with this degree of selectivity, we say, "Yes, it's trying to point out to us the existence of yet another specific component". Chloramphenicol is a case in point; we have known for years that this is an inhibitor of protein synthesis in bacteria. Recent work with *in vitro* systems has shown that, although chloramphenicol inhibits microbial protein-synthesizing systems, it has no significant effect in mammalian systems. Ehrenstein and Lipmann (1961) suggest that this indicates the presence of a special, probably additional, feature in the protein-synthesizing mechanism of the microbial system. Thus these highly selective agents can be used as tools to indicate to us differences between the specific components of the organisms we are studying.

Then there is the specific myoneural mechanism of *Ascaris* which is blocked by piperazine, as Dr. Bueding told us in his exposition of selective toxicity in helminths. Dr. Broome has suggested that factors other than the unique structure of nematode muscle may also play a part, and that matters of differential penetration and metabolism might be involved. Then Dr. Bueding told us also of a respiratory enzyme present in *Litomosoides* which is specifically blocked by cyanine. Cyanine has no effect on the cells of the cotton rat host which do not appear to possess a similar enzyme.

While we are thinking in terms of two members only of the triad in the title of our Symposium, we must consider the possibility of specific stimulation of the host's defence mechanism. The obvious factor here is antibody response. Professor Belyavin has pointed out to us that the antibody response is one of the best ways of blocking the virus surface, but other contributors to the Symposium have dealt more with complications that arise in our field of study as a result of antibody response. Dr. Weitz discussed the results of antigenic variation in trypanosomes, and suggested that such variation may have some connection with drug-resistance in those organisms. Both Professor Stoll and Dr. Soulsby showed us that chemotherapeutic measures can be too effective in dealing with helminths in that, if we kill the parasite too quickly, we may prevent the onset of an adequate immune response in the host, with the result that the host is then susceptible to further infection. We need to have careful regulation of the administration of the drugs in these cases so that we get, as Professor Stoll put it, "not mass murder but mayhem."

Amongst the defence mechanisms of the host, there is a further mechanism, interferon, of which we have heard from Dr. Burke. This is a type of mechanism that is new to us and we do not, as yet, know much about it, how complex it is or how it works in opposing virus infection. Then we had a rather surprising contribution that must come under this general heading of defence mechanisms: Dr. Rose pointed out to us that a number of the successful antileprotic drugs are also goitrogenic, so that stimulation of the thyroid may well be a factor in the antileprotic action.

2. *Difference in affinity for the chemotherapeutic agent of receptors in the host and organism.*

When we cannot deal with our problem in terms simply of agent and organism, or agent and host, we have to think in terms of three components and of using an agent to differentiate between host and organism. The first factor we can consider involves a difference in affinity for the drug of the receptors in the two biological systems. This was one of the points made by Ehrlich in his early studies with dyestuffs when he discovered that insensitive organisms did not fix the dyes; this led him to propound the famous aphorism "*Corpora non agunt nisi fixata*".

Dr. Newton pointed out that the relationship between drug and receptor is not necessarily an all-or-none one but that it may be possible to differentiate between host and organism on a basis of differing affinities of the drug for the receptors in the two systems. He showed us that the ability of quinapyramine to precipitate ribosomal material from extracts varies with the organism from which those extracts are made, and that there may be a relationship between this effect and the sensitivity of the organism to the drug. Dr. Bueding found the exciting fact that phosphofructokinase of the schistosome has eighty times the binding power for antimonials that the same enzyme of the host cell has. Dr. Hitchings has told us that there are differences in the properties and fine structure of folic reductase from different organisms, and suggested that we should be able to exploit these differences between host and infecting organism. Professor Alving suggests that the effect of the aminoquinolines in differentiating between plasmodium and erythrocyte may be due to the fact that the enzymes of the pentose pathway in the parasite are more sensitive to oxidative damage than are those in the host cell. Dr. Pollock told us that the binding of penicillin by organisms is related to their sensitivity to that antibiotic.

3. Difference in ability to penetrate into host and organism.

Next there is the possibility that there are differences in the ability of the drug or of some essential metabolite to penetrate the two organisms concerned. We have not heard of any clear-cut case of differing permeability towards the drug, although Dr. Broome suggested that the irreversible paralysis of nematodes by methyridine can be attributed to selective permeability under alkaline conditions. Dr. Gönnert and Dr. Sadler mentioned that lipid solubility correlates with activity in the series of compounds they were considering, and it seems possible that such a correlation may be due to the ability of the derivatives concerned to pass across lipid membranes. Professor Belyavin has suggested that we could attack viral infections by the use of amphipathic agents which affect the permeability of the membranes through which the virus particles have to pass.

The ability of an essential metabolite to penetrate the cell can provide a most important basis for selective action as Dr. Hitchings has shown us. Organisms appear to be divided into two classes: those that can assimilate folic acid from the medium and those that synthesize folic acid from precursors such as p-aminobenzoic acid —and organisms in the latter class cannot normally assimilate preformed folic acid by an active transport mechanism. Bacteria and protozoa synthesize folic acid; mammalian cells assimilate folic acid. This gives us an excellent way to differentiate between the host and the parasite, since inhibition of folic acid synthesis will lead to death of the parasite while the host will continue to utilize folic acid provided in the diet *via* the blood stream. It seems probable that we can explain the selective toxicity of variants on the sulphonamide and antifolic acid scheme by variations in the abilities of organisms to synthesize or assimilate folic acid. Such considerations must be relevant to the problems put before us by Dr. Rose and Dr. Bishop in their discussion of the sensitivity of leprosy bacilli and malaria parasites to drugs of the sulphonamide series.

In the anthelmintic field, Dr. Bueding spoke of the action of dithiazanine and certain dibenzylamines in inhibiting the penetration of glucose into the worms they affect.

4. *Different metabolic pathways leading to an essential product*

This can be looked upon as another facet of the matter we have just discussed; where an essential product is synthesized from precursors by one organism and assimilated in a preformed state by another. We do not seem to have had any example, in this Symposium, of a product which is formed by different metabolic paths in different organisms—as we get, for example, in the synthesis of lysine through diaminopimelic acid in bacteria and through α-aminoadipic acid in fungi. However Professor Woods suggested in the course of the discussion that folic acid synthesis in the tubercle bacillus may be different from that occurring in other bacteria, and that this might be the explanation of its different response to sulphones and sulphonamides. Dr. Newton has found that the synthesis of ribonucleic acid in *Strigomonas oncopelti* is more sensitive to quinapyramine when adenine is the source of purine than when glycine is supplied as precursor but information on these syntheses in other organisms is not yet available.

5. *Differing rates of metabolism in host and organism*

A number of effective agents—atoxyl, prontosil, the amino-quinolines—must be metabolized to active derivatives before they are effective *in vivo*. Dr. Mitchison, however, has taken another line by investigating the destruction of the agent by the host—the inactivation of isoniazid by tuberculous patients. He found that patients could be divided into slow and fast inactivators, and this enabled him to test whether it is the peak concentration, or the period for which the drug is present in the blood, which is the important factor in treatment. He tells us that it is the peak concentration which is the main consideration in ridding the host of the tubercle bacillus, while it is the period for which the drug is present which is of importance in the toxicity of isoniazid towards the host. In fact, Dr. Mitchison has revealed the truth of yet another of Ehrlich's aphorisms: with a good chemotherapeutic drug it is necessary "*frapper vite et frapper fort*".

Finally we have the possibility of imposing a stress on limiting metabolism. Where a parasite is rapidly synthesizing an essential component which is also necessary for the host, there is the possibility that a given stress will have more effect on the parasite than on the host which is leading a more leisurely existence. Although we have not had any direct examples of this sort of effect, it could be an interpretation of a number of the results that have been put before us. It might even explain the action of interferon which, we have been told by Dr. Burke, is a poor uncoupling agent;

perhaps a poor uncoupling agent will have a bigger effect on the viral system, which is synthesizing nucleic acid much more rapidly than the host, than it will on the host where the stress will be less.

6. *Combinations of drugs to increase selective toxicity*

With so many possible ways of differentiating between host and infecting organism, it would seem that it should be possible to increase the degree of selectivity by combining drugs with different sites of action. We have had two examples described to us. Dr. Bueding found that the combination of dibenzylamine, which inhibits the transport of glucose into schistosomes, with stibophen, which inhibits phosphofructokinase, resulted in a very marked decrease in the effective dose of the antimonial. Dr. Hitchings showed us the very effective use that can be made of multiple blocks in folic acid synthesis as a further means of differentiating between "synthesizing" and "assimilating" organisms.

Resistance

Drug-resistance proves to be one of the main problems in the practical application of chemotherapeutic drugs. Mr. Whiteside showed us the problem as it actually occurs in the field in trials and in practice. Dr. Bishop outlined the complications that arise from cross-resistance in plasmodia, while Dr. Williams Smith has given us a fascinating survey of the changes occurring in the flora of the alimentary tract during the administration of antibiotics, showing us the ease and speed with which the normal flora can be replaced by an antibiotic-resistant one.

Drug-resistance becomes of importance when an organism, previously sensitive, becomes insensitive to the drug to a degree that effectively abolishes the selective nature of the drug between the organism and its host. Resistance is therefore a facet of selective toxicity and any of the factors, discussed above, that differentiates between a sensitive organism and an insensitive host can likewise be involved in the change from sensitivity to insenstivity in the organism itself. I do not intend to work through these factors again but will give brief consideration to a new basis of resistance: the development by the organism of enzymes which will inactivate the drug. The outstanding example of this is penicillinase, which has been discussed by Dr. Pollock. The development of penicillinase-producing staphylococci has become the major problem of the clinical use of penicillin. At the moment, the problem has been overcome—or by-passed—by the production of new penicillin molecules which, while retaining antibiotic activity, have so small an affinity for the enzyme that their rate of hydrolysis at bactericidal concentrations is negligible. This is a further tribute to the enlightened empirical approach : what, in this case, has amounted to an exercise in enzyme kinetics.

The Future

"It's a poor sort of memory that only works backwards" remarked the Red Queen, and we must not leave this Symposium without a look at what we can—and what we ought to—do in the future.

The contributions to this Symposium have given us a grand series of selective agents derived by chemical research. We must press on with their investigation on the biochemical, on the physiological, and on the genetic planes. We must develop further biological systems which we can dissect by biochemical methods. This means that we must be able to culture the sensitive organisms: most bacteria we can; worms and protozoa in most cases we cannot. What is the basis of the highly exacting nutritional requirements of pathogenic protozoa which has made it almost impossible to culture them? Must we wait until we can culture them before we can press on with a rational chemotherapy of protozoa? Dr. Newton says no. He says that we can take our drugs and we can work with them on sensitive but simpler organisms which can be

12*

cultured in the laboratory, and that, just as investigation of antibiotics on *Escherichia coli* provides information on their mode of
action on other bacteria, so we can obtain useful information about
the mode of action of antiprotozoal drugs by using simple laboratory systems. The same attitude is expressed by Dr. Bueding who
tells us that "the sensitivity of a parasite ... to ... agents is determined to a much greater degree by biochemical than by morphological or taxonomic characteristics". In my opinion this is one of
the important Thoughts for the Day that has come out of this
Symposium.

Selective toxicity is an essay in comparative biochemistry. But
when we look at our knowledge of comparative biochemistry, we
find that it is really about on a par with our knowledge of chemotherapy. We have talked of differences in the properties and structures of membranes, but we have little real knowledge. We are
beginning to know that there are differences in the properties of
enzymes with the same catalytic function but from different sources
Within the last few years biochemists have described enzymes,
from the same cell, which have the same catalytic function but
different physical properties and different sensitivities to inhibitors: the isoenzymes. Are isoenzymes involved in the development
of resistance? Dr. Newton has found that ribosomal materials from
different organisms differ in their binding capacities towards certain
drugs. Have we been negligent in the past in making too easy an
assumption that like components from different cells are alike in
structure and composition? And should we not now turn concentrated attention to the physical and chemical properties of membranes, ribosomes, enzymes and other cell components to see
whether we can exploit their fine structure on a comparative basis?

Lastly there is the exciting prospect before us of the control of
characteristics and the control of differentiation. If selective toxicity
can be based upon small differences in the fine structure of enzymes,
then surely we should, at some time in the future, learn how to
control these differences. Recently it has been possible to change a

penicillin-sensitive organism to a penicillin-resistant one by trans-duction whereby the appropriate pencillinase gene is inserted into the sensitive organism. This is a laboratory experiment that is far removed at present from any practical application but our know-ledge of the biochemical processes involved in control has advanced so rapidly during the last three months that we need not be too timid about our predictions for the future.

REFERENCE

EHRENSTEIN, G. V. and LIPMANN, F. (1961). *Proc. nat. Acad. Sci., Wash.*, **47**, 941.

INDEX TO SUBJECTS

Printed by Spottiswoode, Ballantyne & Co. Ltd., London and Colchester